Contents

Preface

Personal training has come a long way since it first became popular in the early 1990s. Since then, the body of knowledge has expanded not only in the area of exercise and physical activity for fitness, but also in the value of exercise in maximizing health and the quality of life. With the release of the U.S. Surgeon General's Report on Physical Activity and Health in 1996, there has never been a better time to promote safe and effective exercise to the American public.

A professional, high-quality personal training instructor plays an important role in helping people achieve their fitness goals. Of all the variables that can affect exercise compliance, perhaps the most significant is the quality of the exercise instructor. A qualified, enthusiastic professional will prescribe progressive exercise to minimize the chance of injury, ensure variety and fun during the session, help the participant establish realistic goals, provide periodic evaluations, keep accurate records, and recognize participants' accomplishments.

This is one of the reasons why the YMCA is introducing this new YMCA Personal Training Instructor Manual and the accompanying certification course. As the demand for quality personal training instruction increases, YMCAs and the exercising public demand better qualified and certified instructors. YMCA personal training instructors will be expected to be conversant with the information presented in this manual, experienced in the techniques and skills required to implement programs, and current on emerging technologies and programs. This new manual represents the most current picture of the knowledge, instructional techniques, and responsibilities YMCA personal training instructors need to provide effective exercise instruction to members. It is a revision and updating of the former YMCA Strength Training Manual, and it is the required text for the YMCA of the USA's YMCA Personal Training Instructor certification course. It focuses on how to lead personal training sessions, covering the following areas:

- The role of personal training instructors in the YMCA
- Basic physiological information on the cardiorespiratory and musculoskeletal systems
- Description of cardiorespiratory and muscular strength training programs
- Guidelines and physiology of flexibility training
- Information on health screening and fitness assessment
- Guidelines on developing individual exercise programs
- Basic nutrition information
- Information on motivating participants
- Communication and teaching techniques
- Methods of avoiding, recognizing, and treating various exercise-related injuries
- Suggestions for program administration

The book also includes practical tools in the appendix such as educational topic outlines and health screening forms, as well as a glossary of fitness training terms.

The text begins with a discussion of YMCA health and fitness programs and the use of personal trainers in the YMCA. It then moves to more technical information regarding the anatomy and physiology of cardiorespiratory fitness and the principles and guidelines for this type of exercise.

The following chapters deal with the anatomy and physiology of muscular strength and endurance and the principles and guidelines for this type of exercise. Flexibility, the third primary component of physical fitness, is discussed in detail in the next chapter, with the science of flexibility presented along with sample flexibility exercises. The next two chapters deal with the important topics of screening personal training participants and then using your knowledge of exercise and their health status to design appropriate programs. They are followed by the topic of good nutrition, a vital area of concern for many personal training participants. Getting participants started is one thing—having them stick with it is another. Keeping members motivated is a challenge most personal training instructors will face, so the next two chapters focus on principles of communication and motivation and the skills you will need to work effectively with members. Finally, the book concludes with suggestions on how to reduce exercise injuries and how to treat them, and ideas about program administration.

As a YMCA personal training instructor, you have an abundance of information at your fingertips. Your challenge is to learn how to apply this information in a way that is effective and enjoyable, brings results, and ensures the long-term success of your participants.

Acknowledgments

The YMCA of the USA would like to acknowledge the contributions of those individuals who helped develop the *YMCA Personal Training Instructor Manual*. The *YMCA Personal Training Instructor Manual* is a revision and updating of the *YMCA Strength Training Manual,* published in 1994 by the YMCA of the USA.

Project Coordinator

Michael Spezzano, YMCA of the USA, Chicago, Illinois

YMCA Contributors

The YMCA of the USA thanks the following staff and YMCAs for their assistance with the initial development of the YMCA Strength Training materials and training program:

Diane Ballek, Sheridan County YMCA, Sheridan, Wyoming

Paul Cramer, West Suburban Family Branch YMCA, Wauwatosa, Wisconsin

Mike Doss, Hutchinson & Reno County YMCA, Hutchinson, Kansas

Carol Happ, Davenport YMCA, Davenport, Iowa

Perry Mecate, Whittier Center Branch YMCA, Whittier, California

Morris Peltz, Downtown Branch YMCA, Richmond, Virginia

Dan Ochs, YMCA of the USA West Field Office, Palo Alto, California

Lynne Vaughan, YMCA of the USA, Chicago, Illinois

Wayne Westcott, South Shore YMCA, Quincy, Massachusetts

David Wetsell, Sewickley Valley YMCA, Sewickley, Pennsylvania

Phil Wortman, West Central Florida YMCA, Lakeland, Florida

The YMCA of the USA would also like to gratefully acknowledge the contributions and cooperation received from the following organizations: the American Council on Exercise (ACE), the National Dance-Exercise Instructor's Training Association (NDEITA), and the American College of Sports Medicine (ACSM).

We also thank the following companies for supplying photos:

Cybex

Nautilus

Universal

Life Fitness

1

Personal Training in the YMCA

Welcome to the team of dedicated YMCA Personal Training Instructors helping members achieve their exercise goals in YMCAs across the nation. You'll soon discover that the members of this team are diverse in age and background. Amidst this diversity, however, a common bond exists among successful instructors. Each has accepted the challenge to become the best instructor he or she can be.

Acquiring the skills to become the best personal training instructor you can be does not happen just by your attending a few workshops, nor does it magically result at the end of your first training session. Commitment to become your best requires time, energy, motivation, practice, a love of learning, and a love of people. Becoming your best is an ongoing process that begins with preparing to work with your first member and continues as you polish your style with every member you teach.

In this chapter we start by explaining how YMCA personal training programs came about, beginning with strength training. We then talk about what a good personal trainer should be able to do and the YMCA's expectations for personal trainers.

Following this, we describe some of the additional YMCA trainings open to you, then discuss how you can share your fitness knowledge with members and apply that knowledge to your programs.

YMCA Personal Training Programs

More and more, YMCA members participating in physical activity are seeking personal attention, guidance, and coaching from caring, well-trained, and knowledgeable fitness staff. This personal instruction helps members understand the many components of physical fitness and provides them with individualized programs that help them become physically fit. Comprehensive fitness programs include cardiorespiratory, muscular strength, and flexibility exercises.

In the early years of the fitness boom, the focus was mostly on cardiorespiratory, or aerobic, exercise, particularly jogging and aerobic dance. However, in the 1990s, participation in strength training grew by leaps and bounds as facilities and equipment improved and became more accessible to the masses. In the YMCA, the use of personal trainers began almost exclusively with strength training, as more and more members added this new component to their workouts. Because strength training was new to many members, they sought assistance from qualified staff, most often called strength training instructors in YMCAs. Gradually these instructors began helping members with their aerobic workouts, as many members preferred individual, mostly machine-based, cardiorespiratory exercise rather than group exercise classes. As the scope of instructors' work broadened, so did their titles, and many YMCAs now have staff who provide personal training and attention to members. Whether it's providing one-on-one coaching, orienting new members, or being available in the fitness center for assistance whenever it's needed, personal trainers perform a valuable member service in today's YMCA.

Strength Training at the YMCA

Beginning in the early 1900s, YMCA gymnasiums included weight-training rooms. This was certainly consistent with the "muscular Christianity" mission of that era, which advocated a strong spirit, a strong mind, and a strong body. Unfortunately, most weight- training rooms were dominated by a small group of strong males, which was somewhat intimidating to others. As a result, for years weight training was considered to be an inappropriate physical activity by most adults and definitely off-limits for youth.

Throughout the 1970s, the typical YMCA weight room was a small space with unfamiliar equipment, muscular men, and loud noises. It remained an uninviting place. However, as larger strength training facilities were introduced, with convenient new weight-training machines and programs based on the philosophy that average men and women could benefit from relatively brief strength training sessions, newcomers were attracted to weight training. Many YMCAs retained the traditional free-weight room for those interested in weightlifting and bodybuilding, and then added a modern new strength training facility for those interested in general conditioning and developing better muscular fitness. Far from being a fad, the interest in strength fitness has continued to increase across the country. Strength training quickly became the fastest growing exercise activity of the 1990s.

Strength training is not to be confused with lifting extremely heavy weights, as in competitive weightlifting, or building extremely large muscles, as in competitive bodybuilding. Very few individuals have the genetic capacity to be successful in these sports. Also, some competitive weightlifters and bodybuilders jeopardize their overall health and fitness in their quest for stronger and larger muscles. The main purpose of YMCA strength training programs is to help individuals improve their overall health and fitness through better muscular development.

Strength training is appropriate for people of all ages as a means to enhance their overall health and fitness. Performing resistance training exercises can stimulate muscle development for all, although within each person's genetic framework. Few have the potential to build exceptionally large muscles, but people of all ages can increase their muscle strength and physical capacity through regular resistance exercise. In addition to helping people look better, feel better, and function better, strength training reduces injury risk, delays the degenerative effects of aging, and enhances the joy of living.

While strength training is the best means for developing and maintaining a strong, functional, and injury-resistant musculoskeletal system, it is only one dimension of health-related fitness. YMCA personal training stresses total fitness, with an emphasis on cardiorespiratory conditioning, flexibility, and muscular strength and endurance. Part of the YMCA philosophy is also to encourage people to participate in leisure sports and activities that provide health benefits and fun.

Being the Best

Good YMCA personal training instructors

- know their stuff. They understand the basic principles of cardiorespiratory and muscular fitness, incorporate safe movements and exercises into individual programs, try to prevent injuries by practicing sound teaching principles, and motivate participants at all skill and fitness levels;
- effectively apply their knowledge and communicate it to participants; and
- implement the YMCA's philosophy of helping each person achieve his or her personal best through sound training and educational programs.

Let's look at each of these areas.

Knowing Your Stuff

As a personal training instructor you must do much more than demonstrate exercises. You are also expected to provide accurate fitness information, to plan effective programs, and to address participants' questions. Knowledge you gain from the exercise sciences will strengthen your preparation to lead. For example, understanding basic principles of fitness will help you better plan each warm-up, workout, and cool-down, and insights from sport psychology can provide useful ways to motivate your participants. Throughout this book you'll become familiar with information from the exercise sciences to apply to training programs. The more you learn about all dimensions of effectively planning and leading personal training, the more you will inspire and benefit your participants.

Reaching Your Participants

As a personal training instructor you may possess a head full of fitness knowledge, but if you can't motivate and communicate with participants, they're not likely to stay with your program very long. Only highly self-motivated persons will stick with an instructor who does a poor job of motivating or communicating with them before, during, and after the workouts.

Some instructors are naturally talented at motivating and communicating with participants; others must do more conscious planning to make sure encouragement comes across. Reading this book will give you some good ideas on how to motivate and communicate with your participants. But reading good suggestions is only one way to improve your skills. Probably the best way to learn good motivation and communication techniques is to watch effective instructors in action. Pay close attention to the good instructors at your YMCA. Note what they say, verbally and nonverbally, as they work with individual members. Exchanging ideas with other YMCA instructors is a rewarding way to learn.

Implementing the YMCA's Philosophy

The YMCA has been a recognized leader in health and fitness for the spirit, mind, and body since 1891. The YMCA views personal training as a means to develop, grow personally, and have fun. The YMCA addresses all aspects of a participant's good health through its comprehensive programs. Preprogram health screening, fitness testing, exercise plans, and education programs all meet tough standards set by physicians, exercise physiologists, and health educators.

Programs should be open to all individuals, no matter what their current level of fitness or their economic status. The YMCA prides itself on offering equal opportunities for persons of any sex, age, shape, or size to participate in fitness programs. Many YMCAs offer classes for a variety of groupings: multilevel, multiage, seniors, visually impaired, hearing impaired, prenatal and postpartum women, the physically challenged, or individuals confined to wheelchairs. YMCA programs are taught in inner cities as well as in smaller urban and suburban communities; they're held in schools, churches, hospitals, and recreation facilities as well as in YMCA buildings.

Every YMCA program shares certain characteristics. Whether a program is offered to individual, families, or the community, it stresses these objectives:

GROW PERSONALLY—Build self-esteem and self-reliance.

CLARIFY VALUES—Develop moral and ethical behavior based on Christian principles.

IMPROVE PERSONAL AND FAMILY RELATIONSHIPS—Learn to care, communicate, and cooperate with family and friends.

APPRECIATE DIVERSITY—Respect people of different ages, abilities, incomes, races, religions, cultures, and beliefs.

BECOME BETTER LEADERS AND SUPPORTERS—Learn the give and take necessary to work toward the common good.

DEVELOP SPECIFIC SKILLS—Acquire new knowledge and ways to grow in spirit, mind, and body.

HAVE FUN—Enjoy life!

The YMCA prizes instructors who genuinely care about and encourage development of program participants. Caring about your members can be shown in many ways. Learning participants' names and their personal goals is a simple way to show that you care. Extending courtesy to all at all times is another characteristic of caring instructors. Good teaching practices, such as patience when you must explain the same movement several times, also show you care. Many member service educational materials are available from the YMCA Program Store.

Working With Different Age Groups

Personal training programs can be designed to meet the fitness needs of all age groups. The YMCA personal training programs you create should be developmentally appropriate for people of various ages and for special populations, and they should take into account individual differences. For example, people of different ages have different exercise capacities and should train accordingly. Consider the following age groups, all of whose members can benefit from well-designed personal training programs:

- **Youth**—Pre-teens (ages 9 through 12) are experiencing normal growth and maturation. However, in today's society few youth get sufficient physical activity, especially progressive resistance exercise. As a result they do not develop the strong muscles, tendons, and bones that should be an integral part of their developmental years. Pre-teens can benefit greatly from systematic strength exercise, but their training program should be basic and brief. They require relatively little resistance exercise to produce excellent strength gains. At this age strength training should be only one component of a physical activity program. Youth need the opportunity to join in active games with their peers that give them opportunities to use their creativity and have fun. Most youth lose their enthusiasm for exercise when they are confronted with lengthy strength training sessions. That's why fun and variety are so important.

- **Adolescents**—Teenagers (ages 13 through 18) continue to experience physical growth and maturation, with the development of secondary gender characteristics. Particularly pronounced among teenage males is enhanced upper body size. Most teens are capable of regular and rigorous resistance training that produces high levels of strength and muscularity. This is a time when many teens, both male and female, are interested in their physiques and are willing to spend considerable time and effort to achieve their physical objectives. They may choose to do longer or harder workouts, performing more exercises and more sets than they did as pre-teens.

- **Young Adults**—Young adults include men and women who have attained physical maturity (approximately age 19) through the beginning of middle age (approximately age 39). This is a rather broad age range, and 19-year-olds typically have greater physical capacity than 39-year-olds. However, as a group, young adults are relatively strong and capable of high-intensity cardiorespiratory and muscle resistance exercise. For many young adults it is difficult to schedule long training sessions due to the time pressures of work, family, recreation, and other commitments, so they may be best advised to perform moderate duration exercise sessions.

- **Middle-Aged Adults**—Middle age means different things to different people, but most 40- to 55-year-olds fit into this category. This may be the most important time of life to perform regular exercise. During these years men and women who do not engage in training lose muscle tissue at a rapid rate. This results in a lower physical capacity, a reduced metabolic rate, and a premature onset of old age. A well-designed personal training program can maintain muscle mass, metabolic rate, and physical capacity at a high level throughout an adult's middle years. Because middle-aged adults typically have busy schedules, they often respond well to brief exercise sessions.

• **Older Adults**—While people in this category have attained a certain quantity of life, too many have sacrificed a desirable quality of life. Because they are sedentary, they function at a much lower level than they should, and they accept their unfitness as part of the aging process. We need to address this problem by introducing older adults to a more active lifestyle. One step is developing individualized exercise for them to increase their muscle strength and physical capacity. Personal training sessions should be of moderate effort and reasonable duration, in the company of other older adults whenever possible.

Knowing What the YMCA Expects of You

Ideally, the YMCA prefers to hire personal training instructors who are already well trained in exercise physiology or who have past experience training others. Although not everyone chosen to train has these extensive credentials, the YMCA does expect certain qualities of all instructors. These characteristics include physical fitness, high motivation, the ability to communicate well, a personable nature, the ability and willingness to work with individuals, and reasonable maturity. The YMCA has found that, although the professional backgrounds of instructors are diverse, these common traits exist in all effective instructors.

Regardless of your background in or knowledge of physical fitness, you will receive additional training upon joining the YMCA staff. In many YMCAs a new instructor is teamed up with an experienced instructor and serves an apprenticeship. This 20- to 30-day internship helps to acquaint you with the YMCA's way of leading personal training and helps ease you into working with your first member. If you aren't currently certified in CPR, you must become certified or renew your expired card. Classes to prepare you to pass the CPR exam are held frequently at the YMCA and in many other community programs. You may be required to attend a two-day YMCA of the USA Personal Training Instructor certification course that covers such topics as exercise physiology, ways to give good instruction, safe exercises, and how to motivate participants.

Attending Additional YMCA Trainings

As a YMCA instructor, you should take pride in improving the quality of your program's content. Making improvements depends heavily on your commitment to continue learning. Many instructors attend additional YMCA Health & Fitness certification trainings and continually search for new ideas. The following are selected YMCA of the USA Health & Fitness courses that are useful for personal trainers:

• **Fitness Specialist**—This training prepares YMCA staff members to perform physical fitness assessments and develop individualized exercise plans. Course participants will be certified to conduct the YMCA Fitness Testing and Assessment battery.

• **Healthy Back Instructor**—This course provides training for instructors of YMCA Healthy Back exercise programs. Content will cover structure of the back, muscle anatomy and physiology related to back function, common causes of back pain, lifestyle habits related to back pain, and a variety of exercise routines to alleviate and prevent back pain. Practical experience in two land sessions is included as a part of this training. To receive Water Back certification as well, additional time for a water practical has been added as an option.

• **Prenatal Exercise Instructor**—This course is designed to certify YMCA staff members and volunteers as instructors for prenatal exercise programs. The material covers specific guidelines for exercise during pregnancy, information on the anatomy and physiology of pregnancy, and recommended exercises. This course adheres to the guidelines set forth by the American College of Obstetricians and Gynecologists (ACOG). Additional course time has been added for participants interested in leading aquatic prenatal exercise programs.

- **YMCA Walk Reebok Instructor**—This training is designed to give YMCA staff members and volunteers all the information they need to conduct walking programs and activities. Course content includes the hows and whys of walking, walking for special populations, equipment selection, evaluation, and how to establish a walking program and club.

- **YMCA Walk Reebok Distance/Interval Instructor**—Developed in collaboration with Reebok University, this second-level training is for those previously certified in the basic YMCA Walk Reebok Instructor course. Techniques for distance and interval fitness training to use with walking program participants will be presented. Course content also includes effective goal setting and strategies for increasing walking mileage and ways to increase conditioning intensity through the use of intervals.

- **YMCA/IDEA Get Real Weight Management Instructor**—This course was developed in collaboration with IDEA, The Health and Fitness Source, and is based on their book *Get Real: A Personal Guide to Real-Life Weight Management.* This course includes techniques and strategies for conducting weight management group classes or individual sessions, or for incorporating this information into exercise and fitness programs. Content covers the critical role of physical activity, sensible nutrition, self-empowerment, and body image as they relate to successful lifelong weight management.

- **YMCA Personal Fitness Program Director**—This course was developed to teach the YMCA's innovative new program for introducing inactive people to regular exercise. The program is based on the science of exercise behavior change, and it teaches instructors how to manage staff, facilities, equipment, and activities to accommodate the needs and motivations of the ready-to-be-fit. Course content also includes effective goal setting and strategies for helping new exercisers identify and overcome barriers to exercise. Course participants will be given a staff training outline for use in training other staff at their YMCAs.

- **Active Older Adult Exercise Instructor (land)**—This training is designed for those who lead exercise classes for older adults. It focuses on exercise adaptations for older adult participants and includes sample exercise classes.

- **YMCA Water Fitness Instructor**—This course, based on latest research, provides participants with the necessary knowledge and skills needed to lead YMCA Water Fitness classes. The course includes all components of fitness principles, information designing purposeful exercises, and methods for targeting specific training objectives.

- **YMCA Active Older Adult Water Fitness Instructor**—This course provides participants with the necessary knowledge and skills needed to lead YMCA Water Fitness classes specifically for active older adults. The focus is on targeting functional fitness for activities of daily living.

These and many other YMCA programs are excellent opportunities to expand your fitness knowledge.

You can continue your quest for information by becoming familiar with the materials available through the YMCA Program Store. These materials can keep you up-to-date on the latest techniques and program ideas.

Most instructors subscribe to reliable fitness-oriented magazines and journals to stay informed of the latest trends. A list of such resources can be found in the book *Principles of YMCA Health and Fitness.* All of these efforts make their programs more complete and more sound.

Being a Fitness Educator

Although education programs are often offered as separate entities at the YMCA, education should be an integral and ongoing part of every fitness program. You can help participants learn by encouraging them to attend education programs simultaneously with their fitness programs and by providing information as part of your personal training sessions. Appendix A has outlines for a number of health and fitness topics that can be shared with participants.

Selecting Reliable Fitness Information

With the abundance of material available, selecting reliable information in the fitness area can be frustrating and confusing. Add to this the need to select information in sports medicine and on leadership abilities, and the task appears overwhelming. The materials available on fitness are plentiful and competitive, but be careful – not all information is accurate or reliable. So how exactly do you choose reliable sources or references to answer questions on exercise-related topics?

Competent authority is the main concern in evaluating fitness information. Whether the information is in books or magazines, or even on television, you should know the credentials of the person or persons presenting it. Become familiar with reputable authorities in the areas in which you need information; otherwise you may get caught in the celebrity name game when you seek fitness information.

What's in a name? Apparently a lot. Books written by celebrities sell quite well, much better than those written by noted exercise physiologists. But don't let the popularity of a celebrity influence your search for accurate information. Your job is to sort out reliable information from all that is available. Subscribe to professional journals and magazines that strive to educate as well as to entertain. *Principles of YMCA Health and Fitness* lists some resources from which you can begin to compile fitness reference materials for you and your participants and to share with other YMCA staff.

Applying Exercise-Science Information to Your Program

As important as finding reliable sources of exercise-science information is being able to read and understand them. While you need to seek knowledge from the exercise sciences, you may not be able to sift through all of the scientific jargon to understand the practical significance of what is being said. Exercise scientists, like other scientists, seem to speak a language all their own. This language is necessary for communicating precisely among fellow scientists, but the specialized terms that enhance scientific communication make it more difficult for lay readers to understand and apply what is said.

You need to work hard at bridging the "technical-term gap" between personal training instructors and exercise scientists. Terms from exercise science appear frequently today in popular as well as academic journals. But beyond merely recognizing these terms, you need to understand what they mean and how they fit into the overall fitness scheme. Each of the following chapters uses the appropriate technical terms to discuss each topic. Once you understand the terms and general principles from each chapter, you can begin to apply them to your program. Having a good understanding of fitness information and how to apply it will vastly improve the quality of your program.

Looking Ahead

The continued success of personal training programs at the YMCA depends on *you*. Programs will stay fresh and alive as long as there are instructors who are creative, innovative, and hardworking. Although this may sound like a formidable task, if you are willing to assess your current abilities and to learn how to develop new skills one step at a time, you will become a top-notch YMCA Personal Training Instructor in no time at all. You are to be commended for taking on the challenge of teaching at the YMCA. As you read the next few chapters, take a close look at yourself – the skills you have, what you may be lacking, and what you can gain from your YMCA experience. You will find information to help you make quick, long strides in becoming the best instructor you can be.

2

Cardiorespiratory Fitness

Individual exercise, primarily using cardiorespiratory exercise machines, is a popular training method to achieve aerobic fitness. When programs are properly structured, participants experience many cardiorespiratory training benefits. Understanding these benefits will help you to design more sound and individualized workouts. Many of your participants will want to compare the training benefits of their workout session to those of other aerobic activities. However, before you can understand and explain the training adaptations that body systems undergo as a result of exercising, you must first be familiar with how the systems function while the body is at rest. Familiarity with the terminology related to each body system will help you comprehend authoritative fitness information and better communicate with your participants.

We begin the chapter by defining what aerobic exercise is and describing the physiological changes that occur as a result of aerobic training. We then give you an overview of the cardiorespiratory system and how aerobic fitness is assessed. Finally, we explain some basics of energy production and the central nervous system as they relate to cardiorespiratory fitness.

What Is Aerobic Exercise?

All aerobic activities have the following common elements:

a. They place a demand on the cardiorespiratory (cardio = heart; respiratory = lungs) system,
b. they use large muscle groups,
c. they predominantly use the aerobic (with oxygen) energy system,
d. they are rhythmic in nature, and
e. they can be safely performed at a moderate level of intensity. Examples of aerobic activities include swimming, walking, jogging, running, cycling, stair climbing, and aerobic dance/exercise.

If performed continuously for 20 minutes or more, aerobic activities prompt adaptations, or training responses, within the cardiorespiratory, muscular, energy, and nervous systems. Understanding how these systems adapt can help you

- realize the importance of individualized fitness,
- plan safe and beneficial workouts,
- understand training benefits gained from aerobic exercise,
- answer questions concerning exercise, and
- react logically to injuries or emergencies.

Understanding Training Responses

Before you can understand how a system responds to exercise, you need a basic understanding of how that system functions at rest; otherwise you may misinterpret some of the physiological changes it undergoes. For example, during moderate exercise the heart beats around 150 beats per minute (bpm). This heart rate may sound dangerously high to someone who does not know that the average resting heart rate is around 68 to 72 bpm. At a moderate level of exercise, the amount of blood pumped through the heart per minute (cardiac output) increases to 15 liters (15.9 quarts), which is three times the cardiac output at rest. The demands placed on these systems during exercise are much greater than those placed on them at rest.

The body's adaptations to exercise can be studied at three general levels:

- Changes at the cellular (biochemical) level, for example, the changes within the muscle cells during different types of exercise. Understanding these responses provides insight about energy production and other chemical processes.
- Changes in the body's systems, for example, the amount of blood being pumped per minute to various sites in the body.
- Other considerations, for example, the influence of environmental factors (such as exercising in the heat and cold) or changes in body composition (fat weight versus lean weight).

To relate every known or probable response to exercise at each of these levels would take volumes. Your task is to select those pieces of information from exercise physiology that are most applicable to designing your program. Not gathering enough information may mean that you will not offer the best program possible or that you will fail to adjust the level of exercise to each individual's needs. Yet if you tried to learn everything known about exercise, you would not have time left to teach your members. A fair compromise, then, is to become familiar with how the major body systems function at rest as well as during aerobic exercise.

The next section examines the resting functions of the major body systems most involved in aerobic exercise. Let's begin by looking at the cardiorespiratory system.

The Cardiorespiratory System

The cardiorespiratory system is actually comprised of two systems — the heart and its vessels (the cardiovascular system) and the lungs (the respiratory system). Let's take a look at each component.

The Cardiovascular System

The heart's function is to pump blood through the body. The pressure of the heartbeat forces the blood to flow in a continuous, traceable route. This path is shown in figure 2.1. Blood enters the right atrium (RA), which is a thin-walled storage compartment that receives blood returning to the heart. The blood is forced by atrial contraction through the tricuspid valve into the right ventricle (RV). The ventricles are the heart's pumping chambers and comprise most of the heart's muscle mass. The right ventricle pumps blood through the pulmonary valve into the pulmonary artery and to the lungs. After oxygen and carbon dioxide have been exchanged in the lungs, the blood returns to the left atrium (LA) through the pulmonary veins. Left atrial contraction forces blood through the mitral valve into the left ventricle (LV). From the left ventricle blood is pumped through the aortic valve and on through the body.

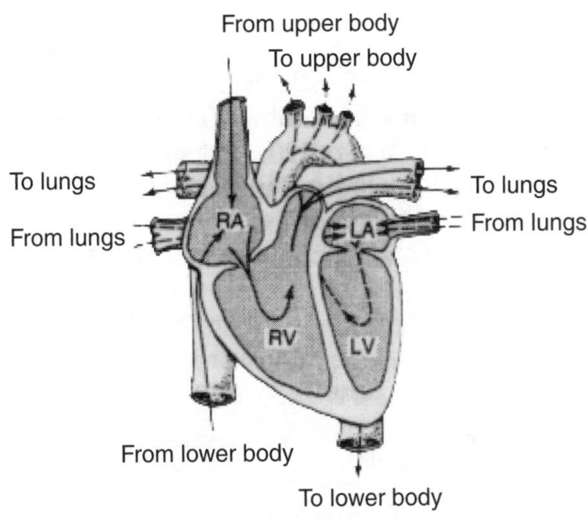

Figure 2.1 Path of blood flow through the heart.

Cardiac Output

The volume of blood the heart pumps per minute is referred to as the cardiac output. This volume is expressed in liters (L) or milliliters (ml) of blood pumped per minute (min). The symbol Q is often used to represent cardiac output in scientific literature or in tables of data. Cardiac output is calculated as the stroke volume (SV; the amount of blood pumped out of the left ventricle in one beat) times the heart rate (HR):

$$Q \text{ (ml/min)} = SV \text{ (ml/beat)} \times HR \text{ (beats/min)}$$

Your cardiac output changes in proportion to the degree of your activity. The average cardiac output of a person lying down in a state of complete rest is approximately 5 L/min. Walking would raise the cardiac output to about 7.5 L/min. Strenuous exercise might raise it to as much as 25 L/min or as high as 35 L/min in a highly trained athlete (Guyton, 1974).

The heart has a maximum rate at which it can pump. Within physiological limits, the heart pumps all of the blood that flows into it at a rate that prevents excessive damming of the blood in the veins. The amount of blood that the heart can pump each minute depends on two major factors: the heart's pumping effectiveness and the ease with which blood can flow through the body and return to the heart.

Blood Pressure

As the heart's left ventricle contracts, blood is forced into the systemic arteries, creating pressure. This pressure can be measured in the larger arteries of the body. Blood pressure varies from person to person and from one measurement to the next in the same person. For example, your blood pressure is higher when you stand than when you sit, and it can be higher during times of stress.

Despite individual variations, there is a range of normal values for blood pressure. In a blood pressure ratio reading such as 120/80 (read "120 over 80") the top number is the systolic pressure. This number (in this case, 120) represents the pressure resulting from the force of ventricular contraction as blood is pumped out of the heart. The bottom number of the ratio (80 in this example) is the diastolic pressure, which represents the pressure in the arteries during the filling of the atria. The example of 120/80 is an average value for normal blood pressure. Mild hypertension is considered to be between 140/90 and 160/95. High blood pressure, or hypertension, is defined by a value greater than 160/95. Regular aerobic exercise may help reduce elevated blood pressure.

Redistribution of Blood Flow

The body has a priority system for the amount of blood each of its parts receives. When the body is at rest, the major organs receive the most blood (see table 2.1). During exercise, however, there is a shift of priorities, or a redistribution, to supply adequate blood to the large muscle groups of the arms and legs.

Heart Rate

During rest, the average heart beats 68 to 72 times a minute. This value would be lower, however, for a regular participant in aerobic exercise. Heredity and age are additional factors that influence heart rate. A higher aerobic capacity (i.e., ability to perform continuous exercise) can be genetically determined; also, as a person gets older, aerobic capacity begins to decrease at a rate that correlates with fitness level.

Each person you train will be at a different level of aerobic fitness. Your job becomes one of challenging the fit person and pacing the less experienced beginner. Those members at advanced fitness levels may be overachievers who tend to push their bodies too far. Beginners, on the other hand, may have cardiorespiratory capabilities that have not been stressed for a long time. To maintain safety, you need to help all participants monitor their heart rate responses to their workouts so that they do not attempt too much or too little in trying to achieve the desired training benefits.

In order to handle the increased workload that vigorous physical activity places on the heart, participants must slowly begin to train the heart to progressively handle a little more work each time they exercise. This gives it time to adapt to pumping faster and to supplying larger amounts of blood to the needed areas. Eventually, the participant's heart will be able to perform at an increased workload with ease. This gradual progression in performance and in giving the heart (and lungs) time to adapt to the added stress is what becoming aerobically fit is all about.

Because heart rate is a reliable indicator of how much work the cardiorespiratory system is doing as one exercises, taking the heart rate has become a routine practice during exercise. As a trainer, you can help individuals measure the amount of work they are doing by having them check their heart rates periodically. It is recommended that heart rates be checked regularly, every 5 to 10 minutes for beginners and 15 minutes for experienced exercisers (American Council on Exercise, 1993), so that exercisers know whether they are working out hard enough to achieve aerobic training benefits. If they are not working out at an adequate intensity, then you need to help them make the necessary adjustments (refer to Step 4 on page 14). A good system for monitoring heart rates involves the following steps.

Step 1: Calculating the target heart rate range.

Teach participants to calculate their target heart rate range at the first training session. Prepare handouts of the formula presented here, and use posters to reinforce your points.

The following simple formula is commonly used to calculate a target heart rate range for a normal, healthy adult. The formula and an explanation of what each number represents follow.

Table 2.1 Approximated Shift of Blood Flow Rest to Exercise

Site	% of flow during rest	% of flow during exercise
Skin	5	10
Bone	5	1
Brain	15	6
Heart	5	5
Liver, stomach, and intestines	30	5
Kidneys	25	3
Skeletal muscles	15	70

Data from *Textbook of Work Physiology* (3rd ed., p. 152) by P.-O. Åstrand and K. Rodahl, 1986, New York: McGraw-Hill. Copyright 1986 by McGraw-Hill.

1. **220 – your age = maximal heart rate**

   The number 220 is a constant or index number representing the heart's anatomical and physiological limits. Age is subtracted because after age 25 the maximal heart rate starts to decline progressively at an estimated 1 beat per year.

2. **Maximal heart rate x .55 = lower limit of target heart rate range**

   Maximal heart rate x .90 = upper limit of target heart rate range

   To train the cardiorespiratory system, participants need to work out at a rate between 55/65 percent and 90 percent of their maximal heart rate. This is the range the YMCA recommends for healthy adults.

These two numbers represent the target heart rate range. When participants perform aerobic activities, they should strive to maintain their heart rates within this range. It represents a pace that is sufficient for achieving cardiorespiratory training benefits and that can be reasonably maintained. If participants stay within this range, they can work out continuously for 20 to 30 minutes, whereas if they exceed this range, they may fatigue after only 10 or 15 minutes. The lower end of the range is a safe goal for beginners, but more advanced participants should work out at the upper end of their ranges.

As an example, let's calculate the target heart rate range at 55/65 percent and 90 percent maximum for a 20-year-old woman.

$$220 - 20 = 200$$
$$200 \times .55 = 110$$
$$200 \times .90 = 180$$

Her exercise target heart rate range would be 110 to 180 bpm.

Step 2: Taking the heart rate.

Teach participants to locate a pulse and to count the heart rate. It is easy to feel the pulse in the carotid artery in the neck (on either side of the Adam's apple). To do so, follow the jawline to the throat and press lightly (see figure 2.2a). The radial pulse, at the edge of the wrist under the thumb (see figure 2.2b), is also easy to locate with the fingers. Major arteries lie close to the skin at these two sites, which creates a strong beat.

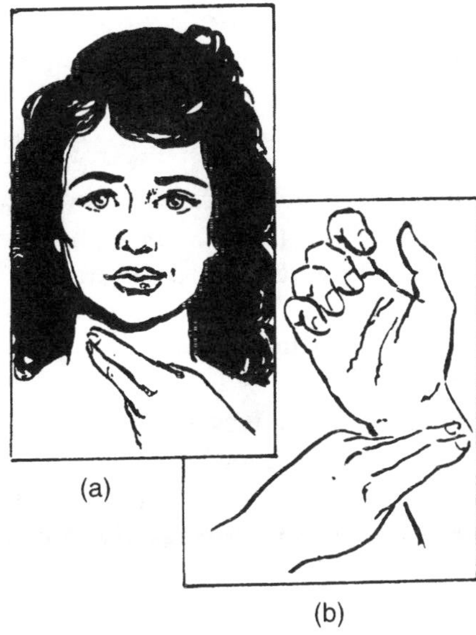

Figure 2.2 Locations for taking the heart rate: *(a)* the carotid pulse; *(b)* the radial pulse.

Have participants take a pulse count with the index and middle fingers. When taking the pulse on the neck, they should apply only light pressure. Under excessive pressure, reflex action may cause the heart rate to slow momentarily.

Have participants practice taking heart rates a few times prior to the first workout. Teach participants to keep moving rather than standing still while counting heart rate. Stopping abruptly can cause blood to pool in the arms and legs, returning to the heart less efficiently. The result can be light-headedness and even fainting.

Have participants check their heart rates during the first 15 seconds after stopping the exercise. Each exerciser should count his or her heartbeats for 10 seconds, beginning the count on a beat, which is counted as "zero," and then multiply that number by 6. This gives the number of beats per minute.

Step 3: Understanding the benefits of staying in the target range.

Explain to participants the benefits and importance of working out within the target range:

a. They can be sure of getting a just-vigorous-enough workout;
b. they won't fatigue as quickly; and

c. once they're familiar with working out within their ranges, they can gauge their participation in any aerobic activity.

Step 4: Making adjustments.

Teach participants how to raise the heart rate by adjusting the level of performance. The heart rate increases when movement speed and/or intensity increases. That is, an individual who is working out below the training heart rate (not too common) can increase workout intensity by doing the exercises more vigorously.

An individual working out above the target range (which is quite common) can adjust by doing just the opposite—decreasing speed and/or intensity. Similarly, the intensity of locomotor skills can easily be adjusted, as in switching from jogging to walking.

As participants continue to train, their resting heart rates will begin to decrease after 6 to 8 weeks into the program due to adaptations of the cardiorespiratory system. Beginning participants' heart rates will rise quickly in response to exercise, but as they become more fit, they will have to work harder to attain and maintain their target heart rates.

Step 5: Using visual aids.

Make posters depicting the heart rate formula, the locations for taking the heart rate, and adjustments that can be made to affect the heart rate. Skillfully designed posters add color and brighten up the workout area. More importantly, posters help reinforce your teaching and remind individuals of the points you've made about working out safely within the target heart rate range.

An alternative method of determining exercise intensity is the rating of perceived exertion (RPE) scale. Based on a subjective determination of how hard they are working, participants rate their efforts on a scale of 6 to 20. This scale, originally developed in 1970 and then revised in 1985 by Gunnar Borg, has proven to be both valid and reliable. The scale is shown in figure 2.3.

RPE can be used either alone or in combination with the heart rate to monitor exercise intensity. It is particularly valuable for participants who take medication that affects their heart rate.

A final method of checking the level of exercise intensity is the "talk test." This simply means that an exerciser should easily be able to talk to someone during a workout. If the exerciser can't be-

6	No exertion at all
7	Extremely light
8	
9	Very light
10	
11	Light
12	
13	Somewhat hard
14	
15	Hard (heavy)
16	
17	Very hard
18	
19	Extremely hard
20	Maximal exertion

Borg RPE/ scale

Figure 2.3 Borg's RPE scale.

Reprinted, by permission, from G. Borg, 1998, *Borg's Perceived Exertion and Pain Scales* (Champaign, IL: Human Kinetics), 47.

cause of lack of breath, the level of intensity is too high and should be lowered.

The Respiratory System

The cardiovascular system is only half of the cardiorespiratory system; the lungs are the other half. The lungs' main function is to aerate blood. During exercise, as well as during rest, carbon dioxide and oxygen are continually exchanged between the tiny air sacs of the lungs and the capillaries of the cardiovascular system. This exchange route can be traced as follows.

Air is inhaled through the nose or mouth and travels down an elaborate system of elastic tubing (see figure 2.4). The trachea divides into bronchi that, in turn, branch into smaller tubes. These tubes (*bronchioles*) continue to branch until they become microscopic air sacs known as *alveoli*, which are surrounded by capillaries. The alveoli are extremely thin-walled structures that allow a rapid exchange of oxygen (O_2) and carbon dioxide (CO_2).

As you saw in figure 2.1, the vascular arrangement between the heart and lungs is quite simple. The right ventricle pumps blood into the pulmonary artery. The blood then flows through the pulmonary artery, finally arriving at the pulmonary capillaries that surround the alveoli. The

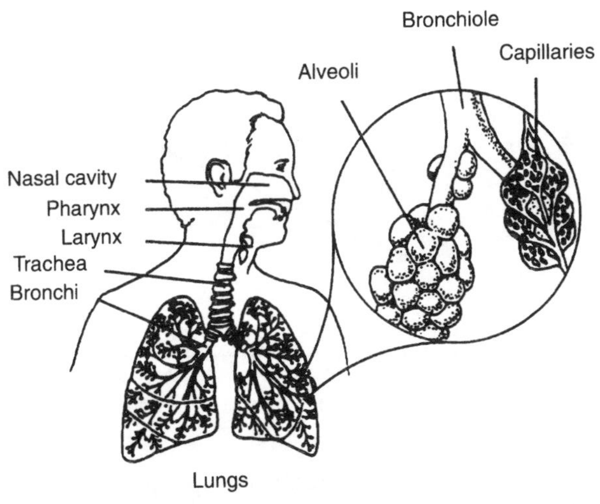

Figure 2.4 The tubular structure of the lungs.

exchange of gases takes place due to the high concentration of these gases in the alveoli and in the surrounding capillaries. The alveoli have a high concentration of oxygen, whereas the capillaries (because they are carrying blood that has already circulated and delivered oxygen throughout the body) have a high concentration of carbon dioxide (see figure 2.5). After the gases are exchanged, the blood flows back through the pulmonary veins and eventually back into the left atrium. From there the blood flows into the left ventricle to the aortic valve and on through the body. The blood delivers oxygen to all body cells, and carbon dioxide is blown off with every exhalation in the lungs.

Aerobic training improves the ability of the heart and lungs to perform this teamwork task of taking in oxygen and delivering it to the working muscles during exercise.

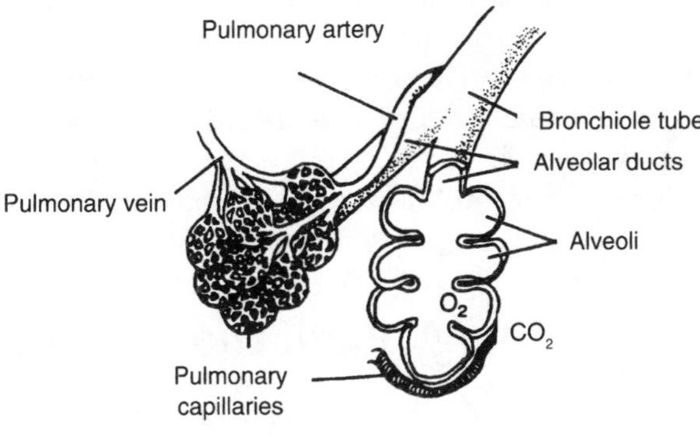

Figure 2.5 Exchange of carbon dioxide and oxygen between the alveoli and capillaries.

How Aerobically Fit Are Your Participants?

Participants in personal training programs are often curious as to how aerobically fit they are compared with participants in other activities. Understanding oxygen consumption will help you begin to see what aerobic fitness is all about. The term for the quantity of oxygen used by the body is *oxygen consumption*. Of the many factors that affect oxygen consumption, three of the most important are the following:

- **Oxygen transport**—This is how much oxygen the blood can carry.
- **Oxygen delivery**—This is how much oxygen can get to the active cells.
- **Oxygen use**—This is how much oxygen the cells can extract from the blood passing by them.

The amount of oxygen being used per minute by an exerciser is another way (like monitoring the heart rate) of determining the intensity at which a person is working out. Oxygen consumption, or $\dot{V}O_2$ as it is symbolically written, is traditionally measured in liters of oxygen consumed per minute (a dot above the V denotes a per-minute measurement). $\dot{V}O_2$ comparisons can be made among persons of different sizes, as $\dot{V}O_2$ measurements are divided by body weight. A $\dot{V}O_2$ measurement, therefore, is expressed as milliliters of oxygen per kilogram (1 kg = 2.2 lb) of body weight per minute, or ml/kg/min. The amount of oxygen being consumed at rest (for example, by sitting and reading this book) is approximately 3.5 to 4.5 ml/kg/min. Depending on the pace or intensity of the exercise being performed, this resting value can increase to 42 ml/kg/min or more.

To determine the intensity of exercise for an individual based on $\dot{V}O_2$, his or her maximal oxygen consumption (max $\dot{V}O_2$) must also be known. Max $\dot{V}O_2$—the maximal amount of oxygen that can be used per minute — is usually determined in a laboratory setting by a maximal stress test. A typical test involves walking, jogging, or running (depending on the individual's level of fitness) on a treadmill under the supervision of a team led by an exercise physiologist. Once a person's max $\dot{V}O_2$ is known, his or her $\dot{V}O_2$ during exercise can be calculated as a percentage of the max $\dot{V}O_2$. The American College of Sports Medicine (1998) recommends that a healthy individual perform aerobic exercise at 40% to 85% of his or her max $\dot{V}O_2$.

Maximal oxygen consumption, like training heart rate, is influenced by age, heredity, and level of physical fitness. For example, after the age of 30 there is a slow but progressive loss of aerobic capacity—by the age of 65 it may have declined 35 percent. Some exercisers inherit larger aerobic capacities and therefore are able to train at higher performance levels. And the more fit a person becomes, the higher the max $\dot{V}O_2$.

The Linear Relationship Between Heart Rate and Oxygen Consumption

Measuring the amount of an exerciser's oxygen use per minute is obviously not as convenient as measuring his or her heart rate per minute. However, research on aerobic exercise has shown that the two values increase and decrease as a pair. In other words, as the heart rate goes up, so does the amount of oxygen being consumed. This linear relationship makes a lot of aerobic fitness measurement calculations possible. For example, if you are working at a certain heart rate during aerobic exercise, it is possible to estimate the amount of oxygen you are using even without the elaborate equipment necessary to measure oxygen consumption. For example, a heart rate of 100 beats per minute (light work) is accompanied by a $\dot{V}O_2$ of approximately 10 ml/kg/min, while a heart rate of 135 (moderate work) denotes a $\dot{V}O_2$ of approximately 20 ml/kg/min (see figure 2.6). This linear relationship is not true, however, for anaerobic exercise (such as weightlifting or sprinting), in which the heart rate may increase much more than the $\dot{V}O_2$.

To convert a liter of oxygen to ml/kg/min you need to know the person's body weight. For the sake of standardizing examples, exercise physiologists have created and use what are known as the reference man and reference woman. The reference man weighs 70 kg, and the reference woman 58 kg. So, a $\dot{V}O_2$ of 20 ml/kg/min with a heart rate of 135 can be converted for a woman to 1160 ml/min (i.e., 20×58) or 1.16 L/min and for a man to 1400 ml/min (i.e., 20×70) or 1.4 L/min.

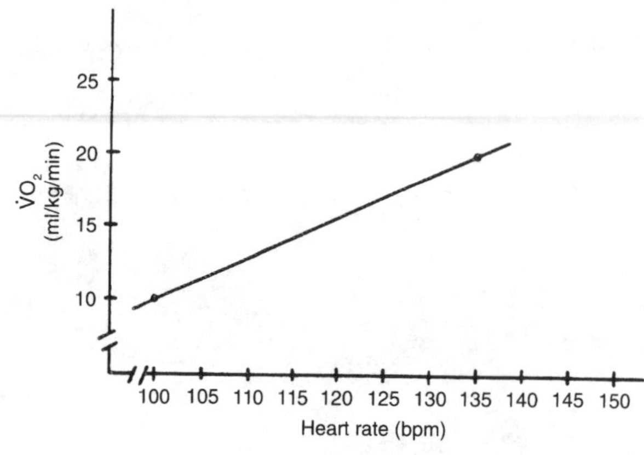

Figure 2.6 The linear relationship between heart rate and oxygen consumption for aerobic exercise.

Caloric Cost of Aerobic Exercise

Another interesting physiological relationship is between oxygen consumption and the number of calories (kcal) expended during exercise. Elementary math teaches us that certain units of measurement can be converted into others; for example, 12 inches equal 1 foot, and 3 teaspoons equal 1 tablespoon. Likewise, the amount of oxygen being consumed during exercise can be converted into the amount of calories being used per minute. For example, when 1 liter of oxygen is used, approximately 5 kcal are expended. Hence, a woman exercising at a moderate pace with a heart rate of 135 beats per minute, using approximately 20 ml/kg/min (1.16 L/min), would expend approximately 5.8 kcal a minute. A man using approximately 1.4 L/min would expend about 7.0 kcal per minute.

Exercise physiologists use this energy conversion to calculate the approximate number of calories expended in aerobic exercise. Most studies confirm that working out at a moderate intensity in your training heart rate range will expend between 6 and 8 calories per minute during aerobic exercise. In table 2.2 you can see how the caloric cost of aerobic exercise compares to that of other activities.

Energy Production

For some, energy is a rather abstract word. Everyone has it, makes it, and uses it, but we often describe it differently. All of the energy in our solar

Table 2.2 Physical Activity and Caloric Expenditure

Work intensity	Heart rate	Calories/min	Activities
Light	Below 120	Under 5	Walking, golf, bowling, volleyball, most forms of work
Moderate*	120 to 150	5 to 10	Jogging, tennis, cycling, hiking, aerobic dance exercise, racquetball, strenuous work, basketball
Heavy	Above 150	Above 10	Running, fast swimming, other brief intense efforts

*Preferred pace for weight control benefits.

Reprinted, by permission, from B.J. Sharkey, 1974, *Physiological Fitness and Weight Control* (Missoula, MT: Mountain Press).

system originates from the sun. Solar energy reaches the Earth as sunlight. The millions of green plants that grow on the Earth store some of that solar energy as chemical energy and use it to produce their food. Unfortunately, people cannot produce their own food in such a manner, and we must eat plants and animals for our energy supply. The food we eat does not supply the energy we need directly. Instead, it is changed chemically into usable nutrients. These nutrients are distributed throughout the body, with some being stored as an energy compound in cells. This energy-rich compound stored within the muscle cells is adenosine triphosphate, commonly referred to as ATP.

The energy that muscles use for contraction is made within the muscle cells. How the energy is made and how fast it is produced depend on the type of activity being performed and on the person's level of physical fitness.

Anaerobic Energy Production

During rest as well as exercise, movement can occur as long as ATP is available at the site of muscle contraction. ATP, however, is available only in very limited amounts, so it must continually be broken down and resynthesized within the muscle cells. Three different energy systems that are capable of resynthesizing ATP have been identified in the body. Two of these systems do not require oxygen to be present to produce ATP. They are called anaerobic energy-producing systems and include the ATP-PC and the lactic acid systems. These systems supply energy for short-term, high-intensity exercise. A slower system requiring oxygen to be present is the aerobic energy system. All three systems actually go into operation during muscle contraction. The amount of energy needed to sustain an activity and the activity's duration denote which system will produce the predominant amount of energy to sustain that activity.

As you begin to work out vigorously, there is a temporary shortage of oxygen being delivered to the working muscles. The energy for the first 2 to 3 minutes of a workout is predominantly supplied anaerobically. The skeletal muscles are prepared to produce energy for approximately 2 to 3 minutes without oxygen. Because an aerobic exercise workout lasts for 45 to 60 minutes, the energy is predominantly supplied aerobically.

A popular term you may have heard related to anaerobic energy production is *lactic acid*. Lactic acid is a by-product of producing energy anaerobically. When lactic acid accumulates to high levels in the blood it causes muscular fatigue. However, the first few minutes of exercise as well as any change of pace during the workout would be hindered without the anaerobic energy system and its accompanying lactic acid production.

Lactic acid is not the villain of exercise it is often made out to be. With training the body becomes better equipped to handle lactic acid. Several efficient changes occur in the body during training that result in decreased production of lactic acid and increased removal of it from the bloodstream.

Aerobic Energy Production

Aerobic exercise periods usually last for 20 to 30 minutes. All of the movements/exercises are performed at a submaximal level of performance, meaning that you work out at an intensity below an all-out, sprinting kind of pace. Because the exercise is submaximal, the cardiorespiratory system has plenty of time to deliver the needed oxygen to the working muscles. Thus, the energy for aerobic exercise is predominantly supplied aerobically.

Aerobic exercise at varying intensity (heart rate) and duration (length of the workout) trains all the energy systems to some degree. Training the aerobic energy system requires gradually increasing the duration, pace, or effort level of an activity to allow the energy system to adapt to its new demands.

The Central Nervous System

What makes the cardiorespiratory system adjust its activity rate from rest to exercise? What makes muscles contract and relax at the right time? Somehow messages must be sent throughout the body to get these systems to speed up or slow down correctly. The main switchboard that organizes these electrical messages is the central nervous system, comprised of the brain and the spinal cord (see figure 2.7). Millions of nerves of varying sizes branch off from the spinal cord and spread much like blood vessels that continually branch out from the main arteries and veins. This network of nerves throughout the body allows you to react to your environment.

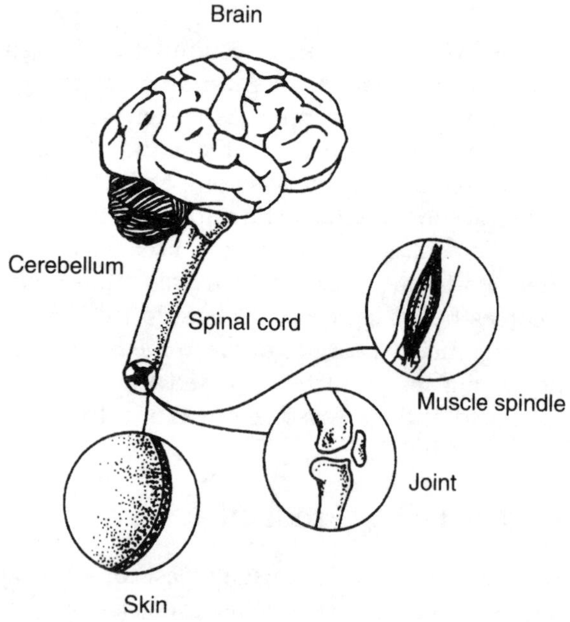

Figure 2.7 The central nervous system.

Let's consider a few functions the nervous system provides for the cardiorespiratory system and the muscles at rest and during exercise. Without these little electrical signals flowing back and forth between the brain and the body systems, nothing in the body could function.

Signals to the Cardiorespiratory System

The heart has its own electrical system (see figure 2.8). The signals sent over this system are responsible for maintaining a regular heartbeat. Any interference with this electrical network results in an irregular beat, meaning that the atria and the ventricles cannot contract in normal sequence.

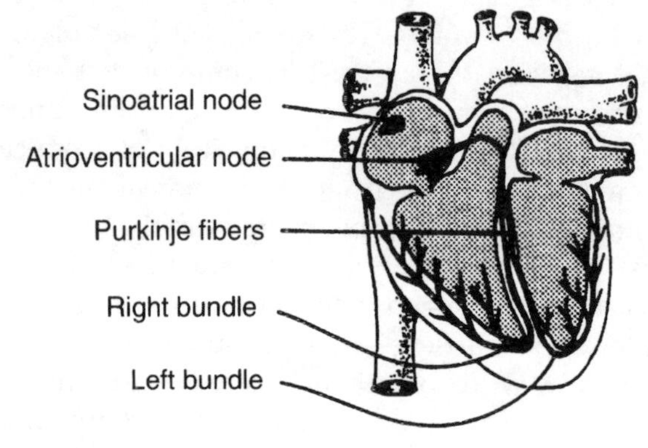

Figure 2.8 The heart's electrical system.

A clump of nerve tissue (the *sinoatrial node*) located in the right atrium receives signals from the brain and sets the pace for the heart to contract. Not surprisingly, this node is often referred to as the heart's pacemaker.

The *atrioventricular node* is located at the junction of the right atrium and the right ventricle. The atrioventricular node receives the electrical impulse from the sinoatrial node and sends it to the *Purkinje fibers*, which form a network that spreads the impulse throughout the ventricles. The fibers are grouped into the right and left bundles.

Electrocardiogram

An electrocardiogram (EKG) is a tool used to assess the heart's ability to transmit its electrical impulses. An electrocardiograph mechanically records the heart's electrochemical activity. When the impulse travels through the heart, electrical current generated at the surface of the heart muscle spreads into fluid surrounding the heart. A minute portion of the current flows to the surface of the body (Guyton, 1974). Electrodes properly placed on the skin around the heart (see figure 2.9) can pick up this electrical current and transmit it to a recording instrument.

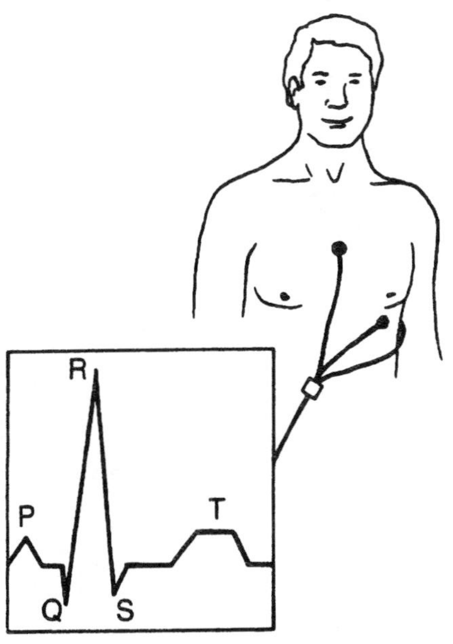

Figure 2.9 Placement of electrodes for and results of a normal electrocardiogram.

Figure 2.9 depicts a normal EKG. Each segment of the line indicates a portion of the conduction of the heart's current. The curve labeled P wave is caused by the current generated as the sinoatrial node initiates an impulse through the atria. The QRS complex results from the impulse passing through the Purkinje system and the ventricles. The T wave of the line represents the recovery of the electrical changes in the ventricles. The atrial recovery is not visible on the EKG because it is masked by the strong QRS complex of the ventricles.

An EKG is often part of an exercise stress test. Because the heart is performing more work during the stress of exercise, abnormalities are more likely to show up then than during a resting EKG.

The Blood Vessels

Before, during, and after exercise, the nervous system regulates the heart rate. Nerve impulses also affect the blood vessels. When necessary, such as during redistribution of blood from the major internal organs to working limbs in preparation for exercise, the nervous system sends messages to the blood vessels supplying certain areas to dilate (become larger) or constrict (become smaller).

Breathing

The rate of breathing during vigorous exercise is also partially controlled by the nervous system. Messages are sent to the muscles that surround the rib cage to contract and help lift the rib cage at a faster rate.

Signals to the Muscles

Skeletal muscle fibers are united with many nerve fibers. When impulses are sent to the muscles via the central nervous system, the muscles contract, and when the impulses stop, the muscles relax. One motor nerve fiber innervates anywhere from 1 to 150 or more muscle fibers. All of the muscle fibers innervated by the motor nerve work as a unit; that is, they contract and relax at the same time. Figure 2.10 shows a single motor nerve innervating several muscle fibers.

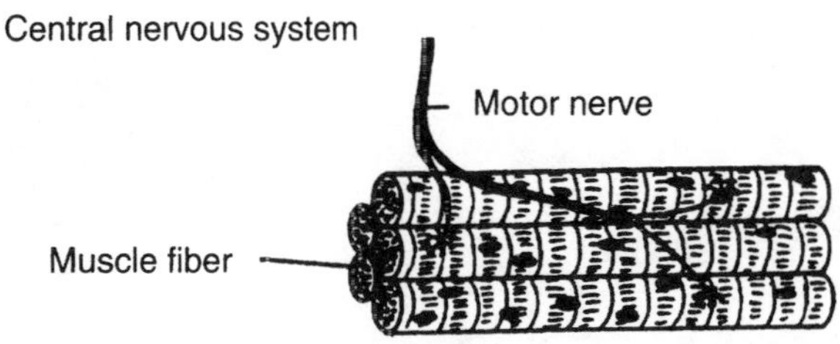

Figure 2.10 A motor unit.

The nervous system helps to coordinate the functioning of the body's systems at rest and during exercise. Like all other systems, it too responds to training. Its ability to send nerve impulses to the correct site, at the proper speed, and for the necessary amount of time are all enhanced through training.

Applying Cardiorespiratory Fitness Information to Your Participants

Studies by exercise scientists have shed light on the training effects of aerobic exercise. From these studies general guidelines have emerged concerning the amount, type, intensity, and duration of exercise needed to achieve improvements in fitness. It's essential that as a trainer you understand and apply certain training guidelines or rules when designing your programs.

Prescribing aerobic activity is a science with rules to be applied, which good instructors use to give their participants the safest, most beneficial workouts possible. More detailed information on this is the subject of the next chapter.

3

Cardiorespiratory Exercise Principles and Guidelines

Ralph LaForge, M.S.

* Ralph LaForge, M.S., is a clinical exercise physiologist with 20 years experience working in clinical cardiology and 12 years experience teaching exercise physiology at the University of California, San Diego. He is currently working with the University of North Carolina, Chapel Hill, department of medicine in the cardiology division. He also is the acting director of the Lipid Clinic Preceptorship Training Program at the San Diego Cardiac Center Medical Group, and has developed and implemented numerous programs in exercise science, applied psychobiology, and cardiac rehabilitation.

Cardiorespiratory fitness continues to receive high acclaim as a centerpiece of physical fitness and cardiovascular health. For health and fitness applications, the terms cardiorespiratory fitness, cardiovascular fitness, and aerobic endurance are synonymous. Cardiorespiratory fitness best describes the health and function of the heart, lungs and circulatory system, and is related to cardiorespiratory endurance, which is the ability to persist or sustain activity for prolonged periods. Cardiorespiratory fitness also describes the capacity of the lungs to exchange oxygen and carbon dioxide with the blood, and the circulatory system's ability to transport blood and nutrients to metabolically active tissues for sustained periods without undue fatigue.

Benefits of Cardiovascular Fitness

The numerous benefits of cardiorespiratory fitness (table 3.1) are related to a variety of adaptive physiologic responses to aerobic exercise. Physiologic responses to training—such as an increase in body-fat utilization, a decrease in peripheral vascular resistance, and an increase in maximal oxygen consumption—help decrease the risk of cardiovascular disease by favorably modifying risk factors like obesity, hypertension, and elevated triglycerides and LDL-cholesterol. When such risk factors are removed from participants' health profiles, they can attain an acceptable level of cardiovascular health. Cardiovascular health goes beyond merely attaining aerobic fitness. It defines the status of the heart muscle, its blood vessels, and the circulatory system it serves. Acquiring and maintaining cardiorespiratory fitness is one of the primary pathways to cardiovascular health.

Likewise, aerobic endurance activities have been effective in other conditioning and clinical therapies, such as cardiac and pulmonary rehabilitation, sleep disorder treatment, diabetic treatment, prenatal/postpartum and renal dialysis conditioning, and anxiety- and depression-management programs. In such clinical settings, aerobic exercise must be prescribed and managed carefully by trained exercise specialists or other qualified clinicians. Experienced and qualified personal trainers may form adjunct relationships with such clinicians in order to effectively manage the patient. Referrals from such programs depend on your relationship and knowledge of local clinical rehabilitation programs and/or affiliated health-care institutions.

Cardiorespiratory fitness also serves as a foundation for other fitness programs. The condition-

Table 3.1 Reported Benefits of Cardiorespiratory Exercise

Health benefits	Adaptive physiologic responses
Reduction in blood pressure	Increased lactate threshold
Increased HDL-cholesterol	Decreased resting heart rate
Decreased total cholesterol	Increased heart volume
Decreased body fat stores	Increased resting and maximum stroke volume
Increased aerobic work capacity	Increased maximum cardiac output
Decreased clinical symptoms of anxiety, tension, and depression	Increased maximum oxygen consumption
	Increased capillary density and blood flow to active muscles
Reduction in glucose-stimulated insulin secretion	Increased total blood volume
	Increased maximal ventilation
Increased heart function	Increased lung diffusion capacity
Reduction in mortality in postmyocardial infarction patients	Increased mobilzation and utilization of fat
	Reduced all-cause mortality
	Decreased anxiety and depression
	Decreased incidence of some cancers

Data from *ACSM's Guidelines for Exercise Testing and Prescription*, 1995. Baltimore: Williams & Wilkins.

ing and health of the heart, lungs, and blood vessels are prime ingredients in the safety and performance of nearly all sports and recreational programs. Activities such as tennis, golf, skiing, dancing, skating, basketball, volleyball, boxing, and nearly all muscular strength-training programs will benefit from attaining acceptable levels of cardiorespiratory fitness. Participants with adequate cardiorespiratory fitness generally have more stamina, which translates to less fatigue and fewer risks for certain types of injuries.

Components of an Aerobic Exercise Program

It is imperative for you to understand the physiologic rationale and application of each component of the cardiorespiratory exercise program. The essential components of the written plan are:

1. Warm-up and cool-down
2. Primary cardiorespiratory activity criteria:
   a. Mode of exercise
   b. Frequency of exercise session
   c. Duration of exercise session
   d. Intensity of exercise session
3. Supportive conditioning exercise (e.g., strength and flexibility)
4. Progression plan
5. Safety and cautions

Each of these components must be discussed with the participant and presented in a legible and succinct written form.

Warm-up and Cool-down

Although most fitness professionals teach a variety of warm-up and cool-down techniques, few fully understand their psychological and physiological rationales (table 3.2). Graduated low-level aerobic exercise is essential for maximizing safety and economy of movement during the cardiorespiratory conditioning phase of an exercise session. The warm-up should gradually increase the heart rate, blood pressure,

Table 3.2 Physiological and Psychological Rationale for Warm-up and Cool-down

Warm-up	Cool-down
1. Permits a gradual metabolic adaptation (e.g., oxygen consumption), which enhances cardiorespiratory performance (e.g., a higher maximum cardiac output and oxygen uptake). 2. Prevents the premature onset of blood lactic acid accumulation and fatigue during higher level aerobic exercise. 3. Causes a gradual increase in muscle temperature which decreases the work of contraction and reduces the likelihood of muscle injury. 4. Facilitates neural transmission for motor unit recruitment. 5. Improves coronary blood flow in early stages of the conditioning exercise, lessening the potential for myocardial ischemia. 6. Allows a gradual redistribution of blood flow to active muscles. 7. Increases the elasticity of connective tissue and other muscle components. 8. Provides a screening mechanism for potential musculoskeletal or metabolic problems that may increase at higher intensities. 9. Provides a psychological warm-up to higher levels of work (i.e., increases arousal and focus on exercise).	1. Prevents postexercise venous blood pooling and too rapid a drop in blood pressure, thereby reducing the likelihood of postexercise lightheadedness or fainting. 2. Reduces the immediate postexercise tendency for muscle spasm or cramping. 3. Reduces the concentration of exercise hormones (e.g., norepinephrine) that are at relatively high levels immediately after vigorous aerobic exercise. This reduction will lower the probability of postexercise disturbances in cardiac rhythm.

Data from McArdle, Katch, F., and Katch, V. *Exercise Physiology,* 1991. Baltimore: Williams & Wilkins.

oxygen consumption, dilation of the blood vessels, elasticity of the active muscles, and the heat produced by the active muscle groups. The warm-up should consist of two distinct components:

1. Graduated aerobic warm-up activity (e.g., walking or slow tempo rhythmic calisthenic movements)
2. Flexibility exercise specific to the biomechanical nature of the primary conditioning activity (e.g., calf, quadriceps, and Achilles stretching prior to running or hiking).

Because a warm muscle is more easily stretched than a cold muscle, the flexibility component should be preceded by five to eight minutes of low-level aerobic activity using the same muscle groups. For instance, a 10-minute walk will increase muscle temperature and circulation of the legs, thereby promoting easier and safer stretching of the same muscle groups.

Table 3.3 lists sample warm-up activities for a variety of aerobic exercises. The intensity of the warm-up should be well below that of the primary conditioning activity. The warm-up duration depends on the level and intensity of the primary conditioning activity, as well as the fitness level of the participant.

The cool-down is an integral part of the exercise program. The purpose of the cool-down is to slowly decrease the heart rate and overall metabolism, both of which have been elevated during the conditioning phase. Low-level aerobic exercise, similar to that of the conditioning exercise, is recommended (table 3.3). Walking, slow jogging, cycling with little or no resistance, and slow aquatic activity or swimming are good examples. Cool-down helps prevent the sudden

Table 3.3 Sample Warm-up and Cool-down Activities (including stretching exercise)

Primary Conditioning Exercise	Warm-up/Cool-down Activity
Aerobics (group exercise)	Graduated low-level aerobic activity utilizing same muscle groups
Circuit weight training	Low-level aerobic activity (e.g., walking or cycling, and/or beginning the circuit training session with a set of relatively high-repetition, low-resistance exercises)
Hiking	Graduate from relatively flat terrain at minimal altitudes to steeper terrain and higher altitudes
Jogging and running	Walking, walk-jogging, or jogging at a slower pace
Outdoor cycling	Begin with relatively flat terrain in lower gears; gradually shift to higher gears and steeper terrain
Racquetball, handball, or squash	Walk-jog and/or graduated tempo volleying
Rope skipping	Graduated walking or walk-jogging pace and/or slow tempo rope skipping pace
Sprinting	Jogging and graduated pace in running intervals
Stationary cycling	Start with cycling against little or no resistance at 2/3 of the pedal crank rpm used in the conditioning phase
Stationary exercise devices	Begin with 50 percent to 60 percent of intended conditioning workload or speed; the duration of submaximal graduated warm-up should be proportional to the peak intensity of the conditioning workload
Step exercise	Low-level aerobic activity (e.g., walking or cycling, stair climber, rowing) and/or relatively low-tempo step exercise
Swimming	Begin with slow crawl and gradually increase arm stroke and pace, and/or begin with short 1- or 2-lap slow intervals
Tennis (competitive)	Walk-jog and/or graduated tempo volleying proportional to the level of the game

pooling of blood in the veins and ensures adequate circulation to the skeletal muscles, heart, and brain. Cool-down may aid in preventing delayed muscle stiffness and reduces any tendency toward post-exercise fainting and dizziness. For high cardiovascular risk participants, a gradual decrease in the intensity of exercise is crucial. Sudden cessation of exercise without cool-down may adversely affect cardiac function because a relatively high concentration of adrenaline remains in the blood from the conditioning exercise. Sudden exercise cessation also may adversely affect filling pressures of the heart, putting a weak heart at risk. The length of the cool-down phase is proportional to the intensity and length of the conditioning phase. A typical 30- to 40-minute conditioning phase at 70 percent of maximum heart rate would warrant a 5- to 10-minute cool-down. The aerobic component of the cool-down phase should be followed by several minutes of stretching those muscle groups active in the conditioning phase.

Primary Cardiorespiratory Exercise Criteria

For maximum effectiveness and safety, the cardiorespiratory exercise program must include specific instructions on the mode, frequency, duration, and intensity of exercise. Most of these criteria originate from the American College of Sports Medicine (ACSM) exercise guidelines and position statements to ensure standardization and validity in the broad field of exercise science (ACSM, 1998).

To avoid confusion, the exercise criteria listed in this section are those needed for measurable improvements in cardiorespiratory fitness (e.g., increase in $\dot{V}O_2$ max). This is an important clarification, since the exercise threshold criteria for health enhancement are generally lower (ACSM, 1995; Haskell, 1994). For instance, the minimum duration and intensity of physical activity required for health enhancement is 15 minutes at 40 percent of $\dot{V}O_2$ max. Here, health enhancement refers to reduced risk of degenerative disease, such as cardiovascular disease.

Exercise Mode

Selection of the exercise mode is made on the basis of the participant's functional capacity, interests, time availability, equipment and facilities, and personal goals. Any activity that uses large muscle groups, is rhythmical and cardiorespiratory in nature, and is maintained continuously can be used. The American College of Sports Medicine classifies cardiorespiratory endurance activities into three groups:

- **Group 1**—Physical activities in which exercise intensity is easily maintained at a constant level, and interindividual variation in energy expenditure is relatively low. Examples are walking and cycling, especially treadmill and cycle ergometry.
- **Group 2**—Physical activities in which energy expenditure is related to skill, but for a given individual can provide a constant intensity: aerobic dance, aerobic step exercise, slide exercise, swimming, skating, and cross-country skiing.
- **Group 3**—Physical activities that are quite variable in both skill and intensity: soccer, basketball, and racquet sports.

Group 1 activities are recommended when precise control of the exercise intensity is necessary, as in the beginning stages of a conditioning program. These activities can be performed in a continuous or discontinuous (interval) format, depending upon the participant's fitness level and personal preference, and are useful during all stages of conditioning. Group 2 activities are useful because of the enjoyment provided by group exercise and settings other than an exercise gym. Adding Group 2 exercise to a training program helps foster compliance and reduce boredom. Because of the skill and variable intensity nature of Group 3 activities, they require a base level of conditioning using Group 1 activities. Group 3 activities tend to be group- or team-sport oriented and, therefore, provide greater interest and compliance for many individuals. Group 3 activities should be cautiously considered for high-risk, deconditioned, or symptomatic individuals.

Exercise Frequency

Frequency refers to the number of exercise sessions per week included in the program. The frequency of exercise depends on the duration and intensity of the exercise session. Lower-intensity exercise performed for shorter periods can warrant more sessions per week. To improve both cardiorespiratory fitness and maintain body fat at near optimum levels, a participant should exercise at least three days per week with no more than two days between sessions. The American College of Sports Medicine recommends three to five days per week for most aerobic programs. When a participant starts an aerobic exercise program, exercising every other day for at least the first eight weeks is appropriate. For those with a poor functional capacity, one to two daily sessions may be recommended. Those with an average functional capacity should exercise at least three times per week on alternate days. In general, participants who are just beginning weight-bearing exercise, such as aerobic dancing, aerobic step exercise, and jogging, should have at least 36 to 48 hours of rest between workouts to prevent overuse injuries and promote adequate bone/joint stress recovery. This is especially true with those who are overweight.

Exercise Duration

Duration refers to the number of minutes of exercise during the conditioning period. The conditioning period, exclusive of the warm-up and cool-down, may vary from as little as 5 to 60 or more minutes. The duration required for cardiorespiratory benefits is dependent upon the exercise intensity. Take a given intensity of exercise, for example, 75 percent of functional capacity, and compare it to an exercise duration of five minutes versus 20 minutes at this intensity. Obviously, more total energy is expended during the 20-minute exercise session. The conditioning response to an exercise session is the result of the product of the intensity and duration of exercise (total energy expenditure). Beginners who are in the lower cardiorespiratory fitness classifications should begin with 10 to 20 minutes of aerobic conditioning. Very deconditioned individuals may be more suited for multiple sessions of short duration, such as five to 10 minutes. Those in the average classification should go for 15 to 45 minutes, and those in the high fitness classification can go for 30 to 60 minutes.

Intensity of Exercise

Intensity refers to the speed or exercise workload. As a rule, the American College of Sports Medicine (ACSM, 1998) recommends a range of 55/65 percent to 90 percent of maximal heart rate (MHR). This range approximates 40 percent to 85 percent of heart rate reserve (Karvonen formula) and maximal oxygen uptake (functional capacity or aerobic capacity). It is important for you to understand that for any given percentage of maximum oxygen uptake, except for maximum exercise intensities, the percentage of maximum heart rate will be somewhat higher (table 3.4).

From a physiologic point of view, this 40 percent to 85 percent of maximum oxygen uptake range is the goal for cardiorespiratory training benefits. Lower intensities, such as 50 percent to 60 percent of maximal oxygen consumption and heart rate maximum reserve, are advised for beginners in the lower cardiorespiratory fitness levels. Persons with very low fitness levels, however, can benefit from training intensities as low as 40 percent to 50 percent of maximal oxygen uptake. Exercise intensities as high as 75 percent to 85 percent of maximal oxygen uptake and heart rate reserve may be more appropriate for those who are apparently healthy and in the higher fitness classifications. Overall, the average exercise intensity for apparently healthy adults is usually between 60 percent and 70 percent of their maximum oxygen uptake.

Table 3.4 Relationship Between Percent Maximal Aerobic Capacity ($\dot{V}O_2$ max) and Percent Maximal Heart Rate

Percent Max Heart Rate	Percent $\dot{V}O_2$ max
50	28
60	42
70	56
80	70
90	83
100	100

Reprinted, by permission, from W. McArdle, F. Katch, and V. Katch, 1991, *Exercise Physiology*. (Baltimore: Williams & Wilkins), 435.

Exercise intensity and health-related outcomes

Years of research on exercise and health has made it clear that such health-related outcomes as increased HDL-cholesterol, decreased blood pressure, improved glucose tolerance, reduced blood clotting tendency (fibrinolysis), and reduced anxiety can result from moderate intensities of exercise (i.e., 40 percent to 60 percent of maximum oxygen uptake). In some cases, even lower intensities are recommended (Haskell, 1994).

Supportive Conditioning Exercise

All cardiorespiratory exercise programs must be supported by flexibility, strength, and even neuromuscular fitness exercise in order to enhance the efficiency of aerobic exercise (exercise economy) and minimize musculoskeletal injury. Although some of this supportive exercise, such as stretching, can be part of the warm-up and/or cool-down, it is prudent to add several separate sessions per week that improve the strength of the back, legs, and abdomen. Stretching and range-of-motion exercises are fundamental to a successful cardiorespiratory fitness program. Incorporating various neuromuscular relaxation activities into the cool-down phase of the program is appropriate for those coming from high-stress work environments who need more than just aerobic exercise. You can help your participants relax both mentally and physically by teaching them easy stretching and mental relaxation skills simultaneously.

Cardiorespiratory Fitness Goals

The goals of cardiorespiratory exercise must be clearly stated in the written exercise plan to reinforce compliance and motivation and for assessment during follow up. The participant's implementation and progression plan must reflect these goals and depict means of achieving them safely and realistically. The following are examples of areas that can be addressed in the formulation of cardiorespiratory exercise and activity goals:

1. Overall acquisition and maintenance of cardiorespiratory fitness (e.g., Kcal/day energy expenditure, mastery of jogging, 20-pound weight loss)
2. Cardiovascular risk factor modification
    a. Body composition
    b. Blood pressure reduction
    c. Cholesterol control
    d. Stress and anxiety reduction
3. Performance objectives
    a. Personal accomplishment (e.g., 10K run, 1-mile swim, or 6-mile hike)
    b. Increase physical stamina

Progression Plan

A written progression plan with periodic reevaluation is crucial. This plan must provide details for a graduated progression in the frequency, duration, and intensity of exercise. There must be sufficient flexibility in the rate of progression so that the plan comfortably adjusts to the participant's cardiorespiratory and musculoskeletal response. The rate of progression depends upon a number of factors:

- individual level of fitness (aerobic capacity)
- age
- health status
- cardiorespiratory response to exercise
- individual preferences and goals
- social and family support
- level of exercise initiative and motivation
- access to appropriate facilities and equipment

Three stages of progression for the cardiorespiratory endurance exercise plan are identified in the American College of Sports Medicine guidelines (ACSM, 1995): the initial conditioning stage, the improvement conditioning stage, and the maintenance conditioning stage.

Initial Conditioning Stage

This stage usually lasts four to six weeks or longer and includes low-level aerobic activities, stretching, and light calisthenics. Exercise frequency should begin with every other day. Depending upon initial level of fitness and functional capacity, duration should start with 12 to 15 minutes and gradually increase according to the participant's cardiorespiratory and musculoskeletal response. For those with low functional capacity (4 to 7 METS or less), it may be appropriate to prescribe low-level aerobic interval exercise of two to five minutes at a time. The most important thing to remember during the initial conditioning stage is to be conservative with the exercise intensity. For example, if the individual has a 9 MET functional capacity (31.5 ml/kg/min $\dot{V}O_2$ max), begin at a conservative 40 percent to 60 percent of this value or at about 4 METS. Here, exercise heart rate should begin at approximately 40 percent to 60 percent of heart rate reserve (Karvonen). This initial intensity range is lower than that previously recommended because of enhanced safety and the number of health benefits that can be realized from lower-intensity activities.

Improvement Conditioning Stage

This is the primary conditioning stage for most aerobic training programs. It may last from 8 to 20 weeks, and the rate of progression in intensity is more rapid. The exercise intensity can be increased to the next highest level than that completed in the initial conditioning stage, and within the 55/65 percent to 90 percent of maximal heart rate (40 percent to 85 percent of $\dot{V}O_2$ max or heart rate reserve) depending on fitness level and age. Exercise duration should be increased every two to three weeks according to the participant's response and goals. It is important to periodically review progress at two- to four-week intervals during this stage, either by direct monitoring or by assessing self-report data (RPE, heart rate, symptoms, caloric expenditure).

Maintenance Stage

When participants reach their target functional capacity or primary goals, the maintenance stage begins. This stage is usually reached after the first 6 months of training, but it may be delayed as long as 12 months, depending upon goals. In any case, it is important to reassess goals at the beginning of this stage. Maintenance of a particular level of cardiorespiratory fitness can be derived from an exercise program that has similar energy requirements to that of the conditioning program. Cardiorespiratory fitness can often be maintained by regularly engaging in a variety of endurance-related sports activities that are fun and enjoyable.

Cautions

The last component of an exercise plan involves using individual information to ensure each participant's exercise safety with specific precautions. List any personal or environmental information that reduces the risk of exercise injury or that may compromise exercise safety. Individualized comments such as those describing hot, humid environments or avoiding musculoskeletal symptoms specific to the participant should be included. Another useful format is to list several cautions that are standard for nearly all exercise programs:

- Do not exercise for at least 90 minutes after a meal.
- Avoid continuing exercise with chest discomfort, lightheadedness, or dizziness.
- Reduce exercise intensity in response to very hot or humid environments or to altitudes above 5,000 feet.
- Avoid exercise with tenderness in a joint (for example, a knee or foot) that tends to worsen with activity.
- Avoid strenuous aerobic exercise during viral infections such as the flu or upper-respiratory tract infection.

Table 3.5 lists some of the reasons for which participants should temporarily stop exercising.

Training Methods

Once the mode, frequency, duration, and intensity of exercise have been established, you must choose the appropriate training method. The choice provides the foundation for the exercise progression plan. Selection requires understanding the physiological response to various training methods and, preferably, personal experience with each of those methods. As with exercise intensity and progression, the training method depends on the functional fitness level and the goals of the participant. There are five major training methods (Heyward, 1984; Wells and Pate, 1988):

1. Continuous training
   a. Intermediate slow distance
   b. Long slow distance

Table 3.5 Reasons to Temporarily Defer Exercise

Recurrent illness
Progression of cardiac disease
Abnormally elevated blood pressure
Recent changes in symptoms
Orthopedic problem
Emotional turmoil
Severe sunburn
Alcoholic hangover
Cerebral dysfunction—dizziness or vertigo
Sodium retention—edema or weight gain
Dehydration
Environmental factors
Weather (excessive heat or humidity)
Air pollution (smog or carbon monoxide)
Heavy, large meal within two hours
Coffee, tea, cola (xanthine and other stimulating beverages)
Drugs
Illicit drugs (e.g., tobacco, amphetamines, cocaine, marijuana)
Decongestants
Bronchodilators
Atropine
Weight-reduction agents

Adapted, by permission, from American College of Sports Medicine, 1993, *Resource Manual for the Guidelines for Exercise Testing and Prescription* (Philadelphia: Lea & Febiger), 315.

2. Interval training
    a. Aerobic interval training
    b. Anaerobic interval training
3. Fartlek training
4. Circuit training
5. Aerobic cross training

Continuous Training

Continuous training involves conditioning stage exercise, such as walking, jogging, cycling, swimming, and aerobic dancing. The prescribed intensity is maintained continuously between 40 percent and 85 percent of functional capacity (maximal oxygen uptake). For those with initially low functional capacities, continuous training may be initiated at 40 percent of functional capacity and is usually preceded by four to six weeks of interval training in the initial conditioning stage. In practice, continuous training is divided into two types:

- Intermediate slow distance: Generally from 20 to 60 minutes of continuous aerobic exercise—the most common type of sustained aerobic exercise for fitness improvement. Body-fat reduction, improvement in cardiorespiratory fitness, and cardiovascular risk factor management all are responsive to this type of continuous training.
- Long slow distance (LSD): 60 or more minutes of continuous aerobic exercise, usually employed for athletic training in such sports as cycling and long-distance running. Cardiorespiratory and metabolic demands are great for LSD training. At least six months of successful intermediate

slow distance training should precede LSD training. Increased risk of musculoskeletal injury (e.g., Achilles tendinitis) accompanies this type of prolonged aerobic training.

Interval Training

Interval training consists of repeated intervals of exercise (e.g., jogging or running) interspersed with intervals of relatively light exercise (e.g., walking). Interval training has useful applications for beginning exercisers, as well as experienced, conditioned participants who wish to improve aerobic power. You can use two types of interval training: aerobic and anaerobic. For aerobic or anaerobic interval training the following four variables should be considered when designing an interval training program:

- intensity of work interval (e.g., speed)
- duration of work interval (e.g., distance or time)
- duration of rest or recovery interval
- number of repetitions or repeat intervals

Aerobic Interval Training

Aerobic interval training is best suited for those beginning in the poor- or low-cardiorespiratory fitness classifications (table 3.6) because it is less intense. Generally, aerobic interval training uses exercise bouts of 2 to 15 minutes at an intensity between 60 percent and 80 percent of functional capacity (modified from Wells and Pate). Those with poor- or low-functional capacity should start with 2- to 3-minute exercise intervals at 60 percent to 70 percent of functional capacity. Rest intervals should take approximately the same time as a complete exercise interval. Intervals can be repeated 5 to 10 times depending on the participant's response and program goals; for example, stationary bicycling for three minutes at a work load intensity of 60 percent to 70 percent of functional capacity with a two-minute "rest period" of cycling at zero resistance or load. Hypothetically, this would be repeated 5 to 10 times or for a total workout of 25 to 50 minutes. Higher-intensity and longer-duration aerobic interval training (e.g., 5- to 15-minute bouts at 70 percent to 90 percent of functional capacity) should be reserved for those in higher cardiorespiratory fitness classifications seeking increased aerobic endurance and speed.

Anaerobic Interval Training

Anaerobic interval training is primarily reserved for those in the higher cardiorespiratory fitness classifications who desire to increase speed, lactate threshold, and overall aerobic power. Such training usually results in greater lactic acid concentrations in exercising muscles, and is accompanied by greater muscular discomfort. Because of the relatively high metabolic and cardiorespiratory demands, beginners or those below a 10-MET aerobic capacity should refrain from anaerobic interval training. Although there are many derivations of anaerobic interval training, the training stimulus is usually between 30 seconds and four minutes at an intensity of 85 percent to greater than 100 percent of functional capacity (maximal oxygen uptake). The probability of musculoskeletal injury is greater because of high muscle contraction velocities and forces. The participant, frequently an athlete, should engage in substantial

Table 3.6 Cardiorespiratory Fitness Level Classifications*

Fitness Level	Oxygen Consumption ml/kg/min	METS
Poor	3.5-13.9	1.0-3.9
Low	14.0-24.9	4.0-6.9
Average	25.0-38.9	7.0-10.9
Good	39.0-48.9	11.0-13.9
High	49.0-56.0	14.0-16.0

* For 40-year-old males. Adjustments are appropriate for those over 65 years and those with cardiovascular disease.

Reprinted, by permission, from American College of Sports Medicine, 1991, *Guidelines for Exercise Testing and Prescription*, 4th ed. (Philadelphia: Lea & Febiger), 108.

low-level aerobic warm-up and stretching before vigorous activity.

Fartlek Training

Fartlek training is similar to interval training; however, the work-rest intervals are not systematically or accurately measured. Work-rest intervals and intensity are usually determined by how the participant feels. Over the years, Fartlek training has blossomed in many aerobic-training regimens, primarily to prevent boredom and to enhance aerobic endurance. One of its most useful applications is in running, where the warm-up consists of running for 10 to 20 minutes, then the pace is significantly varied every 5 to 10 minutes. Like long, slow distance aerobic training, this form should be reserved for those in the average or above-average cardiorespiratory fitness levels because of the relatively high demand on the cardiorespiratory system.

Circuit Training

Circuit training takes the participant through a series of exercise stations, with relatively brief rest intervals between each station. The number of stations may range from 4 to 10. Historically, circuit training was designed for enhancing muscular endurance and incorporated mostly muscular endurance exercises such as sit-ups, the bench press, and the leg press. A circuit of 4 to 10 stations with a low-level aerobic warm-up and cool-down station (for example, the stationary bicycle) could be followed by exercise stations using either free weights and/ or single-station weight machines. A good example of circuit training in a more natural environment is par course exercise. This method intersperses walking or jogging with a variety of flexibility, muscular endurance, and strength exercises.

For the last decade or so, aerobic circuit training programs have become popular. Between four and eight aerobic exercise stations with one to five minutes per station and a 15-second rest break between stations constitute a circuit. Stations may include stationary cycling, treadmill exercise, moderate stair climbing, and rowing. Depending on the number of stations, the number of circuits completed would be equivalent to 20 to 50 minutes of aerobic exercise. One key to success is to avoid excessive workloads at each station. Each station should be set at 50 percent to 70 percent of the participant's functional capacity.

Aerobic Cross Training

Aerobic cross training is an individualized combination or composite of all aerobic-training methods, and is characterized by a variety of intensities and modes. It is primarily for those in the maintenance phase of conditioning who want variety and an intensity corresponding to how they feel during a given exercise workout. A good example is a 50-minute workout where the participant warms up by jogging 15 minutes to a nearby pool, then swims for 20 minutes, and then jogs 15 minutes back home. Another example is bicycling 20 minutes to a track or running course and, after 20 minutes of running, cycling back home. Combining a group of aerobic activities into one workout at steady or various intensities is an excellent method of cross training to fight boredom from the same daily workout mode and intensity. This method can also be applied to circuit training in a gym by combining a continuous, relatively low-level aerobic session, such as 20 minutes of stationary cycling, with 10 to 20 minutes of a variety of higher-intensity aerobic intervals on various aerobic ergometers, and concluding with a 5- to 10-minute cool-down of stationary cycling. The many obvious permutations of this method should begin and end with a continuous low-level cardiorespiratory exercise effort for effective physiological warm-up. This method instills variety and is a mini-version of a "training triathlon."

Guidelines for Cardiorespiratory Activity

The best resources for detailed aerobic activities are those that adopt sensible progression guidelines with adequate instruction for each form of exercise (e.g., Greenberg and Pargman, 1989; Howley and Franks, 1992; and Nieman, 1990). Following are guidelines for popular aerobic and sport activities.

Walking

Walking is the easiest aerobic-conditioning activity and is often preferred because of its low injury rate, relative simplicity, and adaptability to busy schedules. Although nearly anyone can incur significant health benefits from walking, several types of participants will respond particularly well to a graduated walking program:

- Those with low functional capacity (2 to 7 METS) who need an initial low-intensity workout.
- Those over 60 years of age who have been sedentary and are just beginning an exercise program.
- Those who are 20 or more pounds overweight.

The energy cost of walking is relatively low compared to that of jogging because of slower speeds; however, at walking speeds of five miles per hour and faster, the oxygen and caloric cost per minute approaches that of jogging or running (table 3.7). There still exists an abundance of misinformation regarding the energy costs of walking versus running. Despite the long-standing claim that walking 1 mile is equivalent to running 1 mile, this is not the case, with the exception of very fast walking speeds of greater than 5 miles per hour (Howley and Franks, 1992; Howley and Glover, 1974). In general, the net caloric cost per mile* of walking is 50 percent to 60 percent of that for running 1 mile. This is an important point if you intend to prescribe and quantify walking mileage for weight management purposes.

Walking is generally less intense than jogging or running, thus longer sessions can be maintained with less likelihood of musculoskeletal injury. When hilly terrain is gradually added to the walking program, there is greater energy expenditure. Perhaps the safest and most effective cardiorespiratory weight-control exercise for those who are 20 to 30 pounds overweight is progressive variable-terrain walking. This walking protocol graduates from walking approximately 2 miles on flat terrain to walking up to 5 or more miles over a variety of grades, such as those found on many urban and rural park and nature trails. It is not difficult to achieve and maintain the walking intensity and duration necessary for acceptable cardiorespiratory fitness. As a general rule, achieving acceptable fitness will require at least 20 minutes (preferably 30 or more minutes) of fast-paced, flat-ground walking or slightly slower variable-terrain walking. When prescribing walking exercise, three things are important:

1. When walking is the primary activity, footwear is important. Specialized walking or hiking shoes are available from many stores, although many walkers will prefer a good pair of running shoes.

*The net cost of exercise is the exercise energy expenditure minus resting energy expenditure. The net cost measures the energy expenditure used over that when just sitting around.

Table 3.7 Energy Costs of Walking (kcal/min)

	Miles Per Hour/METS						
Body Weight (lb)	**2.0/2.5**	**2.5/2.9**	**3.0/3.3**	**3.5/3.7**	**4.0/4.9**	**4.5/6.2**	**5.0/7.9**
110	2.1	2.4	2.8	3.1	4.1	5.2	6.6
120	2.3	2.6	3.0	3.4	4.4	5.6	7.2
130	2.5	2.9	3.2	3.6	4.8	6.1	7.8
140	2.7	3.1	3.5	3.9	5.2	6.6	8.4
150	2.8	3.3	3.7	4.2	5.6	7.0	9.0
160	3.0	3.5	4.0	4.5	5.9	7.5	9.6
170	3.2	3.7	4.2	4.8	6.3	8.0	10.2
180	3.4	4.0	4.5	5.0	6.7	8.4	10.8
190	3.6	4.2	4.7	5.3	7.0	8.9	11.4
200	3.8	4.4	5.0	5.6	7.4	9.4	12.0
210	4.0	4.6	5.2	5.9	7.8	9.9	12.6
220	4.2	4.8	5.5	6.2	8.2	10.3	13.2

Reprinted, by permission, from E. Howley and B.D. Franks, 1992, *Health Fitness Instructor's Handbook*, 2d ed. (Champaign, IL: Human Kinetics), 133.

2. Always warm up and cool down. Begin each session by walking for about five minutes and then stretch the Achilles tendon, calf, and low-back muscles. After the primary conditioning phase, cool down by walking at a slower pace and stretching the muscles that were previously stretched.

3. Give special emphasis to graduating the duration—for example, from 15 to 60 minutes—over the length of the program. Progression in intensity should follow successful duration progression. Emphasize duration first, then gradually add faster-paced walking. Keep in mind that adding hilly terrain increases the intensity, so be sure that the terrain is within the participant's capacity.

Jogging and Running

Jogging and running are superb cardiorespiratory endurance activities. The essential difference between the two is that jogging is "slower running," or as some authorities define it, jogging is running slower than eight minutes per mile. For beginners, a natural sequence of progression might be:

1. Walk/jog intervals: walk 50 yards, jog 50 yards, repeat 10 to 20 times; over time, gradually increase the jogging interval to 2 or more miles.
2. Jogging: gradually increase jogging distance to desired distance or energy expenditure.
3. Running: as jogging endurance improves, increase stride frequency and stride length to a comfortable running style.

It is not necessary to graduate to running if desired goals can be achieved by jogging. However, running is a natural progression for those who orthopedically and psychologically respond well to jogging. Table 3.8 shows the energy cost in calories per minute for jogging and running. Note that the energy cost increases proportionately with increasing speed. These proportional increases in energy cost mean that a participant who runs a mile at 9 miles an hour (6.6 minutes per mile) will finish the mile twice as fast as when jogging 4.5 miles per hour (13.3 minutes per mile), but energy cost per mile is about the same. Numerous benefits can be obtained from successful jogging and running programs that are adequately balanced with appropriate muscular strength and flexibility exercises. Some of these benefits include increased maximum oxygen uptake, improved body composition (decrease in body-fat stores), coronary risk reduction, increased bone strength, and enhanced psychological well-being.

Table 3.8 Energy Costs of Jogging and Running (kcal/min)

	Miles Per Hour/METS							
Body weight (lb)	3.0/5.6	4.0/7.1	5.0/8.7	6.0/10.2	7.0/11.7	8.0/13.3	9.0/14.8	10.0/16.3
110	4.7	5.9	7.2	8.5	9.8	11.1	12.3	13.6
120	5.1	6.4	7.9	9.3	10.6	12.1	13.4	14.8
130	5.5	7.0	8.6	10.0	11.5	13.1	14.6	16.1
140	5.9	7.5	9.2	10.8	12.4	14.1	15.7	17.3
150	6.4	8.1	9.9	11.6	13.3	15.1	16.8	18.5
160	6.8	8.6	10.5	12.4	14.2	16.1	17.9	19.8
170	7.2	9.1	11.2	13.1	15.1	17.1	19.1	21.0
180	7.6	9.7	11.8	13.9	15.9	18.1	20.2	22.2
190	8.1	10.2	12.5	14.7	16.8	19.1	21.3	23.5
200	8.5	10.8	13.2	15.4	17.7	20.1	22.4	24.7
210	8.9	11.3	13.8	16.2	18.6	21.1	23.5	25.9
220	9.3	11.8	14.5	17.0	19.5	22.2	24.7	27.2

Reprinted, by permission, from E. Howley and B.D. Franks, 1992, *Health Fitness Instructor's Handbook,* 2d ed. (Champaign, IL: Human Kinetics), 136.

Four things are important when prescribing jogging or running exercise:

1. Wear appropriate footwear. A comfortable pair of running shoes designed for distance jogging/running should have adequate sole cushion, good heel support, and sufficient sole flexibility.

2. Always accompany jogging or running exercise with appropriate flexibility exercise. Stretching the Achilles tendon, calf, hamstrings, quadriceps, foot, and low-back muscles will help improve jogging and running efficiency.

3. For beginners, jog every other day or no more than four days per week with a day of rest between workouts to allow for adequate recovery of the weight-bearing joints, ligaments, and tendons. Limit the initial duration to no more than 25 to 30 minutes per workout for the first six to eight weeks.

4. Increase jogging pace and add hills only gradually. Emphasize a gradual increase in distance at a relatively slow pace, and then slowly increase pace or speed. Aerobic interval training will facilitate a safe and gradual increase in distance.

Cycling

Cycling is another excellent cardiorespiratory activity with benefits similar to jogging and running. It is a good alternative for those who do not like to jog or run, or who have orthopedic limitations to weight-bearing exercise. Two types are outdoor cycling and indoor stationary cycling. Both have advantages and disadvantages; however, with sufficient frequency, duration, and intensity, both can be an excellent stimulus to cardiorespiratory fitness.

Outdoor Cycling

The benefits of outdoor cycling are sunlight, fresh air, adequate cooling, and variety of terrain and scenery. And it can be a good source of inexpensive transportation. Most participants find cycling outdoors makes it easier to prolong duration of exercise because of distances between destinations and more interesting environments. Disadvantages include inclement weather, nightfall, and some unsafe city environments. However, convenient outdoor cycling, combined with indoor stationary cycling, can be a stimulating year-round program.

Guidelines for outdoor bicycling include the following:

1. Use a bicycle with at least 10 speeds so that the cyclist can easily adapt to nearly any change in grade or wind.
2. For beginners, keep a relatively constant pedal crank speed by adjusting the gears to variable grades and headwinds. This pedal crank speed can vary depending on fitness and comfort, but will usually be between 70 rpm and 90 rpm per leg. This will help minimize fatigue and maximize blood flow and nutrients to the legs.
3. Bicycle seat height should be high enough so that the leg that is on the downstroke is not quite completely extended when the ball of the foot is on the pedal.
4. Use toe clips, especially with significant hill climbing. Toe clips improve pedaling efficiency by delivering more muscular power to the pedal crank axis throughout the entire revolution.
5. Wear bicycling apparel. Always wear a cycling helmet. Padded shorts and gloves will increase comfort for cycling lasting longer than 45 minutes.

Indoor Stationary Cycling

The advantages of indoor stationary cycling include its convenience and relative safety. Most health clubs and fitness centers have two types of stationary cycles: those with mechanically braked flywheels and those that are electronically braked. Either type will provide a good aerobic or anaerobic workout; however, the electronically controlled cycles generally display digital workload information that may be helpful to motivate participants. On electronically controlled cycles, some beginners do not always get an adequate warm-up when selecting certain exercise programs on the display monitor. Regardless of the type of cycle, always warm up by cycling against low pedal crank resistance for at least 5 to 10 minutes. Many stationary cycles are not accurately calibrated, so there may be noticeable differences in pedal crank resistances for similarly indicated workloads between cycles.

The following guidelines apply to stationary cycling machines:

1. Ensure proper ventilation. If necessary, a fan gives adequate cross ventilation to enable good evaporative heat loss. Cooling the body by the evaporation of sweat is necessary to prevent a rapid rise in body temperature. Unlike outdoor bicycling, indoor cycling requires adequate ventilation for prolonged exercise.
2. As in outdoor bicycling, adjust seat height for a slight bend in the knee at the downstroke position.
3. Adjust the handlebars so that the participant is relaxed and leaning slightly forward.
4. Hold pedal crank speed relatively constant for beginners in the range of 70 rpm to 90 rpm per leg.
5. Always warm up and cool down with 5 to 10 minutes of low resistance cycling.

Water Exercise

Exercising in the water is another excellent way to develop physical fitness. Many participants may benefit greatly from training in the water, especially those who have problems with balance or coordination, or who need to begin exercising at a very low intensity. In addition, participants who want to achieve a high-intensity workout with reduced impact can use the surrounding resistance of water as an effective exercise environment.

Integrating water exercises into a personal training program can provide participants with unique training benefits. Water provides an opportunity for people to explore how the body moves without the constraints of gravity and the fear of falling. It also provides postural training, as the core muscles of the trunk (abdominals, erector spinae, and obliques) are constantly stimulated, learning new patterns in response to the water pushing and pulling against the body. Two of the greatest benefits of water exercise are that it allows participants to adjust the impact of activity and that the water provides accommodating resistance (the harder one presses against the water, the harder it presses back). These two benefits give participants more control over the intensity of their own workouts.

Personal training instructors should recognize that both muscular conditioning and cardiorespiratory training can be achieved in the aquatic environment. Water aerobic exercise can consist of either the "vertical" exercise typically found in water fitness classes or "horizontal" exercise such as lap swimming. Muscular development can also be achieved in the water by using the water's resistance, often with the help of exercise equipment such as webbed gloves, fins, kickboards, styrofoam dumbbells, belts, and "noodles." By including water fitness as a component of participants' exercise programs, personal training instructors provide participants with another choice of activities to achieve training results. Participants develop lifetime skills that they can "modify" as their exercise needs develop and change over time.

Many healthy adults who enjoy the water will want to use it to cross-train for new challenges and variety; however, the water is particularly conducive to exercise for those with specific health conditions and/or concerns. Personal training instructors can work with physicians and other health professionals to develop appropriate exercise programs for the following individuals:

- Athletes who want to decrease impact and to overload patterns of movement in the safety of the water
- Obese participants who need to decrease impact and increase exercise duration while enjoying the added benefit of the privacy water exercise affords
- Participants with orthopedic conditions such as arthritis, total hip or knee replacement, post-rehabilitation from knee and shoulder surgery, low back pain, fibromyalgia, and osteoporosis
- Participants suffering from neurological conditions such as multiple sclerosis, stroke, and Parkinson's disease, who may benefit from the support of water
- Participants who need to carefully regulate exercise intensity due to cardiorespiratory conditions such as cardiovascular disease, pulmonary disease, and hypertension
- Those with general medical conditions such as pregnancy, diabetes mellitus, and recovery from mastectomy

The following are some guidelines for teaching water exercise effectively:

1. **Account for land and water differences.** Understanding the water's effect on the body is essential: Water provides continuous resistance to movement. A biceps curl performed on land utilizes gravity and a weight to provide concentric muscular work, while the same movement performed in the water with a buoyant dumbbell works the triceps concentrically.

2. **Teach participants personal balance, stabilization, and safety.** Participants need to develop basic skills for moving safely and effectively through the water. These skills include sculling to enhance balance, recovering to a stand, and keeping good body alignment. When working in a YMCA pool with lifeguards, know your responsibilities as a member of the emergency response team. An emergency action plan must be in place and be understood by all parties at all times.

3. **Teach proper technique.** Those interested in horizontal fitness swimming should have a qualified person assess their stroke techniques in the water. If stroke work is needed, include some swim instruction during workout time or have participants register for swim lessons. For additional help in developing an effective workout for lap swimmers, consult with a YMCA aquatic director, swim instructor, or swim team coach.

4. **Choose a water depth.** Participants can work in three water depths: shallow (navel to nipple), transitional (nipple to top of the shoulder), and deep (any depth where the feet cannot touch bottom). The depth depends on the facility, the objective of the workout, the availability of equipment, and the skill level of the participant. A person who needs to reduce impact may want to work out in deep water using a buoyancy belt for support, while someone who wants to improve a functional skill such as speed walking might choose shallow water.

5. **Monitor water temperature.** The temperature of the water affects exercise design. Competitive athletic training conducted at a high intensity (above 4.2 METs) should be performed in water 80 to 83 degrees F, while vigorous aerobics (4.2 METs) or moderate-intensity activity (below 4.2 METs) should be performed in water 83 to 86 degrees F.

6. **Teach participants how to regulate exercise intensity.** Participants will need to learn to feel the water and to discover their own resistance levels by practicing movements through progressions. Speed, surface area, water currents, and buoyancy all need to be managed to achieve appropriate levels of work and rest. Equipment may need to be added to appropriately overload different muscle groups. For example, webbed gloves may provide sufficient overload for triceps work, while the biceps may require the larger surface area of a fitness paddle.

7. **Use equipment effectively.** In water, iron dumbbells are replaced by foam ones. The surface area and/or buoyancy of equipment moving through the water is utilized to provide resistance. Many types of water exercise equipment are available, and you will need to understand how using various equipment affects both exercise design and safety. Teach participants the skills unique to using each piece of equipment.

For additional information on water fitness, refer to the *YMCA Water Fitness for Health* manual available from the YMCA Program Store.

Rowing

Rowing machines have become popular in gyms and fitness centers for cardiorespiratory exercise, as well as for attaining a reasonable degree of arm, back, and thigh muscular endurance. As with any stationary aerobic exercise device, a fan should provide air circulation to facilitate sweat evaporation and prevent overheating. There are numerous manufacturers of rowing machines, some very basic and some quite sophisticated with hydraulic action of the arm movement and work-load display monitors. However, most operate on the principle of coordinated effort of lower extremity muscular work with arm rowing action. Rowing intensity (rowing motion resistance) can be varied in most machines by changing the force angle of the rowing arm of the machine, by changing the hydraulic pressure in the pressure cylinder, or via electronic programming. Intensity also can be varied by increasing the rowing rate or number of rows per minute. Those just learning should note that several sessions are required to learn how to perform repetitive, efficient rowing motions that require synchronizing the arms, back, and legs. Several guidelines may be helpful:

1. Secure feet in the anchors on the front part of the machine.
2. Use a smooth rowing action (coordinate arm and back rowing movements with leg extensions).
3. Begin with a relatively low intensity (low resistance) with approximately 8 to 10 rows per minute for 5 to 10 minutes.
4. Graduate the speed to approximately 15 to 30 rows per minute and gradually increase duration to 15 to 30 minutes.
5. Gradually increase intensity according to heart rate and perceived exertion.

Stair Climbing

Stair climbing can be an effective means of attaining cardiorespiratory fitness. The participant may use either a staircase or one of the electrically braked stair-climbing machines that are popular in fitness centers. The advent of computer-interactive, electrically braked stair-climbing machines has brought effective and well-controlled stair climbing to the health club and fitness center. They allow for a more effective warm-up and cool-down as well as a variety of training intensities because most of these devices regulate the intensity of climbing based on step rate and training method. You should also note that many people incorrectly support their weight by holding on to guard rails so the actual work performed is less than that indicated on the monitor. Most people find these machines fun, and they can provide an interesting addition to circuit training programs or be a primary means of attaining cardiorespiratory fitness.

Safety precaution: A fan or other means of convective cooling should always be used because of the tendency to overheat on stationary exercise machines.

Because the energy cost of actual stair climbing is largely dependent upon body weight, a large anaerobic component is possible for those who are overweight or unaccustomed to regular stair climbing. Adequate warm-up and cool-down periods must be incorporated due to the potentially large energy costs. Walking for 5 to 10 minutes on relatively flat terrain, either on a track or treadmill, usually provides adequate warm-up or cool-down. Interval-training methods are best when beginning a program with regular stairs or steps in a stadium. After warming up, repeating a sequence of walking four flights of stairs and taking a 60-second walk on flat ground 4 to 10 times is one example of an interval approach.

Aerobic Dance

Studies on the effects of aerobic dance show it to be an excellent form of cardiorespiratory endurance exercise. To gain significant benefits, the participant must maintain the aerobic phase for at least 20 to 30 minutes, three to four times per week. The tempo (speed or pace) should be adjusted to fit the desired intensity or heart-rate range. Like swimming, aerobic dance requires a degree of motor skill and coordination, and may take more time to learn than walking, jogging, or cycling. For those who are significantly overweight or have a history of orthopedic injuries, this type of exercise may create undue demands on the cardiorespiratory and musculoskeletal systems.

For aerobic-dance exercise, the following guidelines apply:

1. Wear appropriate footwear. An aerobic shoe should adhere to four standards: cushion, support, flexibility, and traction compatibility.
2. For beginners, recommend low-impact aerobics—a form of aerobic dance that features one foot on the ground at all times, reducing the risk of musculoskeletal injury, and may include the use of light weights.
3. For beginners, recommend a class that will adapt appropriately to the beginner's functional capacity and skill level.
4. Lower the target heart rate slightly, because aerobic-dance exercise may elicit heart rates 10 to 15 beats per minute higher than running or cycling for the same percentage of aerobic capacity (Parker et al., 1989). This disproportionate relationship between oxygen consumption and heart rate is generally true for most aerobic-exercise routines using upper-body muscle groups.

Refer to the *YMCA Exercise Instructor Manual*, published by the YMCA of the USA (1995), for more information on aerobic instruction techniques.

Step Aerobics

Step aerobic exercise has gained wide popularity in fitness centers and health clubs across the United States and many parts of Asia and Europe. More than 30 studies now confirm that the energy cost of step aerobic training (7 to 11 METs) is commensurate with that of traditional aerobic exercise, such as running and cycling, and is an adequate stimulus of aerobic endurance. Choices of step bench height generally range from 4 to 10 inches, with a standard stepping rate of 120 to 130 steps per minute. Beginners should be advised to begin with smaller step heights of 4 to 6 inches with a goal of 8 inches after four to eight weeks of successful training. The addition of hand-held weights should be discouraged for beginners and those who are coronary-prone, because of the increased blood pressure response for any given step rate and step height. For more information on step aerobics, refer to the ACE *Aerobics Instructor Manual*, published by the American Council on Exercise (1993).

Tennis, Racquetball, and Handball

Tennis, racquetball, and handball are all popular sports and deserve special attention for their ability to increase cardiorespiratory fitness. Each requires various motor skills and neuromuscular coordination, and the level and duration of play depend on these skills. For the beginner, racquet sports demand more from anaerobic energy systems than aerobic. However, as one becomes more skilled and efficient with movement and play, it is easier to prolong the activity and obtain more cardiorespiratory benefits. Improvements in cardiorespiratory fitness are dependent upon several factors:

- skill level and style of the player
- level of competition (intensity)
- total duration of each point played
- time interval between points and games
- total duration of entire exercise session

As the intensity and duration of these sports meet the criteria for cardiorespiratory endurance fitness (that is, 50 percent to 85 percent of maximal oxygen uptake for 20 to 60 minutes), they become more of a cardiorespiratory stimulus.

Racquetball and handball often are played in hot, unventilated environments, and require more attention to regular fluid intake and signs of dehydration. Generally, these racquet sports require at least average cardiorespiratory fitness and are excellent activities for developing and maintaining fitness.

Hiking and Backpacking

Hiking and backpacking activities can require high levels of cardiorespiratory endurance. Although most participants do not engage in these activities more than once a week, they are an excellent adjunct to a cardiorespiratory fitness program using fundamental aerobic activities such as jogging, cycling, or aerobics. The energy cost (oxygen uptake and calories expended) per minute is lower for hiking and backpacking, depending on grade, packloads, and altitude. The duration of such activity is usually prolonged (two to eight hours) and, therefore, the total energy cost is well above most routine aerobic workouts. It is important to be in at least average cardiorespiratory fitness, preferably the "good" classification (table 3.6), before attempting prolonged variable-terrain hiking. One of the most important concerns with prolonged hiking is dehydration. Be sure to carry adequate water and glucose replacement on trips lasting longer than 60 minutes.

Many factors govern the cardiorespiratory and metabolic cost of hiking and backpacking. The following are among the most important:

- body weight of hiker
- duration of the hike
- number and size of the grades
- altitude at which the hike occurs
- speed of movement
- pack load
- air temperature

Monitoring Cardiorespiratory Exercise

Monitoring cardiorespiratory exercise performance is necessary for assessing exercise response, regulating exercise intensity, documenting progress, and assuring safety. Essentially, three techniques are used to monitor cardiorespiratory exercise: heart rate, ratings of perceived exertion, and laboratory monitoring techniques.

Monitoring Heart Rates

As mentioned earlier, heart rate is a good guide for exercise intensity and cardiorespiratory responsiveness. The heart rate can be obtained by palpating (feeling) the pulse or by using a cardiotachometer or electrocardiogram. From a practical standpoint, palpation or feeling the pulse is the easiest method to assess heart rate. The pulse may be palpated in the neck (carotid artery), the head (temporal artery), the wrist (radial artery), or the chest (apical artery). For example, the carotid pulse may be felt by gently placing the index and middle finger over a carotid artery in the neck on either side of the larynx. It is important not to apply too much pressure as there are carotid sensors in these arteries that are sensitive to pressure and may induce a sudden drop in heart rate. Assessing the radial pulse in the wrist is done by placing the first two fingers (index and middle) on the underside and thumb side of the wrist.

Heart Rate Response to Training

There are two trends to look for when monitoring the heart rate response to cardiorespiratory exercise training. First is the tendency of the heart rate, for any given level of exercise, to decrease with training. This tendency primarily applies to submaximal exercise, such as that between 60 percent and 80 percent of maximum functional capacity. For example, expect a decrease in heart rate for the same submaximal work load on a stationary cycle after several weeks of training. The actual decrease in exercise heart rate and the length of time required to elicit this change is variable between participants, but is primarily dependent upon age, initial level of fitness, length of the training program, and the exercise program intensity. Resting heart rate also tends to decrease with training along with the decrease in submaximal exercise heart rate. You must understand that there are other physiological reasons why resting heart rate may be low beyond that induced by endurance exercise training. A low resting pulse rate by itself is not by any means a perfect predictor of fitness.

Required Time for Expected Increases in Aerobic Capacity

For young and middle-aged adults, the usual improvement in aerobic capacity will be 15 percent to 20 percent over 10 to 20 weeks of training (Pollock). However, aerobic capacity may increase up to 45 percent to 50 percent depending upon the following factors:

- initial level of fitness
- age
- frequency of training
- intensity of training
- duration of exercise and total training programs
- genetics (oxidative processes, muscle fiber type ratio, etc.)

Those who begin a moderately intense cardiorespiratory conditioning program with a relatively high aerobic capacity can expect little improvement in aerobic capacity compared to those with initially low capacities. Age is not a detriment to increasing aerobic capacity in itself; however, training generally shows smaller improvements in aerobic capacity because of lower exercise intensities.

Overall, you can expect greater improvements with greater intensity and/or duration of exercise up to a point. This range for aerobic improvement is reflected in the mode, frequency, duration, and intensity standards previously mentioned. For most participants, cardiorespiratory changes, including aerobic capacity, continue to take place over many months, perhaps up to 24, as depicted in figure 3.1. This figure illustrates the relationship between initial functional capacity represented by

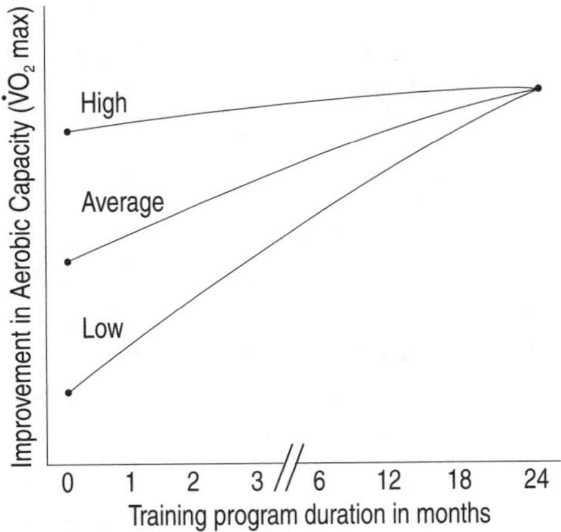

Figure 3.1 The relationship between initial functional capacity and approximate times required to increase aerobic capacity.

three cardiorespiratory fitness levels and approximate times required to increase aerobic capacity (Pollock, 1973; Saltin et al., 1977; McArdle, Katch, and Katch, 1991). This will provide you with a general estimate of expected aerobic capacity changes compared to program duration. Note that endurance performance (increasing exercise duration) may increase with little or no further increase in aerobic capacity. This is more likely to occur during the latter stages of training, such as the maintenance stage. The time required for other changes to occur, such as body-fat reduction and coronary risk modification, will vary considerably.

Special Considerations and Safety

You are responsible for determining current health status, developing an exercise program and following up on a variety of participants. Two areas of special importance are understanding and differentiating the various sources of cardiorespiratory exercise fatigue, and maximizing exercise safety.

The ability to recognize and differentiate exercise fatigue is especially helpful when evaluating self-report progress and teaching exertion limitation and safety precautions. This chapter will discuss only basic sources of endurance exercise fatigue and list their basic characteristics. These sources often overlap. For example, during longer exercise bouts, there may be heat fatigue, glycogen depletion, and lactic acid accumulation. Becoming cognizant of each source of fatigue will better enable you to understand the spectrum of exercise responses. Following are six basic sources and manifestations of fatigue observed in cardiorespiratory exercise programs:

1. Exercise fuel depletion. Liver and muscle glycogen (storage forms of carbohydrate) are at relatively low levels after 60 to 80 minutes of intense cardiorespiratory exercise, depending on the level of endurance fitness. This form of fatigue is focused in the exercising muscle groups and, if exercise continues, leads to increasing anaerobic work.

2. Anaerobic accumulation of lactic acid. This form of fatigue usually comes with over-pacing at too high an intensity, usually at levels of greater than 80 percent of maximal oxygen consumption or as a result of inadequate warm-up. Anaerobic accumulation of lactic acid may also occur with exercise in hot weather or exercise at relatively high altitudes (more than 5,000 feet). This fatigue has a relatively fast onset. It is characterized by the inability to sustain a pace or intensity, shortness of breath, and by transient muscular weakness.

3. Hyperthermia-dehydration. This is a gradual increase in body temperature from prolonged aerobic exercise in hot, humid conditions and/or inadequate water replenishment during prolonged exercise. Elevated body temperatures, high heart rates, inability to sustain usual aerobic exercise intensities, and mental confusion can characterize this form of exercise fatigue.

4. Musculoskeletal (orthopedic). Musculoskeletal discomfort exhibits "fatigue-like" qualities. This discomfort is often the result of overuse, with prolonged repetitive movements or unusual stress on a joint or bone from weight-bearing exercise, such as jogging. This form of fatigue is nearly always focused on the muscle, ligament, tendon, or joint that is stressed, and is characterized by increasing joint or muscular tenderness that tends to worsen with repeated activity.

5. General overtraining syndrome or staleness. This syndrome refers to the final stage in a proposed continuum of increasingly severe chronic fatigue states that develop as a result of overtraining, especially high-volume endurance overtraining. Overtraining syndrome is characterized by persistent plateau or worsening in performance that is not improved by short-term rest periods or reduced training. It also is associated with disturbances in mood and sleep, loss of appetite and weight, muscle soreness, a propensity for overuse injuries, or increased resting heart rate. Refer to Raglin (1993) for a current and detailed review of overtraining and staleness syndrome monitoring. Ketner and Mellion (1995) have also written an excellent review of the pathophysiology of overtraining and treatment strategies.

6. Abnormal cardiac symptoms or chest discomfort (angina). Although uncommon, this form of "fatigue" would represent a contraindication to continued exercise and justify a physician referral. This symptom usually characterizes coronary artery disease and someone who is prone to heart attack. Symptoms include chest discomfort (aching, pressure, burning, or tightness) that tends to come with physical effort and is relieved by

rest. You should always ensure the participant understands the seriousness of the symptoms and discontinues exercise, and should require the participant to report these symptoms to a physician without delay.

Maximizing Exercise Safety

You should be aware of and understand the behavioral and environmental factors that can either alter the response to exercise or predispose the participant to increased risk of injury or cardiovascular complications. These factors include post-meal exercise, thermal stress, air pollutants, drugs and other substances, and the presence of unusual symptoms.

Exercise Following Meals

Vigorous aerobic exercise soon after a full meal can cause the heart to work harder, compromise oxygen and nutrient delivery to the working muscles, and cause gastric discomfort. Consequently, you should advise waiting at least 90 minutes after a full meal before beginning to engage in moderate- and higher-level aerobic exercise. The level of exercise and the amount and type of food ingested both affect the amount of time required for digestion to be completed before beginning exercise. The higher the exercise level and/or the greater the number of calories of food ingested, the longer the individual should wait between eating and exercise.

Thermal Stress

Exercise in hot, humid environments can place the participant at risk for heat injury, as well as affect the usual intensity of exercise. Methods recommended by the American College of Sports Medicine and others (Vogel et al., 1993) can prevent thermal or heat stress.

1. Allow 10 to 14 days for acclimatization to a hot, humid environment.
2. Defer exercise if the heat index is in the "high-risk" zone. (See Vogel et al., 1993).
3. Avoid training during the hottest part of the day, usually between 10 a.m. and 2 p.m., during summer months.
4. Drink 13 to 16 ounces of cold water about 20 minutes before exercising and 10 ounces every 20 minutes during activity. Before and during exercise, fluid replacement should be accomplished with either water or approximately 6 percent glucose solution.
5. Wear loose-fitting clothing that will allow for the evaporation of sweat.
6. Adjust training intensity down by monitoring heart rate.
7. Incorporate compulsory rest periods of at least 10 minutes for every 45 to 50 minutes of physical activity.
8. Closely monitor daily body weight. If losses are greater than 3 percent of body weight they should be replaced by drinking before the next training session.
9. Give special consideration to, and use caution with, the following heat-susceptible persons: those unacclimatized to the heat, the obese, the unfit (low cardiorespiratory fitness classifications), the dehydrated, and those with a previous history of heat stroke.

Air Pollutants

The principal air pollutants that may concern those who exercise outdoors in or near big cities are ozone, carbon monoxide, and sulfur dioxide. The major factors in determining the dose are the concentration of the pollutant, the duration of the exposure, and the volume of air inhaled. Since ventilation increases with the level of exercise, the effects of the pollutant will also depend on the intensity of exercise. See *ACSM's Resource Manual for Guidelines for Exercise Testing and Prescription* (1993) for a more detailed description of air pollution hazards and exercise.

Perhaps the most problematic of these pollutants is ozone or smog (not stratospheric ozone) that is formed by the reaction of a combination of ultraviolet light and emissions from internal combustion engines. The level of ozone we breathe is a function of weather patterns, traffic density, and industrial output. Ozone exposure may impair lung function during moderate aerobic exercise at concentrations as low as .08 parts per million, which is at or below most air quality standards.

Carbon monoxide is another common air pollutant that can substantially reduce aerobic capacity. A 10 percent increase in carbon monoxide in the blood results in an approximate 10 percent reduction in maximal oxygen consumption. Moderate submaximal exercise in healthy individuals does not appear to be significantly affected by a 10 to 15 percent increase in blood carbon monoxide. Cardiac and pulmonary patients are generally affected by as little as a 5 percent increase in this pollutant. It also is noteworthy that because of the relatively slow removal of carbon monoxide from the blood (the clearance half-time is two to four hours), exposures that occur hours before an exercise session, on crowded freeways, or in smoke-filled rooms could influence aerobic performance.

Sulfur dioxide is most frequently produced in smelters, refineries, and other stationary sources and is not a major irritant for most apparently healthy individuals. However, those persons with asthma or bronchospasm tendencies may be quite sensitive to sulfur dioxide.

Particulate matter (e.g., dust and smoke) is minute particles that are generally 3 to 10 microns in size that may arise from dust in windy conditions, or smoke from burning firewood. Smaller particles of 3 to 5 microns can easily penetrate the upper respiratory track whereas those less than 3 microns can settle in the alveoli. Such particulate inhalation can cause bronchoconstriction (asthma symptoms) and inflammation and congestion of the lower respiratory track.

You should be aware of the environmental air quality in your county. An excellent resource for local trends and standards of air quality is the county Air Quality Board or local Environmental Protection Agency. In most cities, one of these agencies or the weather bureau will periodically measure these pollutants and combine them into a Pollution Standards Index (PSI) that ranges from 0 to 500. Generally, PSI levels above 100 will affect those who are very unfit or who have cardiovascular or pulmonary disease, while levels greater than 150 are required to impair cardiorespiratory performance in healthy normal participants. By understanding environmental air quality standards and being knowledgeable of resources for more information, you can minimize unnecessary fatigue and respiratory distress in participants.

Drugs and Other Substances

There are a number of substances that, when combined with moderate- to high-level aerobic exercise, can increase the risk of cardiovascular complications and/or affect the response to exercise. These substances are certain prescription medications, alcohol, tobacco, strong stimulants, and over-the-counter medications. Although each is briefly discussed here, refer to a comprehensive review of drugs and substances and their effects on exercise performance in *ACSM's Resource Manual for Guidelines for Exercise Testing and Prescription* (1993).

Virtually all beta-blocking drugs and some of the calcium-channel blocking medications prescribed for a variety of hypertensive and cardiac disorders lower the heart rate response to exercise. Although these medications may, in fact, increase the participant's ability to perform safe exercise, it is important to understand that the heart rate response to both submaximal and maximal exercise will be blunted. Psychological medications can have side effects that could make exercise more difficult. Some anti-anxiety medications, such as phenothiazines, can reduce blood pressure and cardiac output, each of which can reduce exercise capacity.

One of the most prevalent categories of drugs employed in medicine, and one that you are likely to occasionally observe in your participants, is antihypertensive drugs (i.e., blood pressure-lowering drugs). The major categories of antihypertensive drugs include diuretics, beta- and alpha-blockers, calcium channel blockers, and ACE inhibitors. Within limitations, all of these antihypertensive agents can make exercise safer for the patient with high blood pressure. Diuretic drugs (e.g., thiazides) can induce a relative depletion of blood volume, which can increase the vulnerability of a patient to hypotension in the post-exercise period. This side effect of diuretics is of greater concern after prolonged exercise when dehydration may compound the problem.

Alcohol consumption before, during, or after exercise can impair normal exercise heat exchange in prolonged exercise in hot weather. Smoking tobacco in any form increases blood carbon monoxide levels, which will decrease the oxygen consumption of the heart and skeletal muscles. Stimulants such as nicotine, amphetamines, and especially cocaine all have the potential to induce abnormal cardiac rhythms and decrease coronary blood flow. These substances also may mask important signs of exercise fatigue which are important for the participant to discern in order to adjust exercise intensity. Mixing these or combining any of these substances with near maximal or maximal aerobic exercise markedly increases risk of cardiovascular complications, even sudden cardiac death.

Over-the-counter medications such as decongestants, antihistamines, and aspirin products are not contraindications to exercise by themselves but warrant attention because of the infections or ailments for which they are taken. You should caution participants who have viral infections to abstain from prolonged and/or intense aerobic exercise because of the potential for complications and cardiac rhythm disturbances.

Unusual Symptoms

Chest discomfort, musculoskeletal pain, dizziness, lightheadedness or malaise are indications to discontinue exercise and, in some cases, consult a physician. Exceptional chest discomfort (not necessarily chest "pain") such as aching, pressure, tightness, or burning in the chest is always an indication to consult a physician. The participant should never exceed the exercise threshold necessary to cause chest discomfort.

When a participant experiences overall listlessness and/or recent onset lethargy (feelings of no energy) for no apparent reason, you should either have the participant abort exercise or significantly decrease exercise intensity and duration. Such vague symptoms can precede viral infections and even be prodromal to cardiovascular complications.

Musculoskeletal pain or tenderness in a muscle or joint which tends to increase with increasing exercise intensity or duration is an indication to discontinue that particular mode and/or intensity of exercise. The beginner should be told to expect some minor muscle soreness and general postexercise fatigue. These minor symptoms usually resolve themselves in several weeks; however, those musculoskeletal symptoms which tend to reproduce themselves over the course of several weeks warrant special attention.

Exercise during viral infections, such as the flu and upper respiratory infections, may lead to complications including worsening of the infections, an increase in body temperature and cardiac rhythm disturbances. You should advise rest and the usual recuperative recommendations as long as malaise, congestion, or fever persist.

References/Suggested Reading

American College of Sports Medicine. (1995). *ACSM's guidelines for exercise testing and prescription* (5th ed.) Baltimore: Williams and Wilkins.

American College of Sports Medicine. (1993). *Resource manual for guidelines for exercise testing and prescription* (2nd ed.) Philadelphia: Lea & Febiger.

American College of Sports Medicine. (1990). The recommended quantity and quality of exercise for developing and maintaining fitness in healthy adults. ACSM position statement. *Medicine and Science in Sports and Exercise,* 22, 265-274.

American Council on Exercise. (1993). Cotton, R.T. (Ed.) *Aerobics instructor manual.* San Diego, CA: American Council on Exercise.

American Heart Association. January 15, 1995. Exercise standards: A statement for healthcare professionals from the American Heart Association. *Circulation,* 91, 2.

Astrand, P.O., and K. Rodahl. (1977). *Textbook of work physiology.* New York: McGraw-Hill.

Borg, G.B. (1982). Psychological basis of perceived exertion. *Medicine and Science in Sports and Exercise,* 14, 377-381.

Bouchard, C., R. Shepard, T. Stephens, J. Sutton, and B. McPherson. (1990). *Exercise fitness and health: A consensus of current knowledge.* Champaign, IL: Human Kinetics.

Carlton, R., and E. Rhodes. (1985). A critical review of the literature on the ratings scales of perceived exertion. *Sports Medicine,* 2, 198-222.

Dishman, R., R. Farquhar, and K. Cureton. (1994). Responses to preferred intensities of exertion in men differing in activity levels. *Medicine and Science in Sports and Exercise,* 26, 783.

Durstine, L., and R. Pate. (1993). Cardiorespiratory responses to acute exercise. *ACSM's resource manual for guidelines for exercise testing and prescription* (2nd ed.) Philadelphia: Lea & Febiger.

Folinsbee, L. (1990). Exercise and the environment. Bouchard, C., R. Shepard, T. Stephens, J. Sutton, & B. McPherson (Eds.) *Exercise Fitness and Health.* Champaign, IL: Human Kinetics.

Franks D., and E. Howley. (1989). *Fitness Facts.* Champaign, IL: Human Kinetics.

Greenberg, J., and D. Pargman. (1989). *Physical fitness: A wellness approach* (2nd ed.) Englewood Cliffs, NJ: Prentice-Hall.

Haskell, W.L. (1994). Health consequences of physical activity: Understanding and challenges regarding dose-response. *Medicine and Science in Sports and Exercise,* 26, 649-660.

Herbert, W., and D. Herbert. *The Exercise Standards and Malpractice Reporter,* 1987 to present.

Heyward, V.H. (1984). *Designs for fitness.* Minneapolis: Burgess Publishing.

Howley, E., and D. Franks. (1992). *Health fitness instructor's handbook* (2nd ed.) Champaign, IL: Human Kinetics.

Howley, E., and M. Glover. (1974). The caloric costs of running and walking 1 mile for men and women. *Medicine and Science in Sports and Exercise,* 6, 235-237.

Ketner, J.B., and M.B. Mekkion. (1995). The overtraining syndrome: A review of presentation, pathophysiology, and treatment. *Medical Exercise Nutrition Health*, 4, 136-145.

McArdle, W., F. Katch, and V. Katch. (1991). *Exercise physiology* (3rd ed.) Philadelphia: Lea & Febiger.

Nieman, D. (1990). *Fitness and sports medicine: An introduction.* Palo Alto, CA: Bull Publishing.

Ockene, I., and J. Ockene. (1992). *Prevention of coronary heart disease.* Boston: Little Brown & Company.

Painter, P., and W. Haskell. (1993). Decision making in programming exercise. In *American College of Sports Medicine's resource manual for guidelines for exercise testing and prescription* (2nd ed.) Philadelphia: Lea & Febiger.

Parker, S., B. Hurley, D. Hanlon, and P. Vaccaro. (1989). Failure of target heart rate to accurately monitor intensity during aerobic dance. *Medicine and Science in Sports and Exercise,* 21, 230.

Pollock, M. (1973). The quantification of endurance training programs. *Exercise and Sport Science Reviews*, 1, 155-188.

Pollock, M., J. Wilmore, and S. Fox. (1984). *Exercise in health and disease.* Philadelphia: Saunders.

Raglin, J.S. (1993). Overtraining and Staleness: Psychometric Monitoring of Endurance Athletes. R.B. Singer, M. Murphey, & L. Tennant (Eds.) *Handbook of Research on Sport Psychology.* New York: Macmillan.

Richie, D. (1989). Medical and legal implications of dance exercise leadership: The role of footwear. *Exercise Standards and Malpractice Reporter,* 3, 61.

Saltin, B. et al. (1977). Fiber types and metabolic potentials of skeletal muscles in sedentary men and endurance runners. *Annals of the New York Academy of Science,* 301, 3.

Shapiro, U., and D. Seidman. (1990). Field and clinical observations of exertional heat stroke patients. *Medicine and Science in Sports and Exercise,* 22, 1.

Van Camp, S. (1993). Pharmacologic factors in exercise and exercise testing. In *American College of Sports Medicine's resource manual for guidelines for exercise testing and prescription* (2nd ed.) Philadelphia: Lea & Febiger.

Vogel, J., P.B. Rock, B.H. Jones, and G. Havenith. (1993). Environmental considerations in exercise testing and training. In *American College of Sports Medicine's resource manual for guidelines for exercise testing and prescription* (2nd ed.) Philadelphia: Lea & Febiger.

Wells, C., and R. Pate. (1988). Training for performance in prolonged exercise. Lamb, D. & Murray, R. (Eds.) *Prolonged Exercise* (Vol.1), 357-389. Carmel, IN: Benchmark Press.

Whaley, M., L. Kaminsky, G. Dwyer, L. Getchell, and J. Norton. (1992). Questioning the routine use of 220 - AGE heart rate formula. *Medicine and Science in Sports and Exercise,* 24, 1173.

Wilmore, J. H., and D. Costill. (1994) *Physiology of sport and exercise.* Champaign, IL: Human Kinetics.

4

Muscular Strength and Endurance

Every movement of the human body involves the muscular system. Muscles are unique in their ability to contract, relax, and produce force and movement. With appropriate exercise, muscles become larger and stronger. As a YMCA Personal Training Instructor, you need to be knowledgeable about the basic anatomy, physiology, and biomechanics of the musculoskeletal system. This chapter defines some key terms and presents essential concepts from these areas of study as they relate to strength-training exercise.

Skeletal Anatomy

In this section we look at the types of bones in the body, the joints, and the movements possible at the joints.

Bones

The skeleton consists of 206 bones that provide protection for the internal organs and a leverage structure for muscles. The skeleton also allows for growth and is the largest store of calcium in the body. There are four classes of bones:

- **Long bones**—These are found in the arms and legs, and they are associated with movement.
- **Short bones**—These are found in the hands and feet. Some short bones, such as the bones in the vertebral (spinal) column, are irregular in shape.
- **Flat bones**—These are found in the upper part of the skull.
- **Irregular bones**—These are found in vertebrae and in the pubic area.

Figure 4.1 shows the front (anterior) and back (posterior) views of the skeleton and identifies the major bones, groups of bones, and anatomical landmarks.

Joints

A joint is the point where bones link or connect. Joints are also called *articulations,* and items associated with joints usually begin with the prefix *arthr-,* as in *arthroscope,* a device that is used to look into the joint spaces of a person with *arthritis.* Joints are classified on the basis of how much movement is permitted between the bones:

- **Synarthrodial joints**—These are immovable joints or those with limited movement, such as the joints between the bones in the skull.
- **Amphiarthrodial joints**—These are joints with slight movement, as seen in the connections between vertebrae in the spinal column.
- **Diarthrotic or synovial joints**—These are joints possessing great potential for movement, as in the knee.

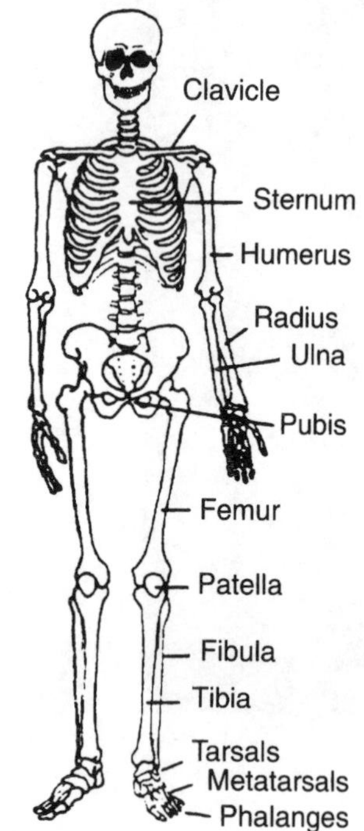

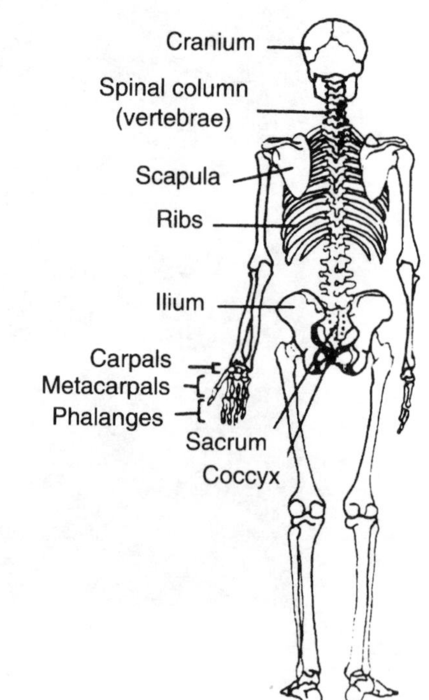

Figure 4.1 Front and back views of the human skeleton.
Reprinted, by permission, from E.T. Howley and B.D. Franks, 1986, *Health Fitness Instructor's Handbook* (Champaign, IL: Human Kinetics), 39.

The diarthrotic or synovial joint is most important in physical activity. Movement occurs when the muscles move the bones through a range of motion within the limits of these joints. These joints are held together by connective tissue—*ligaments*, which cross over the joint, and *tendons*, which attach muscles to bones and also cross over joints to lend additional support. Because these joints move a great deal, the structure also provides slippery surfaces and a lubricant. The slippery surface in each movable joint is the *articular hyaline cartilage* that covers the ends of the bones. This cartilage also absorbs some of the shock of impact to reduce the chance that the bony surface will wear out. *Synovial fluid* is the lubricant secreted by the *synovial membrane* within the joint housing or capsule. In addition, *bursae*, or sacs containing synovial fluid outside the joint space, help to lubricate the movement of tendons, ligaments, and muscles over bony structures. Some of these joints (e.g., the knee) have additional cartilage in the joint space between the bones to take up some of the shock of impact. This is the type of cartilage that can be torn as a result of high-impact forces, while the smooth articular cartilage is the type that can be damaged by arthritis.

Diarthrodial (movable) joints are classified on the basis of the type of movement permitted:

- **Ball and socket joints**—These allow movement in all directions. An example is where the head of the humerus (the bone of the upper arm) fits into the shoulder.
- **Hinge joints**—These allow movement in one plane of motion. The elbow is an example.
- **Saddle joints**—These allow movement in all directions. The metacarpal-carpal joint of the thumb is an example.
- **Pivot joints**—These allow rotation around the long portion of the bone. The radio-ulnar joint is an example, as it allows us to rotate our wrist to make the hand face up (supinated position) or down (pronated position).
- **Gliding joints**—These allow only gliding or twisting. An example is found in the joints between the wrist bones (carpals) or the ankle bones (tarsals).

Movements

The types of movements possible at each joint are dependent on the type of joint. It is important to know the terms that describe these movements before we present a summary of the muscles involved:

- **Flexion/extension**—Flexion describes a motion that decreases the angle of a joint, and extension is a movement that increases the joint angle. If your arm is hanging straight down, flexion is the movement of your hand toward your shoulder around the elbow joint; lowering the hand back to its starting position is extension. The term *hyperextension* refers to a movement beyond a joint's ordinary resting position.
- **Abduction/adduction**—Abduction describes a movement away from the center line of the body; adduction is a return to the ordinary anatomical position. Moving the leg to the side, away from the body, is an example of abduction.
- **Rotation**—Rotation is movement around the long axis of a bone and describes a movement either toward (*inward* or *medial rotation*) or away from (*outward* or *lateral rotation*) the center of the body. With your forearm at a 90-degree angle relative to your upper arm and your hand in front of your body, movement of the wrist and lower arm toward the center line of the body is an example of medial rotation.
- **Pronation/supination**—If the forearm is held at a 90-degree angle relative to the upper arm, hand in front of the body with thumb up, pronation describes a movement of the forearm such that the palm turns downward, and supination the reverse. These terms are also used to describe the manner in which the foot lands when walking or running. A person who lands with the inside or medial aspect of the foot striking first is said to be a "pronator." Many running shoes are designed to control this problem.
- **Dorsiflex/plantarflex**—These terms describe the movement of the foot from its normal position either toward the lower leg (dorsiflex) or toward the bottom of the foot (plantarflex).

See figure 4.2 for specific examples of these movements.

ANKLE EXTENSION (PLANTAR FLEXION)

Muscle Group

Gastrocnemius and soleus

Increasing the angle between the foot and the leg.

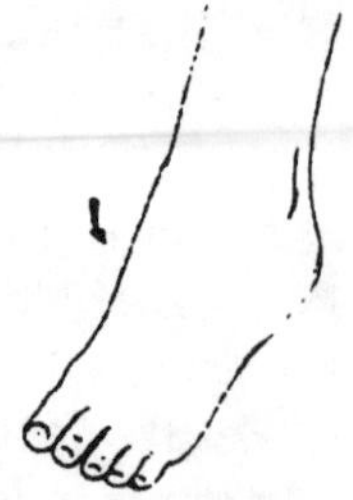

ANKLE FLEXION (DORSIFLEXION)

Muscle Group

Tibialis anterior

Decreasing the angle between the foot and the leg.

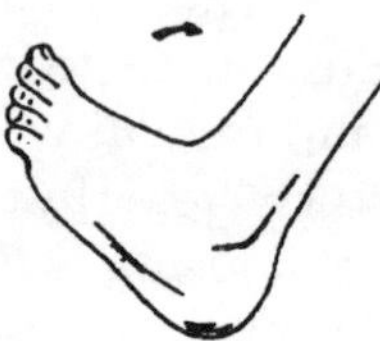

KNEE EXTENSION

Muscle Group

Quadriceps: rectus femoris, vastus lateralis, vastus medialis, and vastus intermedius

Increasing the angle between the thigh and the leg.

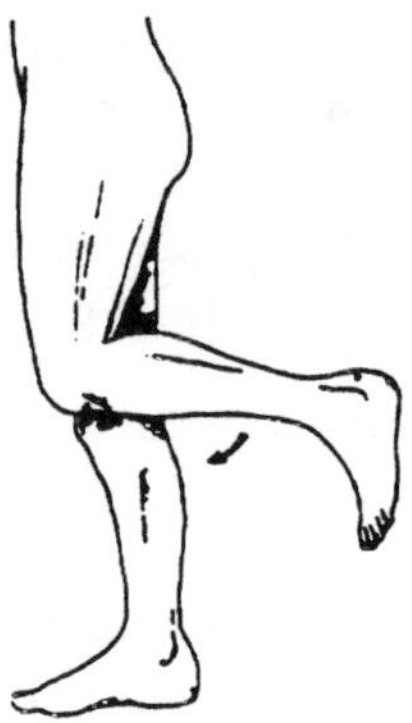

KNEE FLEXION

Muscle Group

Hamstrings: biceps femoris, semitendinosus, and semimembranosus

Decreasing the angle between the thigh and the leg.

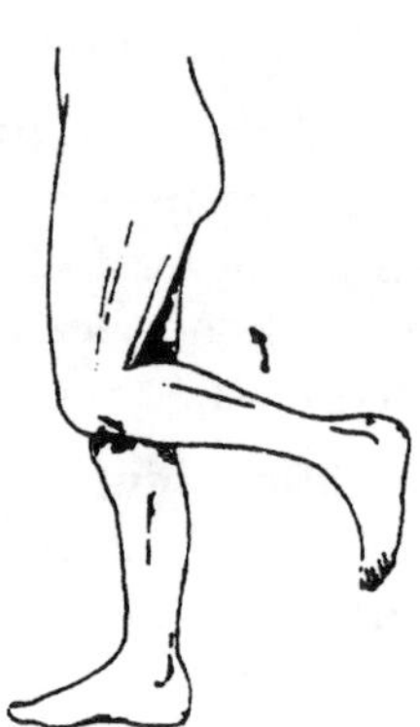

Figure 4.2 Examples of possible joint movements.

HIP ABDUCTION

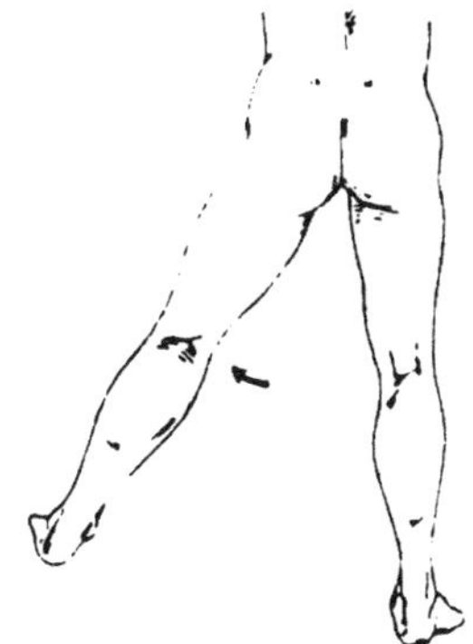

Muscle Group

Hip abductors: gluteus medius and tensor fascia latae

Increasing the angle between the thigh and the midline of the body (outward-sideward movement).

HIP ADDUCTION

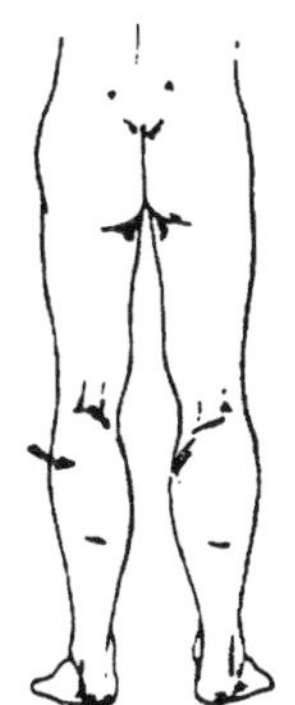

Muscle Group

Hip adductors: adductor magnus, adductor longus, adductor brevis, pectineus, and gracilis

Decreasing the angle between the thigh and the midline of the body (inward-sideward movement).

HIP EXTENSION

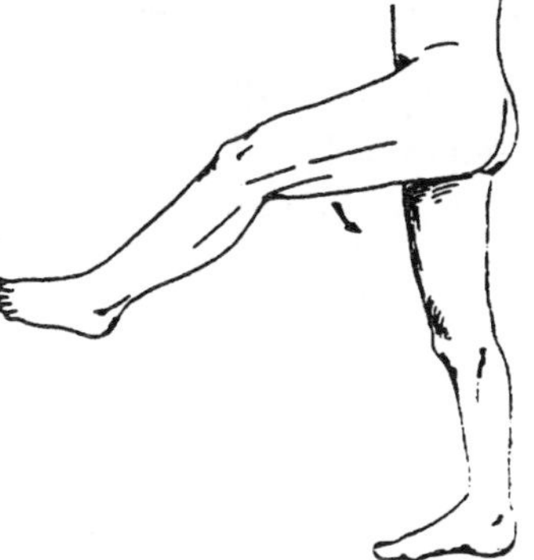

Muscle Group

Gluteus maximus and hamstrings

Increasing the angle between the thigh and the torso.

HIP FLEXION

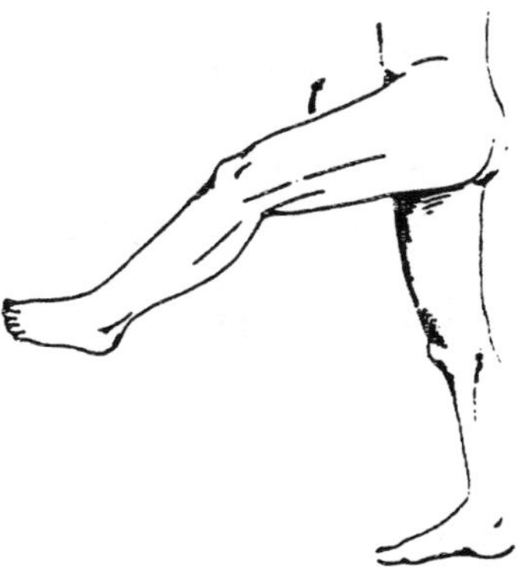

Muscle Group

Rectus femoris and iliopsoas

Decreasing the angle between the thigh and the torso.

Figure 4.2 *(continued)*

TRUNK EXTENSION

Muscle Group

Erector spinae

Increasing the angle between the chest and the abdomen.

TRUNK FLEXION

Muscle Group

Rectus abdominis

Decreasing the angle between the chest and the abdomen.

SHOULDER ABDUCTION

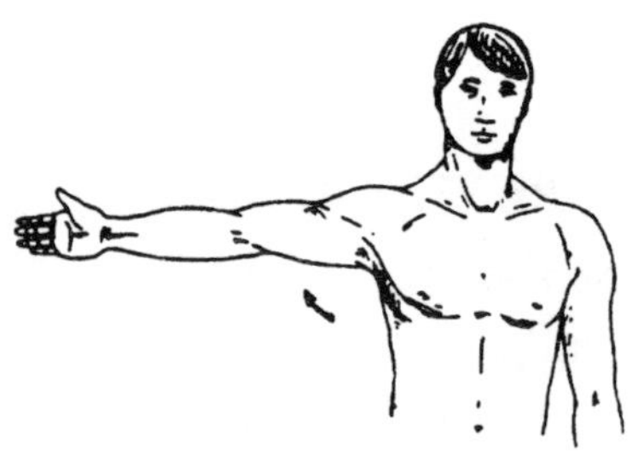

Muscle Group

Deltoids

Increasing the angle between the arm and the side (upward-sideward movement).

SHOULDER ADDUCTION

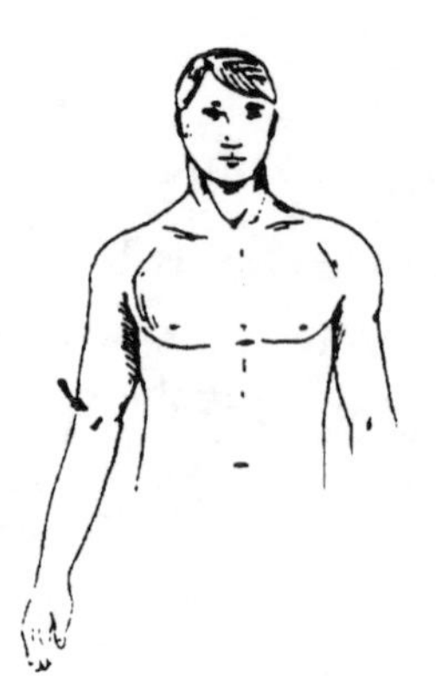

Muscle Group

Latissimus dorsi and pectoralis major

Decreasing the angle between the arm and the side (downward-sideward movement).

Figure 4.2 *(continued)*

SHOULDER FLEXION

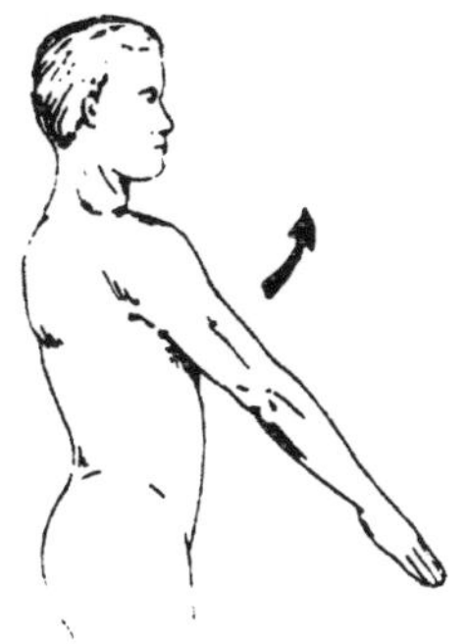

Muscle Group

Anterior deltoid

Increasing the angle between the arm and the chest (upward-forward movement).

SHOULDER EXTENSION

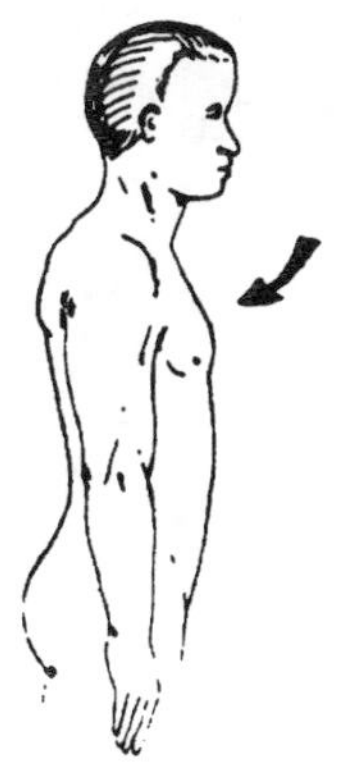

Muscle Group

Posterior deltoid and latissimus dorsi

Decreasing the angle between the arms and the chest (downward-backward movement).

SHOULDER HORIZONTAL FLEXION

Muscle Group

Pectoralis major and anterior deltoid

Decreasing the angle between the arms and the chest (forward movement with arms perpendicular to the chest).

SHOULDER HORIZONTAL EXTENSION

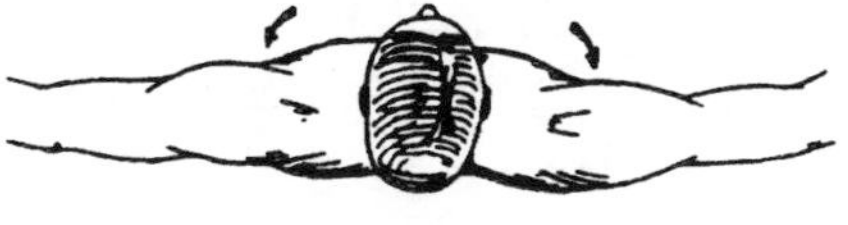

Muscle Group

Posterior deltoid and latissimus dorsi

Increasing the angle between the arms and the chest (backward movement with arms perpendicular to the chest).

Figure 4.2 *(continued)*

ELBOW FLEXION

Muscle Group

Biceps brachii

Decreasing the angle between the arm and the forearm.

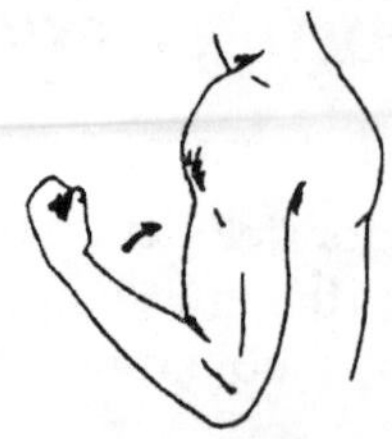

ELBOW EXTENSION

Muscle Group

Triceps brachii

Increasing the angle between the arm and the forearm.

WRIST FLEXION

Muscle Group

Forearm flexors: flex carpi ulnaris, palmaris, longus, flexor carpi radialis, and others

Decreasing the angle between the palm and the underside of the forearm.

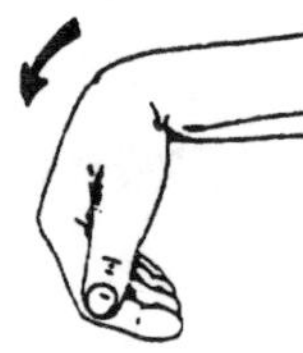

WRIST EXTENSION

Muscle Group

Forearm extensors: extensor carpi ulnaris, extensor digitorum, extensor carpi radialis, and others

Increasing the angle between the palm and the underside of the forearm.

Figure 4.2 *(continued)*

Muscle Anatomy and Physiology

Regardless of how well the cardiorespiratory system might function, no one could move were it not for the muscles and their phenomenal ability to contract. Muscles make up about 40 to 50 percent of total body weight. They are composed essentially of water (72 percent), lipids (8 percent), and proteins (20 percent). The muscle proteins are the keys to muscle contraction, as they perform a unique function.

It is muscles' anatomy that allows muscle contraction and relaxation to take place. This produces force, which takes the form of isometric, concentric, or eccentric contractions. Two types of muscle fibers are present—fast-twitch and slow-twitch, each best suited for a different type of performance. Muscles have both strength and endurance, which are different ways of exerting force.

The muscles can be overloaded using isometric, isotonic, or isokinetic exercises. How large muscles become or how quickly they develop as a result of overloading depends on the factors of muscle length, gender, and age. Each exercise movement uses three sets of muscles: the prime movers, the antagonists, and the stabilizers.

Muscle Anatomy

Muscles are composed of muscle fibers, individual muscle cells that are the functional components of muscles. As shown in figure 4.3, muscle fibers are cylindrical strands that contract as a unit when stimulated by an appropriate nerve impulse. *Myofibrils* are smaller cylindrical strands that run lengthwise within the muscle fiber. Each myofibril consists of numerous protein filaments that are sectioned into individual units called *sarcomeres* (see figure 4.3). Sarcomeres are the smallest units of contraction within muscles. As illustrated in figure 4.3, they form adjacent sections of each myofibril. Also shown is how sarcomeres are structured from two proteins that form a specific pattern and perform a specific function. Each sarcomere has thin actin proteins that surround thick myosin proteins. The thin actin proteins are coupled to the ends of the thick myosin proteins by means of small cross-bridges (see figure 4.3).

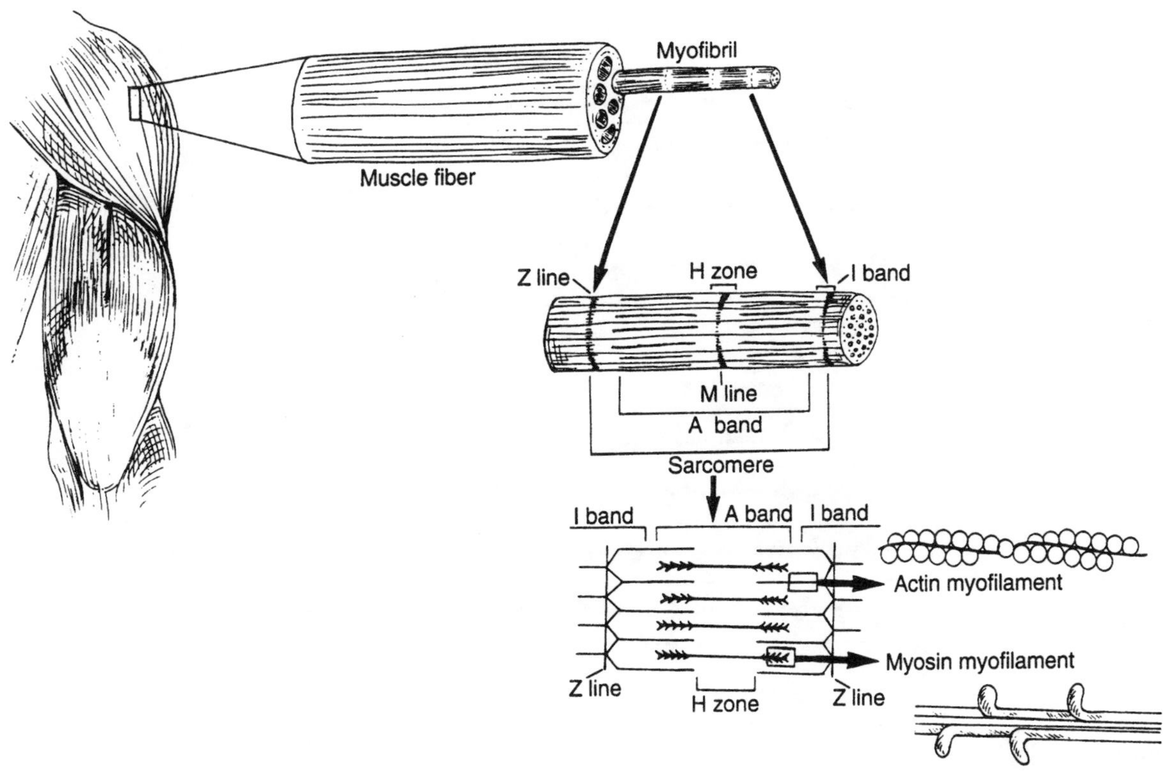

Figure 4.3 A sarcomere.

When properly stimulated, the thin actin proteins are pulled from both ends toward the center by the thick myosin proteins. As illustrated in figure 4.4, this results in a shortening of the activated muscle fibers and a bulging of the muscle.

Muscle Contraction and Relaxation

The pulling action between the actin and myosin proteins that produces the muscle contraction involves electrical, chemical, and mechanical interactions. The electrical stimulus arrives by means of a motor nerve, which is part of a motor unit. A *motor unit* consists of a single motor nerve and all of the individual muscle fibers that are activated by that nerve. As illustrated in figure 4.5, a typical motor unit involves several individual fibers throughout a muscle. Whenever a motor nerve sends a sufficient stimulus, all of the attached muscle fibers contract with maximum force. This is referred to as the *all-or-none principle of muscle contraction.* Consequently, to produce low force only a few motor units are activated, and to produce high force many motor units are activated.

The chemical process centers around the splitting of adenosine triphosphate (ATP), which produces the energy for muscle contraction. The ATP-splitting process appears to occur at the cross-bridges, providing energy for the actin-myosin linkage and pulling action that produces muscle contraction.

The mechanical interaction between the actin and myosin proteins is accomplished through the coupling and pulling movements of the connecting cross-bridges. During this process, the thin actin proteins are pulled toward the center by the thick myosin proteins, which shortens and bulges the muscle (see figure 4.4). The sliding action between the actin and myosin proteins produces muscle friction that alters the effective force output.

When the nervous stimulation that triggers muscle contraction ceases, the coupling and pulling movements between the actin and myosin proteins no longer occur and the muscle relaxes. Muscle relaxation is essential for every movement, because as one muscle group contracts and shortens, the opposing muscle group must relax and lengthen. Fortunately, our nervous systems precisely regulate concurrent muscle contraction

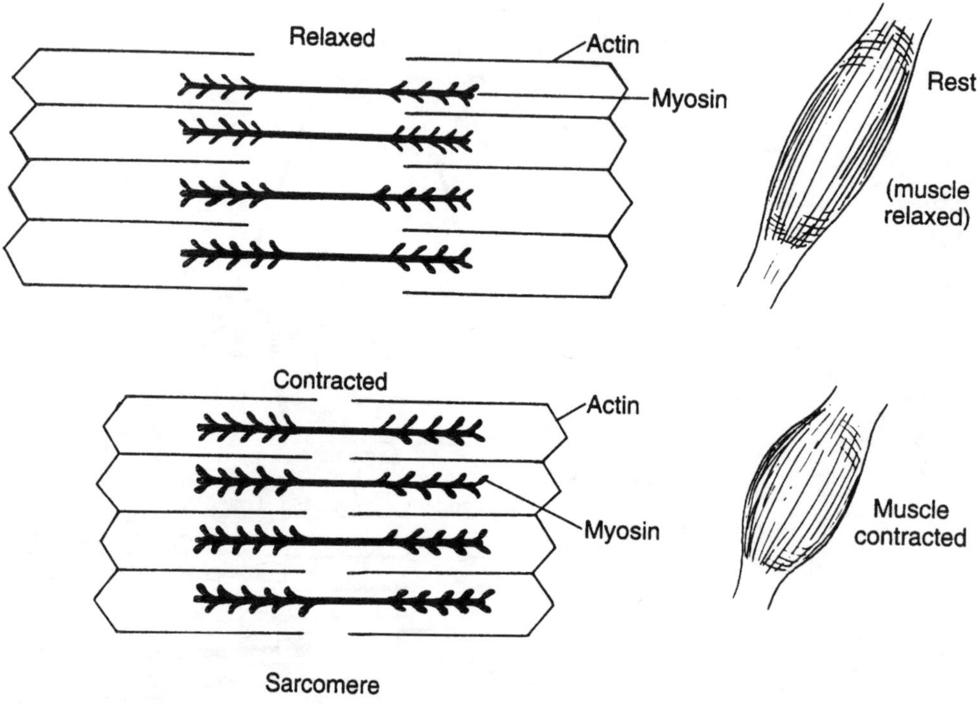

Figure 4.4 Shortening of muscle fibers.

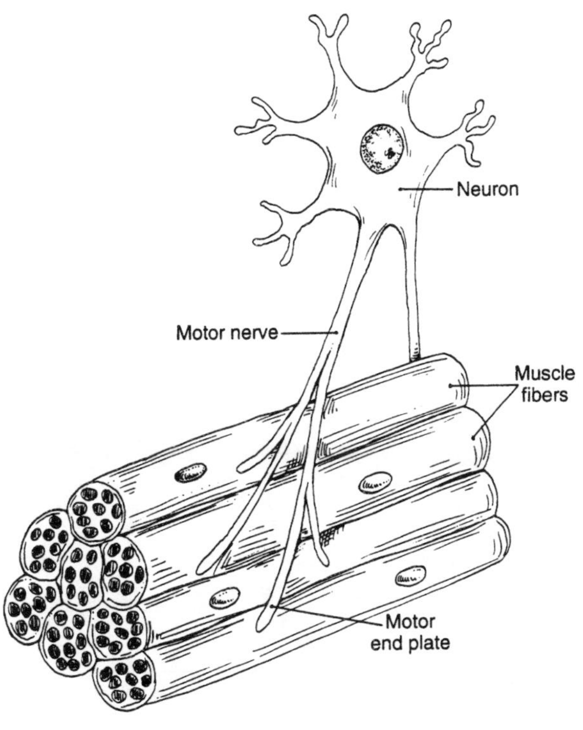

Figure 4.5 A motor unit.

and muscle relaxation to produce smooth movements with the desired degree of force and speed. The blocking of nerve impulses to muscles that oppose a desired movement is termed *reciprocal inhibition.*

Muscle Force Production

A muscle possesses many motor units, and the tension that a muscle develops is dependent primarily on the number of motor units called into play. When little muscle force is required, the number of motor units activated is small and the frequency of nerve impulses is low. When a high level of muscle force is required, the number of motor units activated is large and the frequency of nerve impulses is high. When a muscle contracts, the ends of the muscle move toward each other. The following terms describe the different types of muscle contractions:

- **Isometric contraction**—An isometric contraction, also called a *static contraction,* occurs when a muscle exerts force and does not visibly change in length. The muscle force equals the resistance force, and the muscle neither shortens nor lengthens. Because there is no movement between the actin and myosin proteins, isometric contractions are not affected by frictional forces. Holding a 50-pound dumbbell at 90 degrees of elbow flexion (by producing 50 pounds of muscle force) is an example of isometric contraction (see figure 4.6a).
- **Concentric contraction**—A concentric contraction, often referred to as a *positive contraction,* occurs when a muscle exerts force as it shortens (generally a lifting movement). The muscle force is greater than the resistance force. The shortening process involves muscle friction that decreases the effective force output by about 20 percent. For example, if you can hold (isometric contraction) a 50-pound dumbbell at 90 degrees of elbow flexion, you should be able to slowly lift a 40-pound dumbbell (concentric contraction). Although you are still producing 50 pounds of biceps force, muscle friction subtracts about 20 percent for an effective force output of 40 pounds (see figure 4.6b).
- **Eccentric contraction**—An eccentric contraction, often referred to as a *negative contraction,* occurs when a muscle exerts force as it lengthens (generally a lowering movement). The muscle force is less than the resistance force. The lengthening process involves muscle friction, therefore increasing the effective force output by about 20 percent. For example, if you can hold (isometric contraction) a 50-pound dumbbell at 90 degrees of elbow flexion, you should be able to slowly lower a 60-pound dumbbell (eccentric contraction). Although you are still producing 50 pounds of biceps force, muscle friction adds about 20 percent for an effective force output of 60 pounds (see figure 4.6c).

Muscle Fiber Types

Two types of muscle fibers exist, each of which has different performance characteristics. *Slow-twitch (Type I) muscle fibers* are better suited for low-force, long-duration activities because they possess more endurance enzymes, more blood capillaries, more mitochondria, and more intramuscular triglyceride stores for aerobic energy utilization. Marathon runners and triathletes typically have a high percentage of slow-twitch muscle fibers. *Fast-twitch (Type II) muscle fibers* are

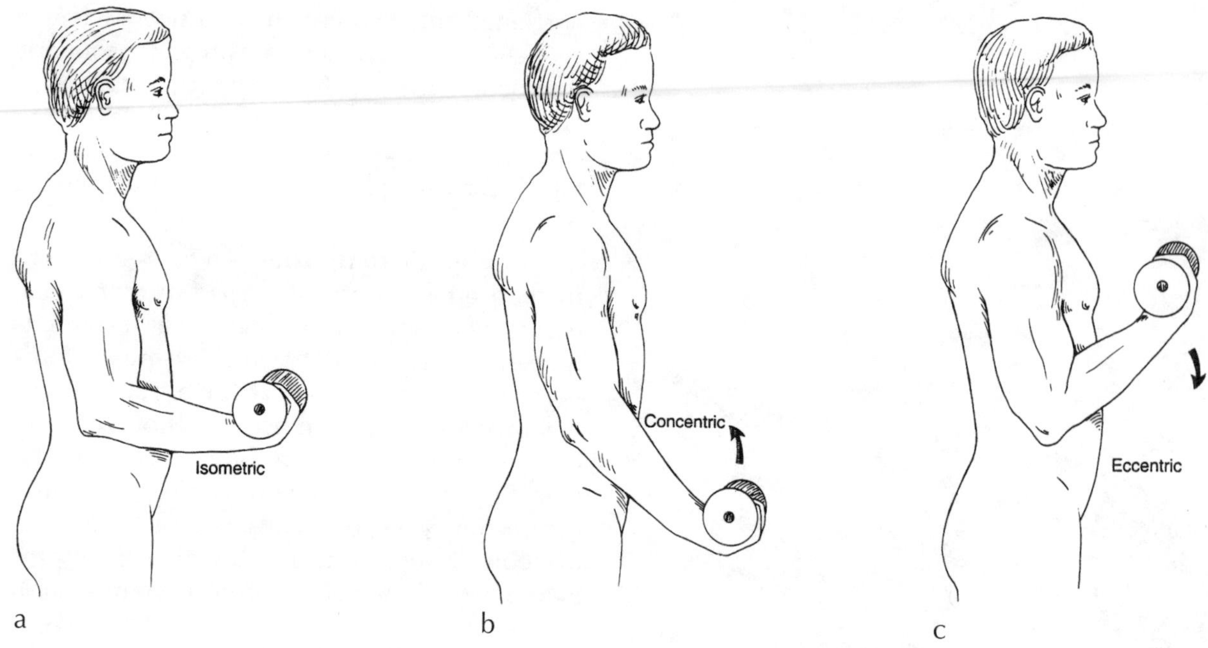

Figure 4.6 Different types of muscle contractions: *(a)* isometric, *(b)* concentric, and *(c)* eccentric.

better suited for high-force, short-duration activities because they possess more glycolytic enzyme activity, more myosin ATP activity, and more intramuscular phosphate stores for anaerobic energy utilization. Sprinters and jumpers typically have a high percentage of fast-twitch muscle fibers.

When maximum strength is required, both slow-twitch and fast-twitch muscle fibers are activated simultaneously. When submaximum strength is required, the slow-twitch muscle fibers are recruited first, followed by the fast-twitch muscle fibers if necessary.

Although it is possible to increase both our muscular strength and our muscular endurance through proper training, it appears that our proportion of fast-twitch and slow-twitch muscle fibers is genetically determined and is not subject to change. However, fast-twitch fibers may take on more aerobic characteristics (Type IIA) or more anaerobic characteristics (Type IIB) depending on the type of training performed.

Muscle Strength and Muscle Endurance

Muscle strength is the ability to exert force against a resistance. It is usually assessed as the maximum resistance that can be performed one time in a given exercise, such as the heaviest weight you can bench press. *Muscle endurance* is the ability to repeatedly exert force against a resistance. It is usually assessed as the number of repetitions that can be performed with a submaximum resistance, such as the number of push-ups you can perform.

Persons with a high percentage of fast-twitch muscle fibers usually score higher on muscle strength and lower on muscle endurance. Conversely, persons with a high percentage of slow-twitch muscle fibers typically score higher on muscle endurance and lower on muscle strength.

In all cases, a rather consistent relationship exists between our muscle strength and our relative muscle endurance. For example, let's say that Ralph can perform one barbell curl with 50 pounds and six barbell curls with 40 pounds. If Ralph increases his strength to one barbell curl with 100 pounds, he will probably perform six barbell curls with 80 pounds. In other words, Ralph's relative muscle endurance (biceps) is six repetitions with 80 percent of his maximum resistance.

Types of Strength Overloads

For many years, strength training programs have been described based on the type of muscle contraction involved during the exercise. The three types of strength training programs are isometric, isotonic, and isokinetic:

- **Isometric exercise—**Isometric exercise is any activity in which the muscles exert force but do not visibly change in length. Pushing against a doorway, carrying a bag of groceries, and water skiing are examples of isometric exercise. Although isometric exercise is effective for increasing muscle strength, it has a few notable drawbacks. First, isometric strength gains are specific to the joint positions that were trained, with relatively little strength improvement in other joint positions. Second, isometric exercise occludes blood flow and often produces unacceptably high blood pressure responses. Third, it is difficult to assess the training effort and strength improvement associated with most types of isometric exercise.

- **Isotonic exercise—**Isotonic exercise refers to activity in which the muscles exert force and change in length as they lift and lower resistance. Strength exercises using a fixed amount of external resistance are now more accurately referred to as either *dynamic constant* or *dynamic variable* resistance exercises. As described in the next paragraphs, these names suggest how the resistance forces and muscle forces interact throughout the range of movement:

  —Dynamic constant resistance exercise— Dynamic constant resistance exercise is characteristic of most muscular activities, such as lifting a baby or pressing a barbell. As the name implies, you lift and lower a constant resistance through a range of movement. Although the resistance does not vary (such as a 90-pound barbell), your muscle force capacity changes considerably throughout the movement range due to leverage factors. Consequently, the muscle force and the resistance force may be closely matched at only one point in the range of movement.

  —Dynamic variable resistance exercise— To better match muscle forces and resistance forces throughout the movement range, many types of strength training equipment incorporate dynamic variable resistance exercise. Through the use of levers, cams, or linkage systems, this equipment automatically changes the resistance in accordance with the muscle force capacity. The equipment provides less resistance in positions of lower muscle force capacity and more resistance in positions of higher muscle force capacity.

  Although dynamic variable resistance exercise definitely provides better matching of muscle forces and resistance forces throughout the movement range, it has not been shown to be more effective for strength development. In both dynamic constant resistance exercise and dynamic variable resistance exercise, the amount of resistance force you select determines the amount of muscle force you produce.

- **Isokinetic exercise—**Isokinetic exercise is any activity in which the resistance forces are closely matched to the muscle forces, thereby maintaining a constant movement speed. For this reason, isokinetic exercise is often referred to as *accommodating resistance.* Water activities are examples of isokinetic exercise, because the water resistance accommodates your muscle force. If you push the water with low force you encounter low resistance, but if you push the water with high force you encounter high resistance. Isokinetic exercise can be performed on a variety of equipment utilizing frictional resistance, hydraulic resistance, or electronic resistance. Although most isokinetic equipment uses only concentric contractions, some electronic machines provide accommodating resistance during both concentric and eccentric contractions. In isokinetic exercise, the amount of muscle force you produce determines the amount of resistance force you encounter.

Muscle Size Factors

Although many factors contribute to our effective muscle strength, the most important one is the cross-sectional size of our muscle. Because most of our muscles produce approximately one to two kilograms of force per square centimeter of cross-sectional area, a larger muscle is usually a stronger muscle. Proper strength training can increase the cross-sectional size of a muscle by adding actin and myosin proteins. As a result, individual muscle fibers increase in size, which leads to a larger muscle circumference. An increase in muscle size is referred to as *hypertrophy,* and a decrease in muscle size is called *atrophy.*

Three factors that affect how large our muscles can become and how quickly we can develop them are muscle length, gender, and age.

Muscle Length Factors

Although everyone can increase muscle strength and muscle size to some degree, one's potential muscle size is related to muscle length. A long muscle with short tendon attachments has more size potential than a short muscle with long tendon attachments.

To see how long your muscles are, try this: Put your arm at a right angle and forcefully contract your biceps muscle. Place as many fingers as will comfortable fit between the end of your muscle bulge and your forearm (see figure 4.7) and count them.

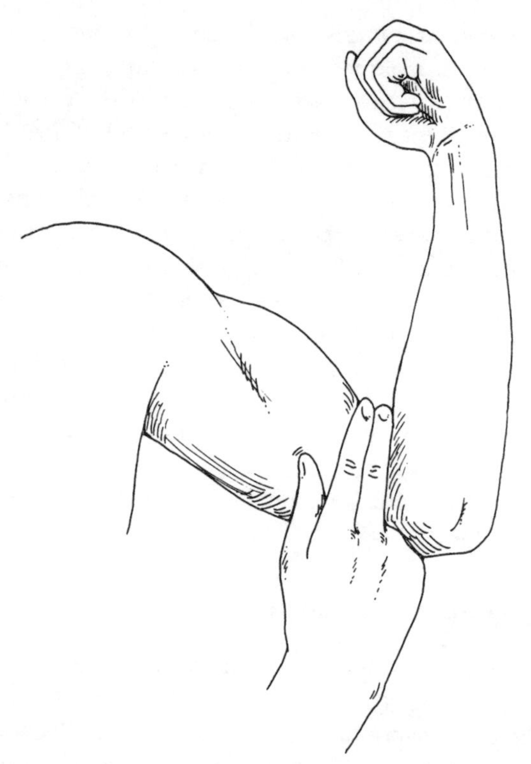

Figure 4.7 Measurement of biceps muscle length.

- If you can fit three fingers, you have a relatively short biceps muscle.
- If you can fit two fingers, you have a medium-length biceps muscle.
- If you can fit only one finger, you have a relatively long biceps muscle.

Persons who possess mostly long muscles are more likely to be successful in competitive bodybuilding and weightlifting activities.

Gender Factors

On a pound-for-pound basis, male muscle tissue and female muscle tissue are essentially the same. The average male is stronger than the average female not because he has better muscle tissue but because he has more muscle tissue. Due to a larger frame size, the average man has more muscle mass than the average woman. Due to having higher testosterone levels (the male sex hormone associated with muscle hypertrophy), the average man experiences larger increases in muscle size and strength as a result of progressive resistance exercise.

Age Factors

Age does not seem to be a factor in regard to strength development; a stimulus-response pattern associated with progressive resistance exercise produces similar strength results in nine-year-olds and ninety-year-olds. However, it does appear to influence the rate of strength development. Research indicates that younger individuals gain muscle size and strength more quickly than older individuals. This is particularly true during the years of normal growth and maturation. Because a strong musculoskeletal system is desirable at every age, sensible strength training should begin in the pre-teen years and continue throughout life.

Muscles and Movements

In each movement we make, muscles are involved. Some provide most of the force for the desired movement, the prime mover muscles; others perform the movement opposite the desired movement, the antagonist muscles; and still others help maintain body posture while movement occurs, the stabilizer muscles.

- **Prime mover muscles**—The muscles primarily responsible for performing a particular movement are called the *prime mover* or *agonist* muscles. For example, in dumbbell curls the biceps muscles are primarily responsible for elbow flexion and serve as the prime mover muscles. More specifically, the biceps muscles contract concentrically to lift the dumbbell and contract eccentrically to lower the dumbbell.

• **Antagonist muscles**—The muscles primarily responsible for performing movement opposite that of the prime mover muscles are termed the *antagonist* muscles. For example, the triceps muscles are primarily responsible for elbow extension and function as the antagonist muscles to the biceps. For smooth elbow flexion, the triceps (antagonists) must lengthen as the biceps (prime movers) shorten. Conversely, for smooth elbow extension, the biceps (antagonists) must lengthen as the triceps (prime movers) shorten. Performance of these movements is regulated through the process of reciprocal inhibition (see figure 4.8).

• **Stabilizer muscles**—The muscles that stabilize certain joints to facilitate the desired movements in other joints are referred to as *stabilizer* or *synergist* muscles. For example, to properly perform barbell curls, the torso must remain erect and steady. This stabilizing function is performed by the low back and oblique muscles, which contract isometrically to maintain the torso in an erect posture.

The major muscle groups are described in figures 4.9 through 4.14, and the action of specific muscles at each joint are listed in table 4.1.

Examples of Muscles Used in Common Activities

The following section presents a summary of the muscle groups involved in some of the most common physical activities. We begin with walking and end with lifting heavy objects.

Walking, Jogging, and Running

Walking, jogging, and running have a lot in common; they differ, however, in terms of the muscular force needed to move forward at different speeds. During walking, one foot is in contact with the ground at all times, but in jogging or running there is a period of "flight" when both feet are off the ground. If a period of flight is involved, a greater amount of energy must be expended to both "take off" and "land." The primary muscle groups involved in each phase of these activities include these:

• **Push-off phase**—The push-off uses the concentric contraction of *hip and knee extensors*.

• **Bringing push-off leg forward**—The concentric contraction of *hip flexors* initiates movement that is modified by the *lateral hip rotators*.

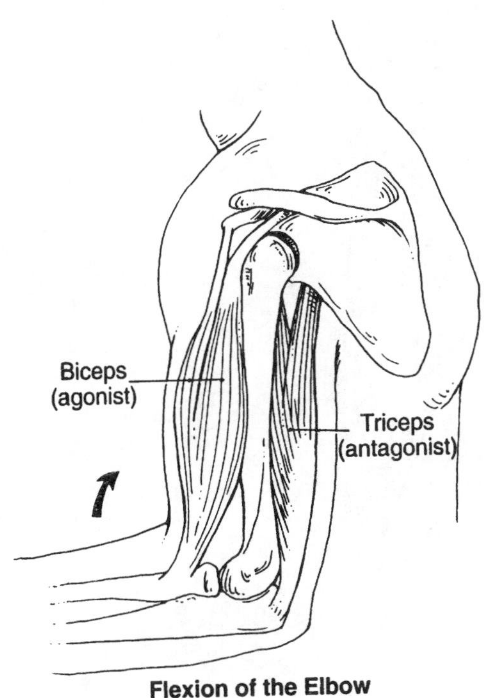

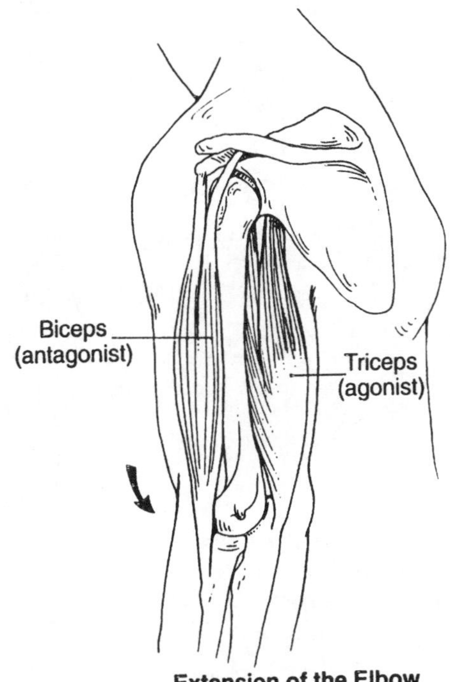

Figure 4.8 Reciprocal inhibition.

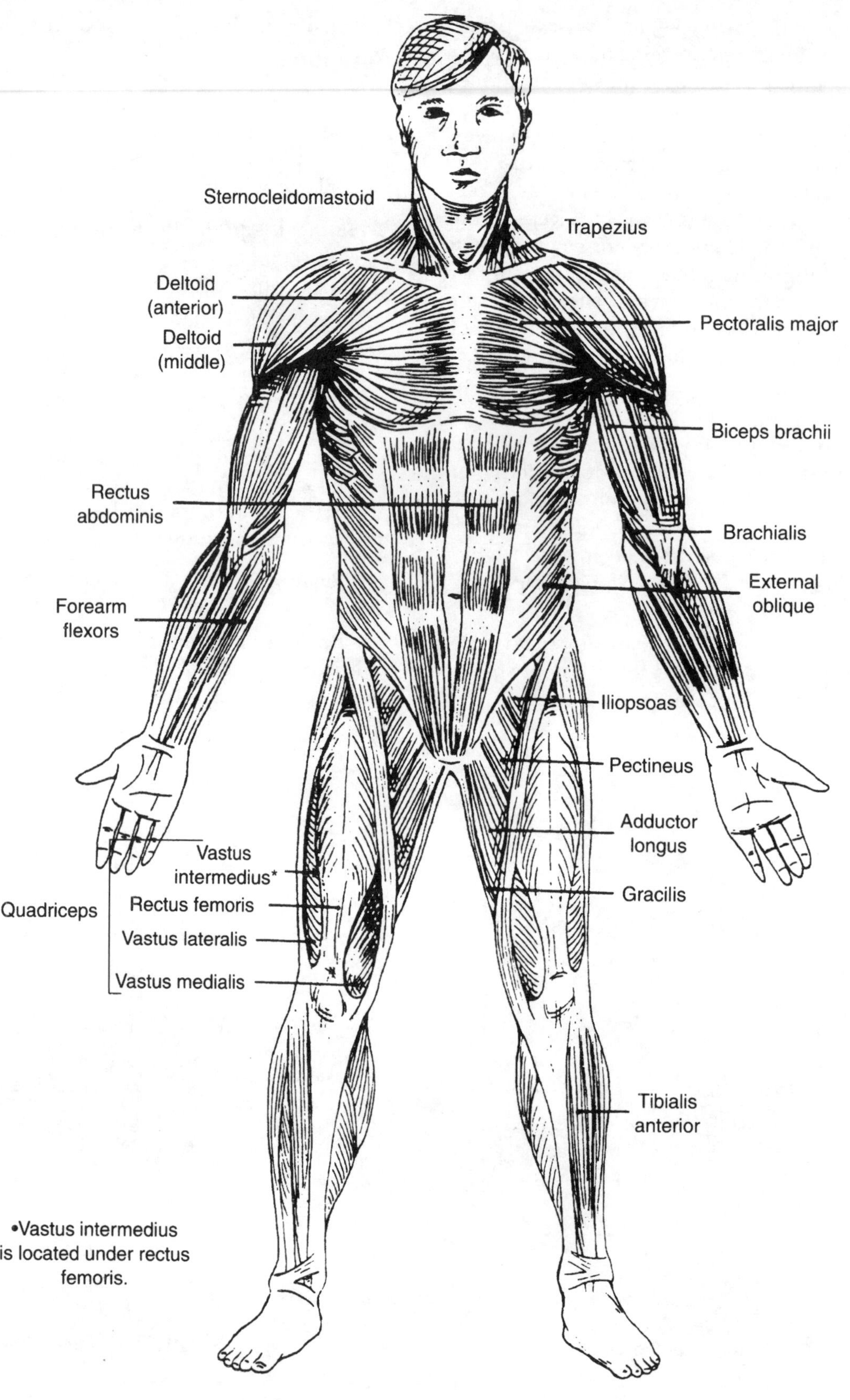

Figure 4.9 Muscles of the human body—anterior view.

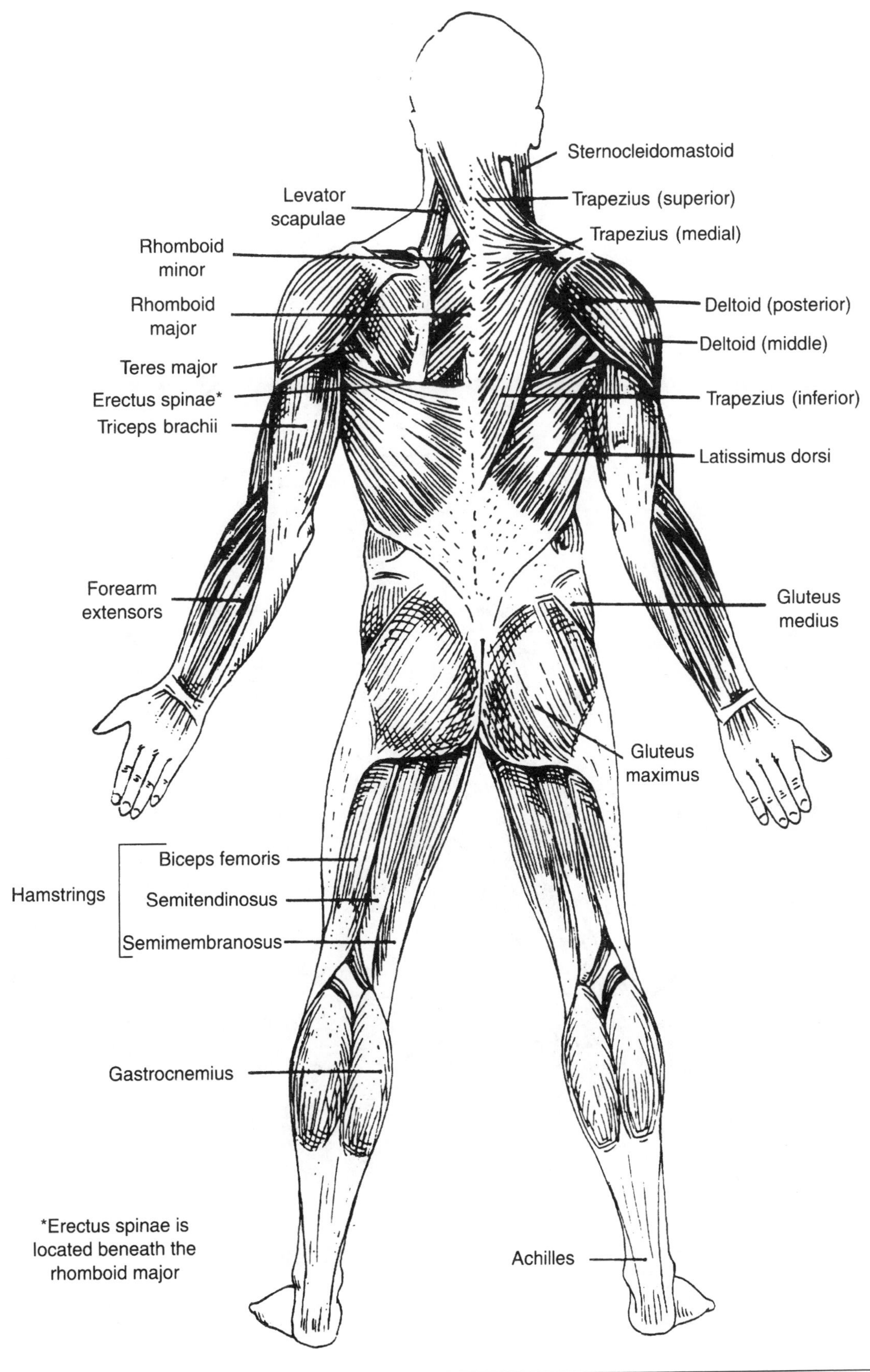

Figure 4.10 Muscles of the human body—posterior view.

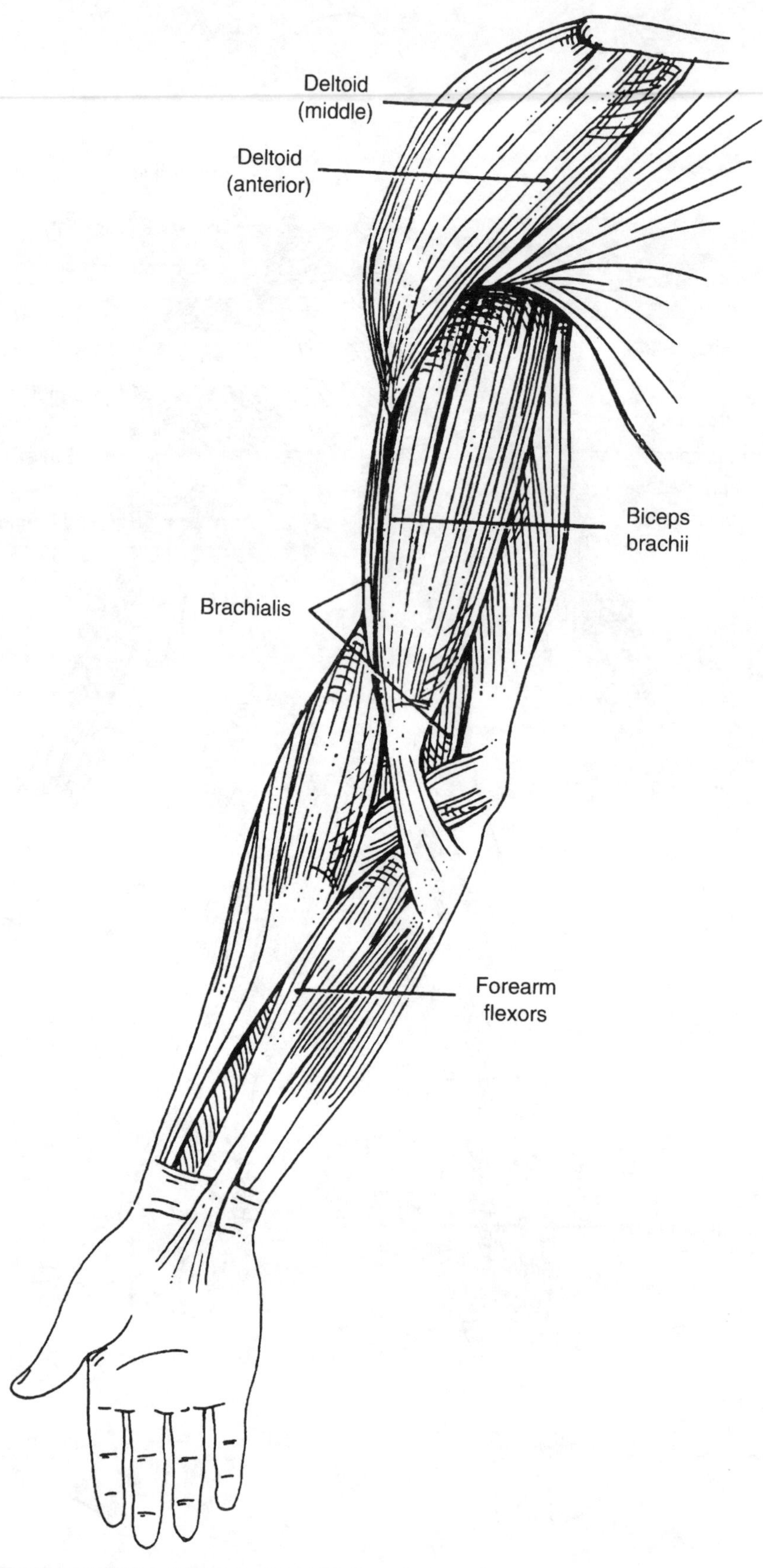

Figure 4.11 Muscles of the arm—anterior view

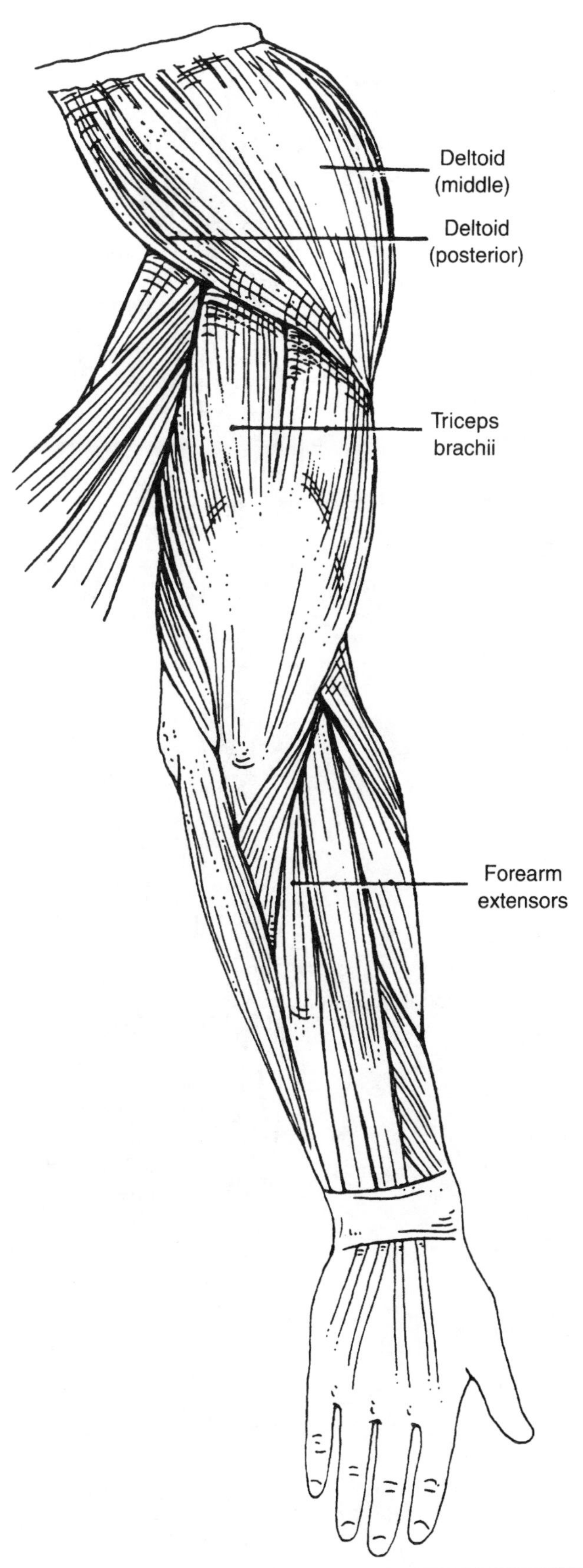

Figure 4.12 Muscles of the arm—posterior view.

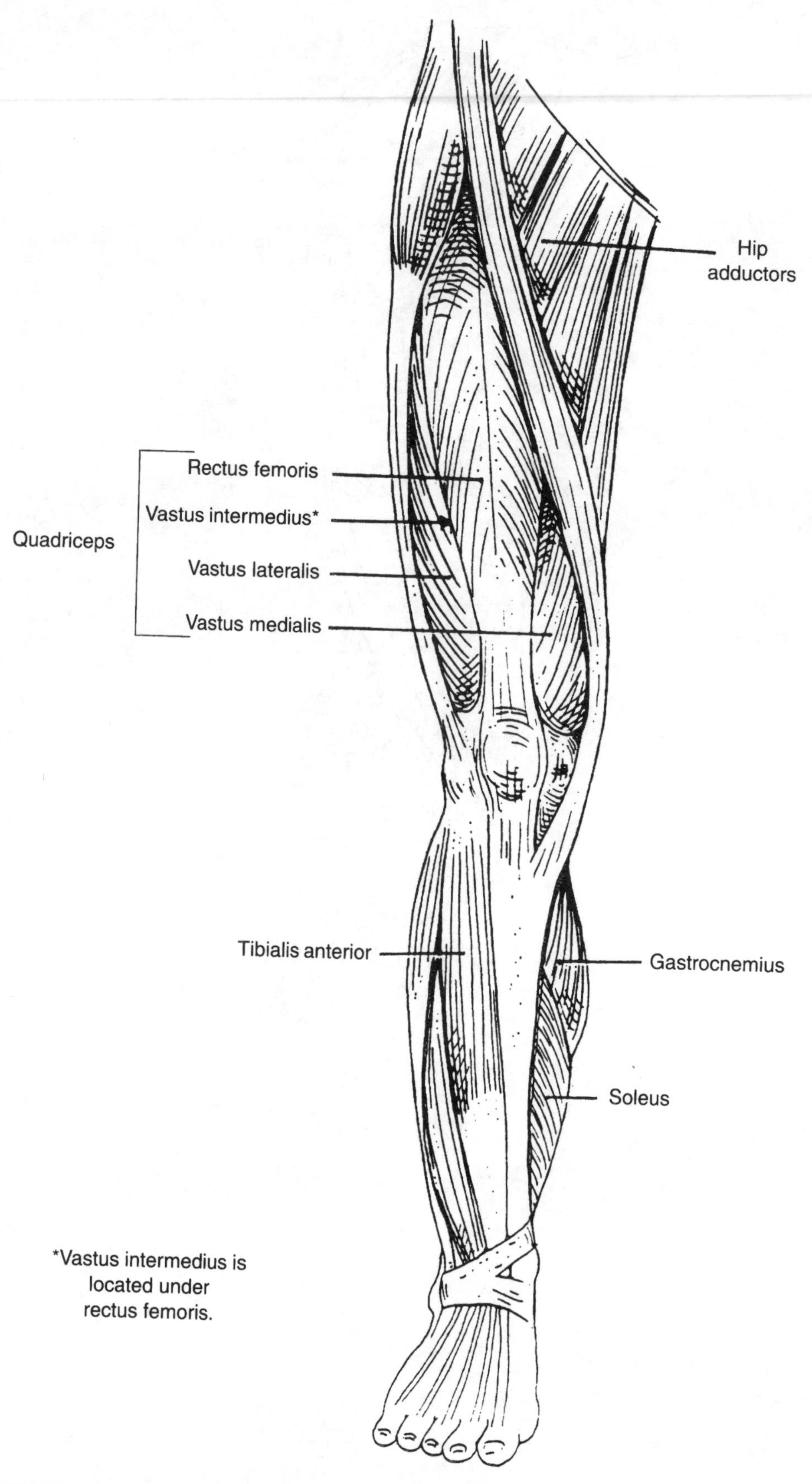

Figure 4.13 Muscles of the leg—anterior view.

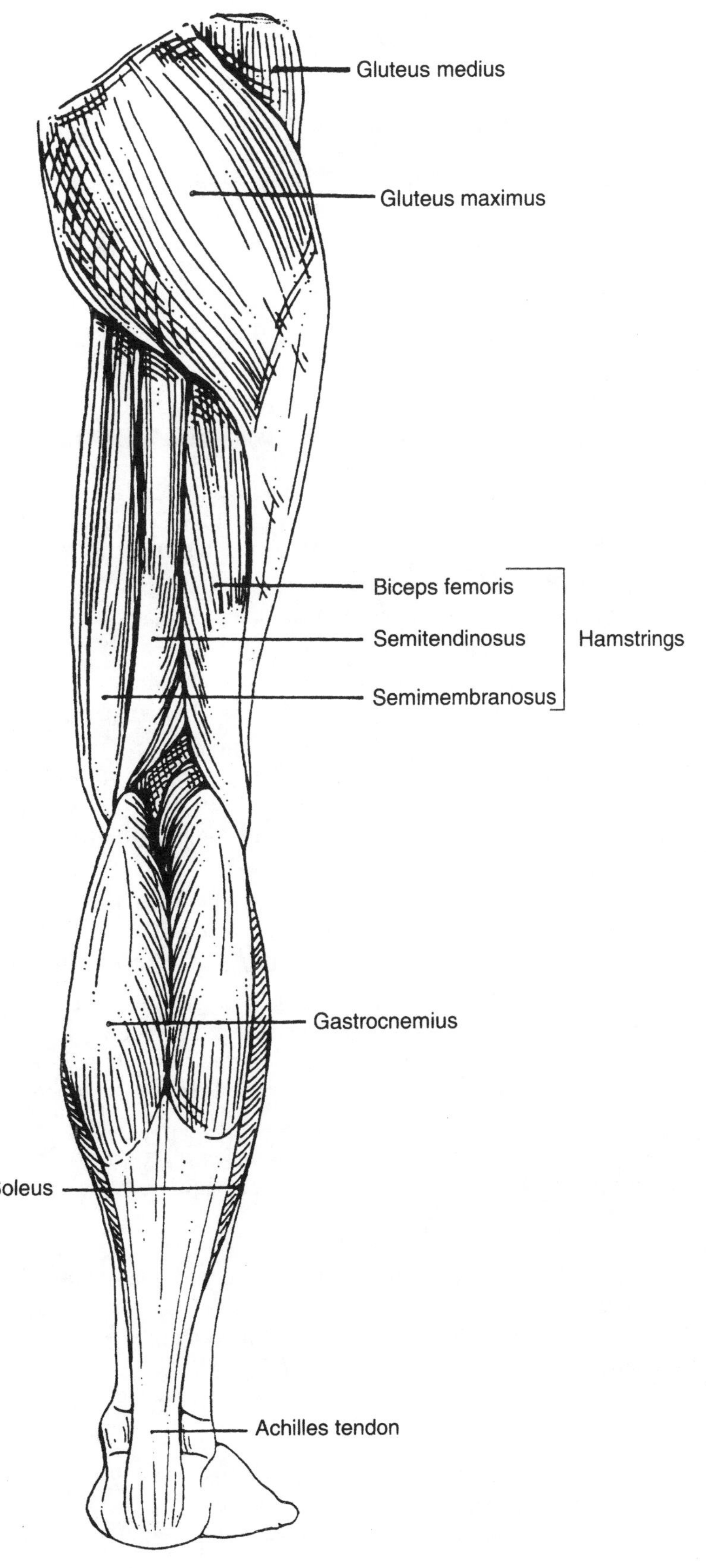

Figure 4.14 Muscles of the leg—posterior view.

Table 4.1 Muscles That Are Prime Movers

Joint	Prime movers
Shoulder girdle	Abductors—serratus anterior, pectoralis minor Adductors—middle fibers of trapezius, rhomboids (upper and lower fibers of trapezius) Upward rotators—upper and lower fibers of trapezius, serratus anterior Downward rotators—rhomboids, pectoralis minor Elevators—levator scapulae, upper fibers of trapezius, rhomboids Depressors—lower fibers of trapezius, pectoralis minor
Shoulder joint	Flexors—anterior deltoid, clavicular portion of pectoralis major Extensors—sternal portion of pectoralis major, latissimus dorsi, teres major Hyperextensors—latissimus dorsi, teres major Abductors—middle deltoid, supraspinatus Adductors—latissimus dorsi, teres major, sternal portion of pectoralis major External rotators—infraspinatus, teres minor Internal rotators—pectoralis major, subscapularis, latissimus dorsi, teres major Horizontal flexors—both portions of pectoralis major, anterior deltoid Horizontal extensors—latissimus dorsi, teres major, infraspinatus, teres minor, posterior deltoid
Elbow joint	Flexors—brachialis, biceps brachii, brachioradialis Extensors—triceps brachii
Radioulnar joint	Pronators—pronator quadratus, pronator teres, brachioradialis Supinators—supinator, biceps brachii, brachioradialis
Wrist joint	Flexors—flexor carpi ulnaris, flexor carpi radialis Extensors and hyperextensors—extensor carpi ulnaris, extensor carpi radialis longus and brevis Abductors (radial flexors)—flexor carpi radialis, extensor carpi radialis longus and brevis Adductors (ulnar flexors)—flexor carpi ulnaris, extensor carpi ulnaris
Lumbosacral joint	Forward pelvic tilters—iliopsoas Backward pelvic tilters—rectus abdominus, internal oblique
Spinal column (thoracic and lumbar areas)	Flexors—rectus abdominus, external oblique, internal oblique Extensors and hyperextensors—erector spinae group Rotators—internal oblique, external oblique, erector spinae, rotatores, multifidus Lateral flexors—internal oblique, external oblique, quadratus lumborum, multifidus, rotatores
Hip joint	Flexors—iliopsoas, pectineus, rectus femoris Extensors and hyperextensors—gluteus maximus, biceps femoris, semitendinosus, semimembranosus Abductors—gluteus medius Adductors—adductor brevis, adductor longus, gracilis, pectineus Lateral rotators—gluteus maximus, the six deep lateral rotator muscles Medial rotators—gluteus minimus, gluteus medius
Knee joint	Flexors—biceps femoris, semimembranosus, semitendinosus Extensors—rectus femoris, vastus medialis, vastus lateralis, vastus intermedius
Ankle joint	Plantar flexors—gastrocnemius, soleus Dorsiflexors—tibialis anterior, extensor digitorum longus, peroneus tertius
Intertarsal joint	Inverters—tibialis anterior, tibialis posterior Everters—extensor digitorum longus, peroneus brevis, peroneus longus, peroneus tertius

Reprinted, by permission, from E. Howley and B.D. Franks, 1992, *Health Fitness Instructor's Handbook*, 2d ed. (Champaign, IL: Human Kinetics), 98–99.

The *knee flexors* first cause knee flexion; then, through an eccentric contraction, control the rate of knee extension prior to the foot touching down. The foot is *dorsiflexed* prior to landing.

- **Landing**—The *hip extensors* that initiated the push-off now contract eccentrically to slow the swing of the forward leg. When the foot touches down, the *knee extensors* also contract eccentrically to control the motion of the foot on the ground.

Cycling

Given that cycling is a restricted activity in that the pedals move in a fixed manner, it should be no surprise that the muscle groups involved in cycling are also somewhat limited. The hip and knee extensors develop the force to move the pedals downward, and, if toe clips are used by a cyclist skilled in their use, hip and knee flexors are involved in the return to the starting position. Without the use of toe clips, flexor activity is considerably less.

Jumping

The force needed to propel the body off the ground is generated by the knee and hip extensors as well as the plantar flexors. To absorb the forces of impact, these same muscles contract eccentrically.

Lifting and Carrying

When a person lifts an object, the large, strong knee and hip extensors should be the primary muscles involved, not the muscles in the arms or along the spine. Keeping the object close to one's body reduces the stress on the back.

Movement Biomechanical Concepts

A variety of basic principles and laws governing the movement of objects and people can, when understood, help you determine proper and improper movements. These include stability, rotational inertia, lever systems, torque, and angular momentum.

Stability

The center of gravity for an average person is near the navel. The stability of an individual is greater the closer the center of gravity is to the ground and the wider the base of support. A person standing with both feet close together is less stable than when standing with feet spread apart.

Rotational Inertia

The concept of rotational inertia as applied to the body indicates the tendency of a body segment to remain at rest and not rotate around a joint. The larger the body segment and the farther the mass of the segment is from the joint (e.g., arm vs. leg), the more rotational inertia the body segment has and the greater the energy required to move that segment through a range of motion. The energy requirement can be reduced by bringing the mass of the segment closer to the joint of rotation; bringing the *flexed* rear leg forward during running is an application of this principle.

Lever Systems

Human movement is possible because of lever systems composed of our long bones, joints, and muscles. Our muscles produce sufficient force to move our bones around our joint axis of rotation. The systems are divided into three classes: first, second, and third.

- **First-class levers**—Whenever the joint axis of rotation is between the muscle force and the resistance force, the system functions as a first-class lever. As illustrated in figure 4.15a, the triceps muscle operates as a first-class lever system because the joint axis of rotation (elbow) is between the muscle force (triceps tendon attachment) and the resistance force (dumbbell).
- **Second-class levers**—Whenever the resistance force is between the joint axis of rotation and the muscle force, the system functions as a second-class lever. As shown in figure 4.15b, the gastrocnemius muscle operates a second-class lever system because the resistance force (body weight) is between the joint axis of rotation (ball of foot) and the muscle force (Achilles tendon attachment).
- **Third-class levers**—Whenever the muscle force is between the joint axis of rotation and the resistance force, the system functions as a third-class lever. As presented in figure 4.15c, the biceps muscle operates a third-class lever system because the muscle force (the point at which the biceps tendon attaches) is between the joint axis of rotation (elbow) and the resistance force (dumbbell).

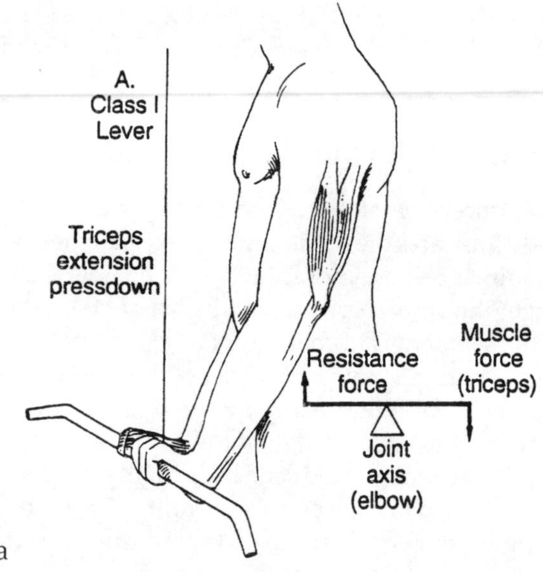

a

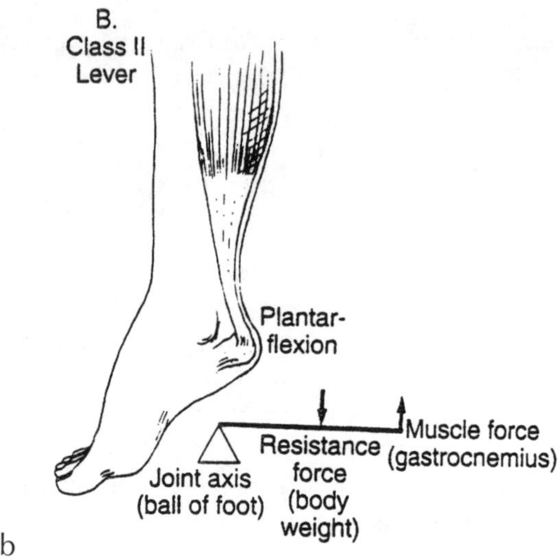

b

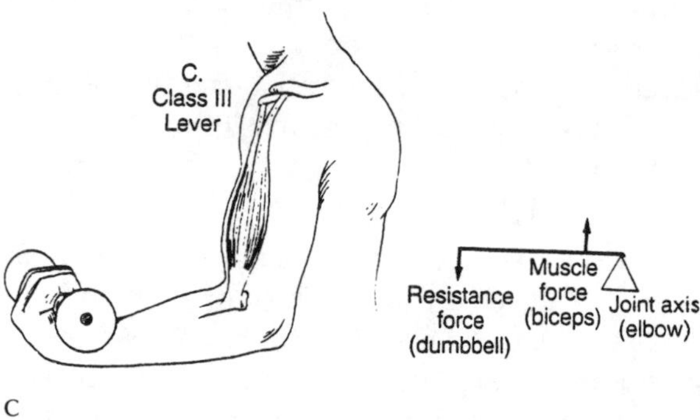

c

Figure 4.15 Lever systems.

The predominantly third-class human lever systems are well designed for range of movement and speed of movement, but they are not very efficient in producing force. Consider the following examples of force relationships in the biceps lever system:

Example

Susan has a 10-inch forearm and her biceps tendon inserts 0.5 inches from her elbow joint. How much biceps force must Susan produce to hold a 15-pound dumbbell at 90 degrees of elbow flexion?

Resistance Arm × Resistance Force =
Muscle Arm × Muscle Force

10 inches × 15 pounds =
0.5 inches × Muscle Force

150 inch-pounds ÷ 0.5 inches =
300 pounds Muscle Force

Susan must produce 300 pounds of force in her biceps muscle to hold a 15-pound dumbbell at 90 degrees of elbow flexion.

Example

Gayle also has a 10-inch forearm, but her biceps tendon inserts 0.75 inches from her elbow joint. How much biceps force must Gayle produce to hold a 15-pound dumbbell at 90 degrees of elbow flexion?

Resistance Arm × Resistance Force =
Muscle Arm × Muscle Force

10 inches × 15 pounds =
0.75 inches × Muscle Force

150 inch-pounds ÷ 0.75 inches =
200 pounds Muscle Force

Gayle must produce 200 pounds of force in her biceps muscle to hold a 15-pound dumbbell at 90 degrees of elbow flexion. She has a distinct leverage advantage over Susan because of her more favorable point of tendon insertion.

These examples demonstrate that typical human lever systems require relatively high muscle force to overcome relatively low resistance force. They also show that small differences in the point of tendon insertion produce large differences in the muscle force requirements.

Torque

This is the effect produced when a muscle contraction (force) causes rotation. We will look at forearm flexion as an example, with the forearm at a 90-degree angle to the upper arm and a 10-pound weight held in the hand. The resistance is the product of the 10-pound weight and the distance from the center of the weight to the elbow joint. The muscular force needed to move that weight is dependent on the distance from the elbow to the tendon insertion on the forearm. The closer the biceps' insertion is located to the hand, the smaller the muscular force needed to move the resistance. In the same way, if the 10-pound weight is moved closer to the joint (to reduce the length of the lever arm), less muscular force is needed to move the resistance. This concept can be extended to the carrying of objects. The reason for carrying an object close to the body is to maintain stability and reduce the force of the back muscles needed to carry the load. If the object is held with arms outstretched, the back muscles must exert more force, which can cause back problems.

Angular Momentum

This term describes the amount of motion that takes place as a limb moves around a joint or a body rotates and is equal to the product of angular velocity and rotational inertia. The *conservation of angular momentum* states that once motion is initiated, angular momentum remains constant until an outside force changes it. This means that a decrease in rotational inertia during a movement results in a higher angular velocity. This is best seen when an ice skater spins around in place; as the arms are brought closer to the body to decrease rotational inertia, the velocity of rotation increases.

5

Strength Training Principles and Guidelines

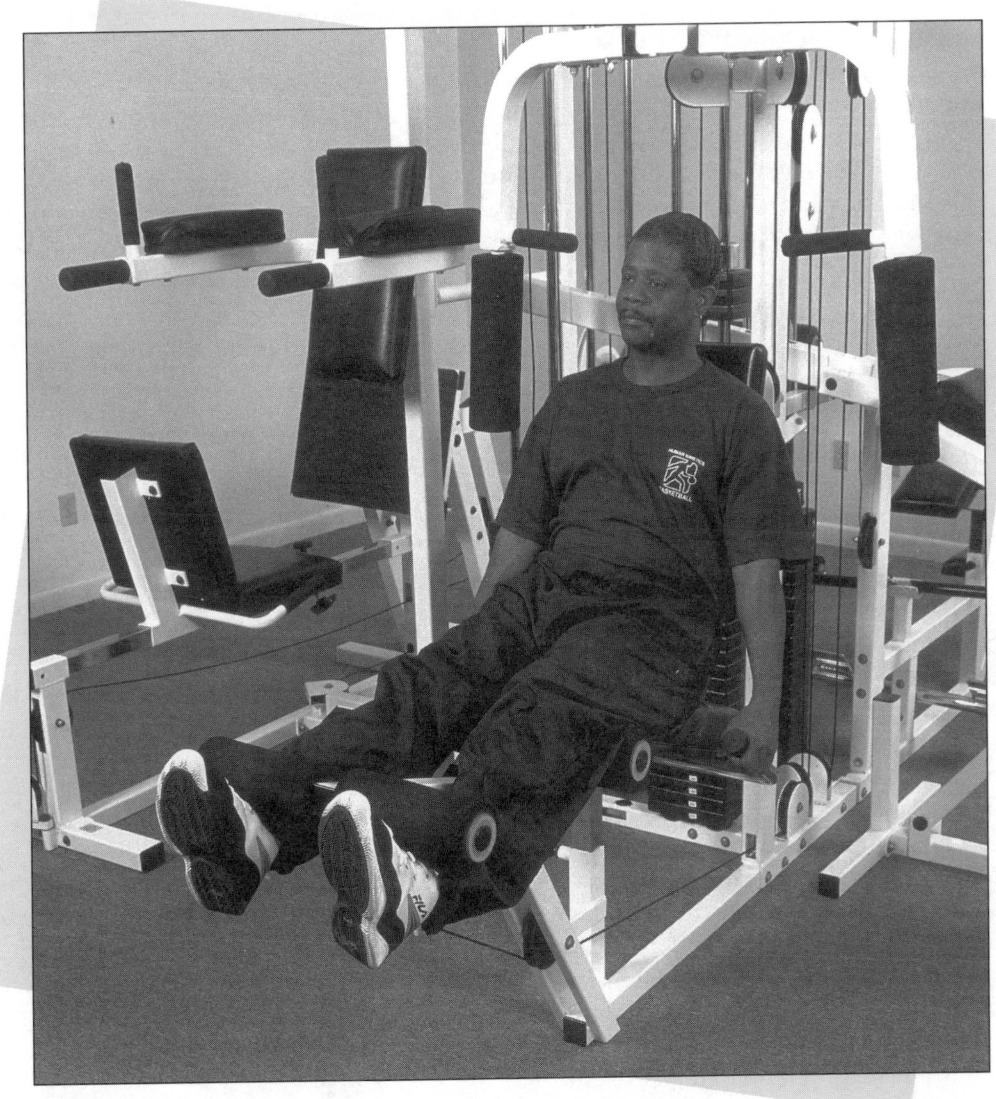

Strength training is a process of systematically applying increasing amounts of stress to muscles. Muscles respond to progressive resistance exercise by gradually becoming larger and stronger. To develop effective strength training programs, you need to understand general concepts about how the body adapts to the progressive overload of strength exercises. Strength training is a highly individualized procedure. As a YMCA Personal Training Instructor, you must assist your members by designing appropriate programs that will challenge them to develop strength.

In this chapter we discuss the many benefits of and reasons for strength training. We describe the principles of strength training, explain special health considerations and precautions related to training, and dispel myths about training. We then present procedures for performing strength training safely and effectively, describe recommended exercises and how to choose them, and show you how to develop effective and efficient programs. We follow this with some advanced training methods that can be used to overcome strength plateaus and a brief discussion of strength training for competitive purposes. Finally, we recommend orientations for beginning, intermediate, and advanced participants, as well as ongoing education for strength training participants.

Strength Training Benefits

Strength training has many benefits for exercisers, some physiological, some physical, and some that lead to better overall health.

Physiological Benefits

Regular strength training produces more myofibrils per muscle fiber, more capillaries per muscle fiber, more intramuscular energy stores, and better muscle fiber recruitment. However, the primary response to progressive resistance exercise is an increase in the muscle proteins, actin and myosin. This produces larger muscle fibers that have greater structural and contractile strength.

The stress applied to the muscles is transferred to the connective tissue (tendons and ligaments) and bones. This produces more collagen proteins in the tendons and ligaments and more osteo proteins in the bones, increasing the structural strength of tendons, ligaments, and bones. The result is a well-developed musculoskeletal system that is strong and injury resistant.

Physical Benefits

A well-developed musculoskeletal system provides many important benefits with regard to functional capacity and quality of life. These include athletic power, injury prevention, physical capacity, metabolic function, and physical appearance.

Athletic Power

Performance power is the key to success in many athletic activities. Sprinting, jumping, and throwing are examples of power activities. So are driving a golf ball, serving a tennis ball, and hitting a softball. Performance power depends on two factors: movement speed and muscle strength. Too little movement speed or too little muscle strength can reduce performance power. The best means for improving performance power is to increase both movement speed and muscle strength. However, having greater muscle strength allows us to move with more power, force, and speed.

Most sports coaches encourage their athletes to strength train in order to enhance their performance power and reduce their injury potential. Coaches have also learned that proper strength training does not hinder movement speed or joint flexibility, and in fact enhances both. All other factors equal, a stronger athlete is indeed a better athlete.

Injury Prevention

Four out of every five Americans experience low back pain, the majority of which is related to poor muscle condition. It is very important to maintain strong postural muscles to counteract the effects of gravity on the musculoskeletal system. In this regard, well-conditioned muscles serve as balancing agents that protect the body from a variety of degenerative processes.

Musculoskeletal injuries can also be a serious problem for many exercisers. For example, runners and group exercise participants frequently experience musculoskeletal injuries caused by repetitive landing forces. Swimmers and tennis players often experience overuse injuries due to using the prime mover muscle groups too much and the antagonist muscle groups too little. Football players and wrestlers are subject to traumatic soft tissue injuries as a result of external contact forces.

In all cases, sensible strength training is the best preventive measure. When performed properly, strength training conditions all of the major muscle groups, thereby enhancing our ability both to absorb external forces and to maintain internal strength balance between opposing muscles. Without balanced muscle strength, it is difficult for athletes to avoid overuse injuries and for nonexercisers to delay degenerative musculoskeletal problems. Because the preferred treatment modality for many musculoskeletal injuries and degenerative problems is progressive resistance exercise under the watchful eye of a medical professional, it makes sense that well-designed and well-supervised strength training programs may be equally useful in preventing many of these problems.

Physical Capacity

Normally, physical capacity is thought of in terms of cardiorespiratory endurance, and that is certainly an important component of overall fitness. While the heart functions as the fuel pump of the body, the muscles serve as the engine. Muscles use energy to produce movement and are essential to all physical activity. Whereas endurance exercise is necessary for improving cardiorespiratory fitness, it generally has little effect on muscular fitness. Progressive resistance exercise is the key to increasing muscular fitness, which has a major impact on physical capacity to perform work, exercise, and daily activities. Weeding the garden, playing tennis, carrying groceries, and climbing stairs all require muscular strength. So does sitting at a desk. Research shows that neck strength decreases considerably between 9 A.M. and 5 P.M. as a result of holding up a 15-pound head. Poorly conditioned postural muscles may also fatigue quickly, limiting physical capacity and lowering quality of life.

Numerous studies have demonstrated significant improvements in muscle strength after only four to eight weeks of regular strength training. The higher strength levels that result from strength training make almost everything we do a little easier. This is because every physical activity requires a certain percentage of our maximum muscle strength. For example, if maximum biceps strength is 25 pounds, carrying a 25-pound bag of groceries is an all-out effort. If biceps strength increases to 50 pounds, carrying the same bag of groceries requires only half of the available muscle force, making the task much easier.

There is a differentiation between muscle strength and muscle endurance, even though they are very closely related. Increased muscle strength results in increased muscle endurance, making it possible to perform more work, exercise, and recreational physical activities.

Metabolic Function

Muscles are responsible for most of the energy used during vigorous physical activity, and they increase metabolic function as much as 20 times above its resting rate. However, muscles have a major influence on resting metabolic function as well. Muscle is very active tissue that requires continuous energy supplies for ongoing cellular processes such as protein synthesis, maintenance, and building. Even when we are sleeping, skeletal muscles are metabolically active, using over 25 percent of the total calorie output. In fact, it is estimated that a pound of muscle uses over 35 calories a day at rest to meet its metabolic requirements. Therefore, muscle mass and metabolic function are closely related. When muscle mass is added, metabolic rate increases, both during activity and at rest. Conversely, when muscle mass is lost, metabolic rate decreases, both during activity and at rest.

Unfortunately, unless regular strength exercise is performed, muscle mass decreases with age. Studies show that after age 25, the average American loses about one-half pound of muscle every year of life through inactivity. The saying "use it or lose it" definitely applies to skeletal muscles. Without an appropriate training stimulus, muscle fibers gradually become smaller and weaker (atrophy). The gradual loss of muscle tissue is largely responsible for the gradual reduction in metabolic rate that appears to be part of aging. Research reveals that resting metabolism decreases approximately 1/2 percent every year of life after age 25.

All vigorous physical activity elevates heart rate, blood pressure, and energy metabolism. However, endurance exercise such as jogging, cycling, or swimming increases metabolic rate only during the activity session and for a brief period of time thereafter. Strength exercise increases metabolic rate during the activity session, but it also raises resting metabolic rate because more muscle tissue is developed. Strength training, therefore, has a double effect on energy utilization. The primary effect is a large increase in metabolic rate during the exercise session. The secondary effect is a small increase in metabolic rate 24 hours per day, 365 days a year (as long as the person maintains a strength training program).

Physical Appearance

Perhaps the most common reason for strength training and the most obvious benefit is improved physical appearance. Essentially, muscles are responsible for overall physique and physical appearance. Although few people have the genetic potential to develop really large muscles, everyone can enhance their muscle firmness and muscle fitness. Consider an average woman who weighs 126 pounds and is 27 percent fat. Even though she is not overweight by most standards, she definitely has too much fat and too little muscle to look and function her best. A sensible program consisting of progressive resistance exercise, endurance activities, and a prudent diet can improve body composition without changing body weight, as shown in table 5.1.

Of course, it is possible to lose 5 pounds of fat by dieting or doing endurance exercise. However, it is unlikely a person will add 5 pounds of muscle without performing regular strength exercise. Although the fat loss is certainly helpful, the muscle gain is even more beneficial in terms of physical appearance and physical fitness. Significant changes in body composition and physical appearance are usually observed after only one to two months of regular strength training. Several studies have found that untrained adults typically gain about three pounds of muscle and lose about three pounds of fat after eight weeks of regular strength exercise. Because the results are apparent to both the exerciser and others, sensible strength training is a reinforcing activity that should become a consistent component of a fitness-oriented lifestyle.

Health Benefits

In addition to the more obvious fitness and performance benefits of regular strength training, a number of outcomes of strength training enhance overall health.

- **Improve body composition**—Body composition can be improved by increasing energy-utilizing muscle tissue and decreasing energy-storing fat tissue. This typically decreases the percentage of body fat (and often decreases body weight), thereby reducing this coronary risk factor.
- **Decrease blood pressure**—Like endurance exercise, strength exercise tends to normalize elevated blood pressure, thereby reducing this coronary risk factor.
- **Reduce sedentary risks**—Obviously, you cannot participate in strength training and remain sedentary. Because sedentary living is a significant coronary risk factor, strength training is beneficial in this respect.
- **Increase HDL cholesterol**—Research indicates that strength exercise may increase levels of high density lipoprotein (HDL; good) cholesterol. Perhaps just as important, persons involved in regular strength training tend to be more concerned about proper nutrition and more likely to follow a low-fat diet.
- **Enhance overall well-being**—Like most physical activities, strength training seems to enhance the overall well-being of most individuals. Many strength trainers report increased ability to accomplish daily responsibilities, improved job performance, and more meaningful recreational activities.

Table 5.1 Example of Body Composition Changes As a Result of Exercise

Preexercise Program	Postexercise Program
14 pounds bone	14 pounds bone
28 pounds organs/skin	28 pounds organs/skin
34 pounds fat	29 pounds fat
50 pounds muscle	55 pounds muscle
126 pounds/27% fat	126 pounds/23% fat

• **Provide psychological benefits**—Strength training may help reduce stress, increase success, improve self-confidence, and enhance self-esteem. Positive changes in physical strength and personal appearance often lead to positive changes in self-image. Without question, strength training is a purposeful physical activity that contributes to self-confidence and personal satisfaction. This may explain why at-risk youth typically respond very well to supervised strength training programs. In addition to improving self-esteem, good strength training programs provide an excellent environment for developing cooperation and leadership skills.

Practical Reasons for Strength Training

Besides bringing health and fitness benefits, strength training also helps individuals with their job training and performance and makes them better able to defend themselves from attack. It makes daily activities easier, whether those activities are chores or recreational. Finally, for those who work out at strength training facilities, it provides the chance for enjoyable interactions with others who are training.

Job Training

Many job training programs incorporate strength training. Police and fire departments use physical fitness testing as part of their evaluation process in hiring. Women who are interested in jobs in the fire and police departments are particularly interested in strength training to develop upper body strength. The armed services (Army, Marines, Navy, and Air Force) stress physical readiness and have an ongoing interest in physical fitness. The Forest Services, Rangers, and Park Services are other examples of occupations vitally interested in physical conditioning. Both men and women seek specific strength training programs and information to help them qualify for careers that require physical strength.

Job Performance

Improved job performance and increased productivity are important to many workers. Some find physical fitness and particularly strength to be a factor in job performance. Those that require physical strength in their jobs directly benefit from strength training programs. But even those who have sedentary professions benefit from strength training because physical strength means less general fatigue, which can maintain and even increase job productivity. Workers who feel better work with more vitality.

Self-Protection

A less obvious reason for strength training is the growing awareness and need for self-protection. Self-defense activities require physical strength. Many authorities believe that a strong and confident person is less likely to be approached or attacked. This, along with the practical ability of being able to deal with a variety of emergency situations, motivates many people to develop strength.

Daily Activities

Routine daily activities and tasks are made easier with increased muscular strength. The homemaker completes household tasks with greater ease. Even grocery shopping is easier because carrying heavy packages from the car to the kitchen, especially up stairs, is not as stressful. Lifting heavy objects, doing yard work, and dozens of daily tasks can be done more easily and without help from others. This is particularly relevant for older adults who wish to live independently as long as possible. The fear of straining or pulling muscles, hurting the back, or overdoing is lessened with muscular fitness. At the end of the day when work and daily tasks are completed, the fit person is ready and able to participate in hobbies and recreational activities, and once again adequate strength is desirable. Strength training and physical fitness enable one to complete the required tasks and work of the day, leaving enough strength, endurance, and energy to participate in enjoyable recreational activities.

Socialization

Today's modern strength training facilities are attractive, pleasant places. Strength training and fitness have become a popular way for people to meet and make friends. Most fitness facilities provide a comfortable and inviting atmosphere for people to interact, making physical activity enjoyable and beneficial. Strength training participants feel good about being with others who share the same experiences and feel the same physical changes. The interaction between people takes place in a variety of ways but usually it occurs naturally. If one wants to meet people, the fitness center is a good place. The self-confidence and comradeship found there may help people reach out in other areas, such as with friends and family and in business. The social aspect of the strength training facility becomes as important to people as the workout itself.

Special Applications for Strength Training

Strength training can be used to help people rehabilitate from injury or cardiac conditions, and it can also give people the chance to engage in competitive bodybuilding and weightlifting.

Rehabilitation From Injury

Strength training is a major modality of many rehabilitation programs. Physicians, physical therapists, and athletic trainers use strength training to rehabilitate many injuries. It is also used as therapy for the chronically ill, the injured, and the disabled. Strength training programs can have a "cross-training" effect; that is, the uninjured side of the body can be exercised to benefit the opposite, injured side. The muscle training may stimulate all parts of the body, so injured areas can improve from the general benefits of exercise. The greater blood circulation, oxygen delivery, and nerve innervation that result from strength training enhance the rehabilitation process.

Cardiac Rehabilitation

A special note is made for those rehabilitating from a heart attack. Previously, strength training was not recommended for postcardiac patients. This was based on the assumption that heavy lifting increased the strain on the heart and circulation and increased blood pressure to dangerous levels. However, if the postcoronary patient is to be rehabilitated, the muscular system must be exercised as well as the cardiorespiratory system. Strength training with light weights is, therefore, highly desirable for the postcoronary patient, because it is the most efficient way muscular strength can be regained and increased. The amount of resistance and the intensity of the exercise must be prescribed by the attending physician.

Bodybuilding

Bodybuilding is a popular activity that attracts a large variety of individuals. The bodybuilder concentrates on the muscle size, definition, and symmetry. The goal involves aesthetics: a well-formed, well-defined, and well-balanced physique. Bodybuilding requires a well-balanced exercise plan, systematically exercising, strengthening, and developing each muscle group to its maximum. The cosmetic effect of bodybuilding has increased its popularity with the general public, although very few reach a high competitive level. It has been suggested that bodybuilding is both a sport and an art form, because posing and highlighting muscle groups and physique are important to the activity.

Weightlifting Competition

Olympic lifting and powerlifting are the competitive aspects of strength training, and for some people these become a major sport. Olympic lifting is a competitive sport that tests one's ability to lift great amounts of weight in two specific lifts: the snatch and the clean and jerk. Agility, speed of movement, power, flexibility, and technique are all facets of Olympic lifting. The foundation of the sport is, of course, strength, and therefore competitive Olympic lifters train for strength. The same is true for power lifting, except there are three different lifts in competition: the squat, the bench press, and the deadlift.

Strength Training and Total Wellness

The physical and practical reasons why people train for strength have been discussed. Strength training can also contribute to the exploration of the whole person. The whole person combines the physical body, the thinking and rational mind, and the emotional and spiritual being, a "wellness" approach to life. Strength training can significantly improve the total person. Individuals may begin a strength training program for the direct and immediate physical or practical goals, but they often continue because of mental and emotional factors, such as

- feelings of self-worth and self-esteem;
- achievement and success;
- acquiring discipline and applying it to other activities;
- substituting a positive habit for a negative one, for example, training instead of overeating; and
- directing motivations such as aggressions and egotism into positive and beneficial activities.

Strength training can be a means for self-exploration. Dealing with the strenuous nature of the activity involves physical exploration. Performing a number of sets and repetitions in a given amount of time contributes to a person's sense of accomplishment. The worth of the activity is seen in a developing body, which brings about a positive and fulfilling feeling and promotes a genuine sense of achievement. The person who trains regularly may take a step further than just physical aspects of training. Strength training may become a part of a person's philosophical approach to living. It can become a method of looking internally for questions not answered in other areas of life and by other physical activities. Experienced weightlifters, bodybuilders, athletes, and fitness participants express feelings about self-discovery, psychological balance, and spiritual realization.

Explanations of total wellness and fitness may differ, yet the theme of training as part of everyday life is apparent. Advanced strength trainers often attribute their continual training as a quest for personal excellence, self-expression, and self-discovery. The scope of strength training can be limited to the physical act of lifting weights, pulling the cables, and pushing the machines, or it can be expanded to all aspects of daily living and mental and emotional well-being. Strength training can be the key to physical development, emotional confidence, and spiritual self-discovery, a model YMCA activity that promotes healthy development of spirit, mind, and body.

Strength Training Principles

An unlimited number of strength training routines and programs are available, most of which work to some degree. The major problem is that many of these programs have an unacceptable injury potential. Although it is important for a strength training program to be effective, it is essential that a strength training program be safe. Several basic training principles should be incorporated into a sensible strength training program. Generally, the probability of experiencing desirable training outcomes depends on how well basic strength training principles are applied to one's personal exercise program. The following principles provide the basis for maximizing strength development and minimizing the risk of injury: stress adaptation, building time, movement speed, movement range, muscle balance, training specificity, and exercise breathing.

Stress Adaptation

To stimulate strength development, the muscles must be stressed. However, the amount of stress is critical. If the stress is too little, the muscles will not respond negatively or positively, and their condition will remain essentially the same. If the stress is too great, the muscles will respond undesirably, resulting in tissue damage and strength loss. If the stress is appropriate, the muscles will respond desirably, resulting in tissue building and strength gain. Simply put, the muscles must do more work than what they are accustomed to in order to develop more strength.

Of course, it is impossible to give a specific training protocol that would be ideal for each individual. However, the best guideline is to systematically increase the exercise stimulus so that each training session places just a little more demand on the muscles. This process must be gradual and progressive to achieve desirable results and to avoid the problems associated with abrupt increases in workloads. The key to attaining muscle strength and avoiding tissue injury is a long-range approach to muscle development.

Several training variables influence muscle demands and the resulting stress adaptation: exercise frequency, exercise resistance, exercise repetitions, exercise sets, exercise intervals, exercise progression, and exercise periodization.

Exercise Frequency

To some degree, how often a strength exercise is performed is a matter of personal preference and time available in one's daily routine. Some exercisers may find a few minutes for brief daily workouts, whereas others may have the time for comprehensive training sessions once or twice a week. The essential factor is the amount of rest necessary for muscles to recover from the training stimulus and build to a slightly higher level of strength. Some people need shorter recovery periods (typically those with a high percentage of slow-twitch muscle fibers), whereas others require longer recovery periods (usually those with a high percentage of fast-twitch muscle fibers). As a general rule, muscles take about 48 hours to recover from a strenuous training stimulus and build to a slightly greater strength level.

If too little recovery is taken between training sessions, muscles will not have time to build new tissue and develop more strength. If too much recovery is taken between training sessions, muscles may temporarily build new tissue and develop more strength, but without an appropriately spaced follow-up workout, atrophy will occur and muscles will return to their original condition.

In a study designed to evaluate the effects of different training frequencies on muscle development, 1,132 men and women were placed into two exercise groups (Westcott and Guy, 1996). Both groups performed 1 set of 12 exercises two or three days per week over an eight-week training period. The group that trained twice a week attained 88 percent as much muscle gain as the group that trained three days a week. The group that trained three days a week achieved the best results, but twice a week training proved to be a highly effective alternative for people with less time availability.

Although most studies suggest that two to four days are most effective, the YMCA recommends training three nonconsecutive days per week for best results. In *Designing Resistance Training Programs*, Fleck and Kraemer summarized research which indicated that three training sessions per muscle group per week is the minimum frequency that causes maximum gains (Fleck and Kraemer, 1997).

Most strength exercisers should train three nonconsecutive days per week for best results. Although some people may prefer to train more often, it is not advisable to stress the same muscle groups on consecutive days. If consecutive day exercise is performed, it may be best to train the lower body muscles one day and the upper body muscles the next day. As muscles become stronger and experience more stressful exercise sessions, it may take longer for them to recover and build to higher strength levels. Consequently, it is always important to evaluate muscle response to the training program. If an individual does not feel at least as strong, and hopefully a little stronger, at each workout, a change in training frequency should be considered. For more information about the effects of rest between exercise sessions, see the section on Building Time later in this chapter.

Exercise Resistance

No specific amount of exercise resistance has been shown to be most effective for strength development. Powerlifters often train with maximum resistance, whereas patients in rehabilitation programs make progress with low resistance. Generally, it is advisable to train between 65 and 85 percent of maximum resistance. A study conducted in 1982 on unconditioned adults concluded that the optimal training for beginners is done with 60 to 80 percent of a person's maximum resistance (Harre, 1982). Research shows that at least 65 percent of our maximum resistance should be used to attain optimum strength development. Empirical evidence indicates that individuals have a much higher risk of injury when more than 85 percent of maximum resistance is used. As a general rule, 75 percent of maximum resistance provides an excellent training stimulus. It is heavy enough to produce positive muscle adaptations and light enough to minimize the risk of injury.

Exercise Repetitions

The amount of resistance used is directly related to the number of repetitions that can be performed. High resistance necessitates few repetitions, whereas low resistance permits many repetitions. The number of repetitions that can be completed with a given resistance is a genetic characteristic closely related to muscle fiber makeup. Consider the results of a research study on 141 men and women, including several outstanding power athletes and endurance athletes. All of the subjects were evaluated for the number of repetitions they could perform with 75 percent of their maximum resistance in a chest exercise. Most of the subjects completed 8 to 13 repetitions. All of the subjects who performed less than 8 repetitions were proficient power athletes who presumably had a high percentage of fast-twitch (low-endurance) muscle fibers. All of the subjects who performed more than 13 repetitions were excellent endurance athletes who presumably had a high percentage of slow-twitch (high-endurance) muscle fibers.

A study by Harre (1982) suggested that beginners should use loads of 60 to 80 percent of maximum with 8 to 10 repetitions in each set. The American College of Sports Medicine (ACSM) recommends 8 to 12 repetitions. Based on these findings, most men and women can complete 8 to 12 repetitions with 75 percent of their maximum resistance and should typically train within this repetition range. Persons who have low-endurance muscles should probably train with fewer (5 to 7) repetitions, and persons who have high-endurance muscles should probably train with more (13 to 15) repetitions. Generally, training with less than 5 repetitions decreases the strength stimulus, and training with more than 16 repetitions increases the injury risk.

Exercise Sets

An exercise may be performed one time or more times during a strength training session. Performing 8 to 10 repetitions of one exercise is referred to as a set. People who prefer shorter training sessions typically perform one set of each exercise. People who prefer longer training sessions generally complete multiple sets of each exercise. Research studies (Atha, 1981) indicate that multiple sets work best for strength development and that gains are achieved faster than with a single-set system (McDonagh and Davies, 1984). However, single-set training effectively stimulates strength development and may be more appropriate for beginners (Fleck and Kraemer, 1997).

Another study compared one, two, or three sets of exercise on upper body strength development as measured by dips and chins with bodyweight (Westcott, 1989). The 77 male and female participants trained three days per week for 10 weeks. The subjects who trained with one set of dips and chins improved their performance by 4.8 repetitions. The subjects who trained with two sets of dips and chins improved their performance by 4.1 repetitions, and the subjects who trained with three sets of dips and chins improved their performance by 5.2 repetitions (see table 5.2). There were no significant differences among the three training groups, indicating that one, two, and three sets of exercise were equally effective for improving upper body (dip and chin) strength. It is suggested, therefore, that the number of sets performed in a given exercise be a matter of personal preference. For most purposes, one to three sets per exercise are recommended for improving muscle strength.

Table 5.2 Comparison of One-, Two-, and Three-Set Strength Training

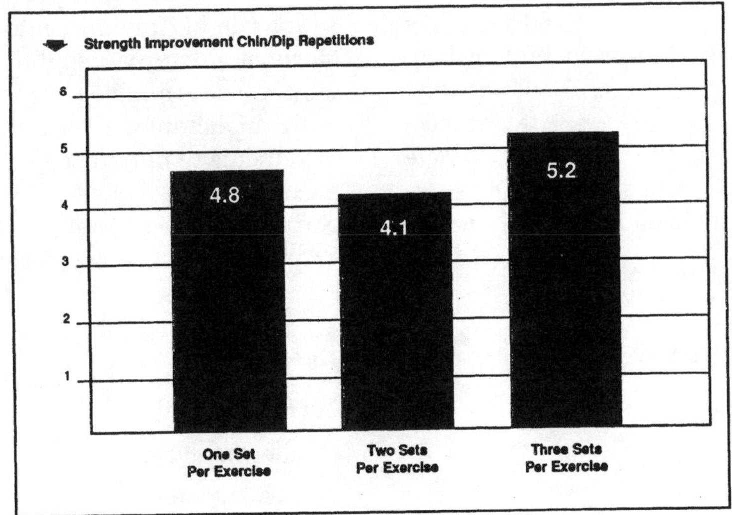

77 Subjects.

For maximum results, finishing a set means attempting to work until no further movement is possible. This point of failure is referred to as a momentary muscle fatigue. Submaximal efforts will produce submaximal results; the correct weight must be determined so that maximum results can be obtained within the 8- to 12-rep range. When a set is completed before the point of failure (momentary muscular failure), the maximum number of muscle fibers has not been innervated. For best results, end a set only when another lift cannot be accomplished. This implies modifying the amount of resistance so that the point of failure occurs at the completion of 8 to 12 repetitions.

Exercise Intervals

If a single set program is followed, the amount of rest required between exercises is minimal, because each set addresses a different muscle group. However, if multiple sets of each exercise are performed, you should allow for longer periods of rest between sets. Powerlifters typically take long rests between sets so they can use heavy weightloads throughout their workout. Bodybuilders generally take short rests between sets to maximize a "muscle pump" during their workout.

Although many physiological and psychological factors influence exercise intervals, energy replenishment is of critical importance. The major energy source for strength exercise is creatine phosphate, which is temporarily depleted after a strenuous set of exercise. The half-life of creatine phosphate production is about 30 seconds. That is, after 30 seconds about 50 percent of the creatine phosphate has been replenished. After one minute about 75 percent of the creatine phosphate has been replenished. After 90 seconds about 88 percent of the creatine phosphate has been replenished, and after two minutes about 95 percent of the creatine phosphate has been replenished.

In other words, a two-minute rest between exercise sets permits almost full restoration of the creatine phosphate energy supply (Fox and Matthews, 1974). For most purposes this provides an appropriate rest period between exercise sets. A two-minute exercise interval is short enough to maintain increased blood flow to the muscle and long enough to train with relatively heavy weightloads.

Table 5.3 shows recommended rest intervals for different types of training.

The amount of rest needed between sets varies with each individual. Although two minutes is a good general rule, some people may need more and some less rest. An instructor's job is to help exercisers understand the effects of exercise on their bodies, which will aid them in judging the amount of rest they need.

Exercise Progression

Strength training is often referred to as progressive resistance exercise. That is, the training resistance is gradually increased as the exerciser becomes stronger. This is unlike bodyweight exercises, such as sit-ups and push-ups, in which there are few ways to progress with the same resistance (perform more repetitions, change the angle or speed of contraction). Although these changes are effective up to a point, there is little strength gain from performing dozens of sit-ups at the same angle or speed of contraction.

It is far more productive to add resistance and exercise for 60 to 90 seconds at a high intensity, that is, to use a resistance heavy enough to cause muscle fatigue within approximately 8 to 12 repetitions. If this training protocol is used, the resistance should increase slightly whenever 12 repetitions can be completed in good form. The average individual should increase the weightload in small increments to minimize the risk of injury and to maximize improvement. The increase should be 5 percent or less. For example, if 12 biceps curls with 50 pounds can be completed, the weight load

Table 5.3 Rest Intervals for Various Types of Training

Emphasis	Rest interval
Muscle hypertrophy	One minute or less
Overall muscle development	Two minutes
Muscle strength	Three minutes

should be increased to 52.5 pounds (or less) next workout. Often, a 5-pound increase is the smallest increment available. If this is the case, the participant must choose between a 5-pound increase and fewer repetitions or performing more repetitions at the same weight until the 5-pound increase can be tolerated. A systematic program of gradual progression is perhaps the most important aspect of sensible and successful strength training.

Exercise Periodization

The key to muscle development is systematic application of the stress adaptation principle. Theoretically, if each training session is a little more demanding than the last one, the individual will continue to gain strength. Unfortunately, the human body does not always respond in this manner. Given the same exercise protocol day after day, muscles become used to the stress and produce little or no adaptation. It is important, therefore, to periodically vary the training program. Such a plan is usually referred to as *strength training periodization*.

Although periodic change of exercise routine is essential for optimum strength results, the exerciser must stay with a given workout routine long enough for it to be productive. For the average lifter, it is advisable to spend three to six weeks on a specific strength training program. A simple and standard form of exercise periodization is a three-month program progressing from higher repetitions and lower resistance to lower repetitions and higher resistance. As presented in table 5.5, the first month's resistance is about 65 percent of maximum with a repetition range of 12 to 16 reps per set. The lower resistance represents a lower percentage of the muscle contractile strength as well as the tendon, ligament, and bone structural strength. This provides a lower risk of tissue injury during the initial conditioning stage.

With beginning strength training participants, the use of high repetitions and low resistance during the first month of their program is particularly important. During this time, the muscles and nervous system are getting used to the movements and stress of strength training. By performing more repetitions, the body is able to learn the movement patterns and get used to moving with added resistance through the repetitive movements. Eighty percent of the strength gained in the first month of training is due to motor learning, a concept that is not unique to strength training. The body learns all new movements in a similar fashion, from learning to type to playing a musical instrument. In the early stages of any new activity, the more you do the movement, the quicker you learn it. This reinforces why it is so important for beginners to learn and practice good technique. They are learning new movements, and should learn to do them correctly.

During the second month, resistance is increased to about 75 percent of maximum with a repetition range of 8 to 12 reps per set. This is definitely a strength-building period that provides a solid foundation for the final high-resistance stage. In the third month, resistance is raised to about 85 percent of maximum with a repetition range of 4 to 8 reps per set. The near-maximum resistance may provide a more effective strength stimulus and should be well tolerated by the muscle and connective tissue after two months of training.

Table 5.4 shows a sample of a three-month exercise plan.

Following three months of progressive resistance exercise, it is usually advisable to take a week of active rest before repeating the cycle. Active rest refers to substituting some non–strength training activities that involve little resistance. Such activities include walking, hiking, jogging, cycling, swimming, racquetball,

Table 5.4 Sample Three-Month Periodization Program

Month	Exercise resistance	Exercise repetitions
First	About 65 percent maximum	12–16 reps per set
Second	About 75 percent maximum	8–12 reps per set
Third	About 85 percent maximum	4–8 reps per set
Active rest	Non-strength training activity for one week	

basketball, tennis, and golf. Although there are numerous periodization variations, the three-month model fits nicely with many seasonal activities. Repeating the three-month training cycle ensures a systematic change in the exercise stimulus, thereby facilitating positive muscle adaptations. Each training cycle should begin at a somewhat higher level of strength. Following a planned periodization program is preferred over a day-by-day trial-and-error approach.

Building Time

The stimulus for strength development takes place during the exercise session. However, muscles do not become stronger at that time. In fact, muscles are weaker after the workout than before the workout. It is only during the recovery period following the exercise session that muscles gradually build to higher strength levels. Building time is an often misunderstood factor that plays a major role in muscle development. According to exercise physiologists, a strenuous strength training session produces some degree of muscle microtrauma (microscopic tissue damage). The time necessary to synthesize actin and myosin proteins and to develop new muscle tissue is called *building time.*

Building time varies among individuals. Research at the University of Florida has shown shorter building time for persons with predominantly slow-twitch muscle fibers and longer building time for persons with predominantly fast-twitch muscle fibers. As suggested in a previous section on exercise frequency, most people respond well to an every-other-day strength training program. However, it is important to carefully monitor progress and evaluate responsiveness. If a participant does not feel a little stronger during successive exercise sessions, building time may not have been sufficient.

Table 5.5 indicates the effects of rest time on the strength level attained.

One way for participants to monitor progress and assessing tissue-building response is through the use of a training or workout log. A workout log contains a record of exercise weightloads and repetitions, as well as a subjective report of feelings during each workout.

Movement Speed

Movement speed is an important factor with regard to strength development, as well as the potential for injury. Although it is not possible to identify an ideal exercise speed, there are several reasons that slow lifting movements may be preferable to fast lifting movements. These include muscle tension, muscle force, momentum, and injury risk.

- **Muscle tension**—Strength exercise produces muscle tension that stimulates strength development. A slow lifting movement provides a longer period of muscle tension than a fast lifting movement. For example, performing 10 barbell curls at 5 seconds per repetition requires 50 seconds of muscle tension, whereas performing 10 barbell curls at 3 seconds per repetition requires only 30 seconds of muscle tension.

The YMCA recommends that exercisers perform all strength training movements in a slow and controlled manner, concentrating on using the prime mover muscles during the exercise. That being said, participants, especially beginners, should be cautioned to not go too slow. Because their muscles are not developed, beginners may place too much pressure on adjacent joints and tendons when performing the exercise too slowly. Instructors should also note that when strength training is being performed to enhance sports performance, faster training movement may be appropriate.

Table 5.5 Effects of Rest Time on Strength Level

Rest time	Effect
Sufficient	Slightly higher strength level.
Too little	Muscle does not build to a higher strength level and may not reach its previous strength level.
Too much	Muscle initially builds to a slightly higher level but returns to its previous strength level by the next workout.

• **Muscle force**—Although muscle tension is an important training factor, muscle force provides the primary stimulus for strength development. Muscle force output is directly related to exercise speed. Muscle force output decreases as the movement speed increases.

• **Momentum**—Every movement involves some degree of momentum. Momentum is the quantity of motion determined by an object's mass and velocity. Fast movements generate more momentum than slow movements. This is significant with respect to strength development because momentum affects muscle force production. Experiments with force recording devices demonstrate that slow barbell lifts require relatively consistent muscle force throughout the movement range. Conversely, fast barbell lifts require high muscle force at the start but almost no muscle force throughout the rest of the movement range due to momentum.

• **Injury risk**—Fast lifting movements require high force levels at the beginning of each exercise repetition. This subjects the muscles, tendons, and joints to high stress levels and increases the risk of tissue injury. Slow lifting movements do not require high force levels at the beginning of each exercise repetition, which significantly decreases the risk of tissue injury.

Movement Range

Research shows that muscle strength increases only in the movement range of a particular exercise. Graves et al. (1989) trained four groups using a bilateral knee extension exercise. One group trained the first half of the range of motion, the second trained the second half, the third trained a full range of motion, and a control group did not train. The results showed that the training result was specific to the range of motion trained, with the group that trained the full range of motion getting the best effect of strength development through the full range. If the goal is to develop muscle strength throughout a full movement range, then training must occur throughout the full movement range.

Consider how an individual's strength typically varies throughout the movement range of the trunk extension exercise. The low back is naturally stronger in a flexed position than in an extended position. However, most individuals have a disproportionately low level of back strength in their extended position. If exercise is done on only the first half of this movement range, only the stronger area will be strengthened, creating an even greater strength differential from flexion to extension. The resulting imbalance may be a predisposing factor for low back problems.

Exercising through a full range of movement also enhances joint flexibility. For example, in the final position of a back extension exercise, the low back muscles are fully contracted and the opposing abdominal muscles are fully stretched. Full-range exercise is advantageous for strength development, flexibility development, and injury prevention.

In certain populations, such as older adults, a full range of motion is not always possible. This may be due to certain medical conditions (arthritis) or deconditioning. Participants who cannot exercise their joints through a full range of motion should focus on the range of motion that is possible for them. As they continue to exercise, their range of motion will gradually increase.

Muscle Balance

When a muscle group is disproportionately stronger than its opposing muscle group, a degree of muscle imbalance results. This reduces joint integrity and increases the risk of overuse injuries. For example, sprinters typically perform strengthening exercises for their quadriceps muscles. However, if they do not strengthen the opposing hamstring muscles, they probably will experience a muscle imbalance. The stronger quadriceps muscles may overpower the weaker hamstring muscles as the sprinter drives off the starting blocks, causing injury to the hamstrings group.

This does not imply that all opposing muscle groups should be equally strong. However, it is important to train all major muscle groups to maintain a desirable muscle balance throughout the body. Although not essential for balanced strength development, it is advisable to train opposing muscle groups in pairs. The following is a suggested sequence for systematically conditioning the major muscle groups in order from larger to smaller.

- Quadriceps
- Hamstrings
- Hip adductors

- Hip abductors
- Chest
- Upper back
- Shoulders
- Biceps
- Triceps
- Low back
- Abdominals
- Neck extensors
- Neck flexors

Balanced strength training is the key to comprehensive muscle development and injury prevention. It is also a necessary counterpart to the principle of training specificity. Individual strength workouts should progress from working the large muscle groups to the smaller, supporting muscle groups. Several implications can be drawn from this.

The order of exercise is one variable of a strength training program. Many practitioners believe that workouts should proceed from large to small muscle groups. Because the largest and strongest muscles of the body, the hip and leg muscles, have the greatest potential for developing overall strength and muscle mass and for providing overall stimulation, these muscles should be exercised first. To fatigue the supporting (and generally smaller) muscles first would make them unable to support the many exercise movements of the larger leg and torso muscles.

Training effectiveness may be influenced by the order in which the exercises are performed. In general, multiple muscle/joint exercises should be performed before single muscle/joint exercises. For example, it is advisable to do bench presses before triceps extensions. If the triceps extensions are performed first and therefore fatigued, that participant would have to use less weight for bench presses, which involve both the triceps and chest muscles. Even though the triceps experience a good workout, the lighter bench presses may reduce the training stimulus to the chest muscles. Performing bench presses first permits a heavier weightload and increases the training stimulus to the chest muscles. Although the extensions must now be performed with less weight, this should not reduce the training stimulus to the triceps muscles if they are worked to fatigue.

Training Specificity

Bodies respond in a specific manner to a specific training stimulus. For example, long-distance running improves a runner's aerobic capacity by increasing cardiovascular endurance, not by increasing the legs' muscular strength. Conversely, performing heavy barbell squats improves the size and strength of the weightlifter's leg muscles, not the weightlifter's aerobic capacity.

Another aspect of training specificity is the rest period between sets of exercise. Bodybuilders take brief rest periods between sets to maintain blood flow to the muscle and stimulate muscle size development. Powerlifters take lengthy rest periods between sets to enable heavy training weightloads and stimulate muscle strength development (see Advanced Strength Training Principles and Techniques section later in this chapter for more information).

Although a few exercises (such as barbell squats) involve opposing muscle groups (quadriceps and hamstrings), most exercises strengthen only one muscle group. For example, leg extensions strengthen the quadriceps but not the hamstrings. Conversely, leg curls strengthen the hamstrings but not the quadriceps. Clearly, strength exercise must be carefully designed to meet specific training objectives. However, it is never advisable to train one muscle group without also training the opposing muscle group. Although a shot putter must strengthen the triceps muscles for peak performance, it is equally important to strengthen the opposing biceps muscles for joint integrity and injury prevention. Always combine the principle of training specificity and the principle of muscle balance for maximum muscle development and minimum risk of injury.

Exercise Breathing

It is very important to breathe continuously during every repetition of exercise. Breath holding during resistance exercise can significantly increase internal pressure in the chest cavity. This situation, known as the Valsalva Maneuver, can limit blood return to the heart and elevate blood pressure to dangerous levels. The preferred method of breathing is to exhale during the lifting movement and to inhale during the lowering movement. In this manner, the air pressure decreases as the muscle pressure increases (lifting movement), and the air pressure increases as the muscle pressure decreases (lowering movement).

Although this breathing pattern maintains a better pressure balance, the most essential consideration is to breathe regularly. As long as the breath is not held for more than a moment, the Valsalva Maneuver should not be experienced. If beginners have difficulty coordinating breathing with the exercise, tell them to breathe normally. Once they learn the exercise and become more comfortable they will be able to switch to a breathing pattern such as described previously.

Summary of YMCA Strength Training Guidelines

Based on what we just discussed, the following are the guidelines for YMCA strength training:

Repetitions	8-12
Sets	1-3
Intervals	2 minutes rest between sets
Resistance	65-85 percent
Frequency	Three times per week (full body workout)
Building time	48 hours rest between workouts
Progression	5 percent or less
Range	Full range of motion as individually possible
Breathing	Exhale on exertion

Special Considerations Regarding Strength Training

Individuals just starting strength training often are concerned about how such training will affect blood pressure, heart rate, and body composition. Also, special precautions must be taken when disabled individuals or pregnant women are strength training.

Strength Training and Blood Pressure

Many men and women avoid strength training because they are afraid that resistance exercise will adversely affect their blood pressure. Research indicates that such fears are generally unfounded. Adults have been correctly cautioned not to perform strenuous isometric activities such as trying to open a sticking window or attempting to move a stalled car. Activities of this type, including isometric strength training, may cause excessively high blood pressure responses and are potentially dangerous for many people.

It is also true that bodybuilders have recorded very high blood pressures during heavy leg press exercises. However, research indicates that sensible strength training does not have a harmful effect on blood pressure. Endurance exercise, strength training for the upper or lower body, and circuit training do not affect blood pressure levels adversely.

- **Endurance exercise**—To place blood pressure response to strength exercise in proper perspective, consider the normal blood pressure response to endurance exercise. In one study, 23 adults were monitored throughout a stationary cycling workout performed at 75 percent of their maximum heart rate. As presented in table 5.6, the results revealed a 35 percent increase in systolic blood pressure from 114 mmHg at rest to 154 mmHg during mid-ride, considered normal. Whenever vigorous exercise is performed, the heart beats faster and contracts harder to pump more blood to working muscles. The circulatory system adjusts to greater and more forceful blood flow by dilating blood vessels and opening additional capillaries, allowing blood to more readily reach the waking muscles.

Table 5.6 Systolic Blood Pressure Response to Different Exercises

Activity	Subjects	Resting systolic pressure (mmHg)	Peak systolic pressure (mmHg)	Percent increase
Stationary cycling	23	114	154	35%
Upper body strength exercises	24	123	165	34%
Lower body strength exercises	25	127	190	50%

• **Upper body strength exercise**—A study was performed to assess blood pressure response during upper body strength exercise. Twenty-four men and women performed 10 biceps curls with the heaviest weightload possible. Their mean diastolic blood pressure measured 75 mmHg both before and immediately after the exercise set. The mean systolic blood pressure increased gradually from 123 mmHg at rest to 165 mmHg during the final repetition. As shown in table 5.6, this represented a 34 percent increase in systolic blood pressure and was well below the 220 mmHg caution level.

• **Lower body strength exercise**—Because lower body strength exercise involves more muscle mass and more muscle force than upper body strength exercise, another study examined blood pressure response during seated leg presses. Twenty-five men and women performed 10 strict leg presses with the heaviest weightload possible. The mean diastolic blood pressure measured 73 mmHg before and 61 mmHg immediately after the exercise set. The mean systolic blood pressure increased progressively from 127 mmHg at rest to 190 mmHg during the final repetition. As presented in table 5.7, this represented a 50 percent increase in systolic blood pressure and was well below the 220 mmHg caution level.

• **Circuit strength training**—A third study examined the immediate effects of circuit strength training on blood pressure. The 100 men and women in this study performed one set (8-12 repetitions) of 11 different strength exercises. Standing blood pressure was measured 30 to 60 seconds before and 30 to 60 seconds after participants completed the 11-station exercise circuit. As shown in table 5.7, their mean pretraining blood pressure was 115/67 mmHg and their mean posttraining blood pressure was 117/65 mmHg. That is, their immediate postexercise blood pressure was almost identical to their preexercise blood pressure. Both the before-exercise and after-exercise readings represented excellent blood pressure levels for these regular strength training participants.

Persons who have high blood pressure, heart disease, or other high-risk characteristics should not perform any type of physical exercise without written consent from their physician. Such participants should be identified during their first visit to the exercise facility by means of a medical history questionnaire.

Although it is strongly recommended that all adults over age 40 consult their physician before beginning an exercise program, there does not seem to be any reason for healthy men and women to avoid sensible strength training. The studies reviewed in this section revealed acceptable blood pressure responses in normal adults during and after sensible strength exercise. In addition, the mean resting blood pressures for all of the strength trained subjects were well within normal limits, indicating that sensible strength training does not adversely affect resting blood pressure.

Sensible strength training is characterized by the following:

- Weightloads that can be lifted for 8 to 12 repetitions in good form
- Continuous muscle movement throughout each exercise set
- Continuous breathing throughout each exercise set

Maximum weight loads, isometric contractions, and breath holding may produce excessive blood pressure responses and should be avoided.

Strength Training and Heart Rate

Like systolic blood pressure, heart rates elevate during vigorous exercise in order to pump more blood to working muscles. And like systolic blood

Table 5.7 Blood Pressure Responses Before and After Circuit Strength Training Session

Subjects	Age (years)	Training time (minutes)	Preexercise blood pressure (mmHg)	Postexercise blood pressure (mmHg)
72 Men	38	29	118/69	119/67
28 Women	34	29	107/62	113/59
100 Total	37	29	115/67	117/65

pressure, heart rate increases gradually and progressively throughout each set of strength exercise. Although larger muscle groups use more oxygen, the heart rate response is similar for lower body and upper body exercises. Beginning from rest, the heart rate typically doubles during an exercise set of 10 repetitions with the heaviest weightload possible. When brief rests are taken between successive sets of exercise, the heart rate may remain at a high level throughout the training session.

Research indicates that circuit strength training may produce some cardiorespiratory benefits (Fleck and Kraemer, 1997), such as reduced resting blood pressure, improved lipid profiles, increased muscle capillarization, and enhanced aerobic capacity. However, much greater cardiorespiratory improvement is obtained through traditional endurance exercise. It is therefore recommended that participants perform strength exercise to develop muscular fitness and endurance exercise to develop cardiorespiratory fitness.

Strength Training and Body Composition

When people are concerned with improving their body composition, they usually think about losing fat by consuming less calories and doing more endurance exercise. Although this approach is effective for reducing fat stores, it may not be the best means for improving body composition, because it doesn't address muscle. Muscle is a major factor in our body composition and physical appearance. Muscle is especially important as we age, because the average adult loses about 1/2 pound of muscle every year of life. Consequently, the 45-year-old man who weighs the same as he did at age 25 may very well have 10 pounds less muscle and 10 pounds more fat. For him, and most Americans, adding muscle is just as important as losing fat. Gaining muscle provides two benefits. First, additional muscle improves body composition and physical appearance. Second, additional muscle increases resting metabolic rate, because muscle is very active tissue with high energy requirements, even at rest. More muscle means more calories for tissue maintenance and building functions.

Consider a research study that examined the effects of strength training on body composition. All 72 participants followed the same dietary guidelines and exercised for the same amount of time. Twenty-two subjects performed 30 minutes of endurance exercise, three days a week. Fifty subjects performed 15 minutes of endurance exercise and 15 minutes of strength exercise, three days a week. After eight weeks of training the subjects who performed only endurance exercise lost 3 pounds of fat weight and 1/2 pound of lean (muscle) weight (see table 5.8). The subjects who performed both endurance exercise and strength exercise lost 10 pounds of fat weight and gained 2 pounds of lean (muscle) weight, for a 12-pound improvement in body composition.

This research indicates that strength training is an excellent means for enhancing body composition. Because it is the only activity that burns fat, builds muscle, and increases resting metabolic rate, strength training should be a key component in fat loss and body-shaping programs.

Strength Training for Individuals With Disabilities

Strength training is a very appropriate activity to consider for people with disabilities. All individuals with disabilities should be carefully screened to determine what type of strength exercise they are capable of doing. With their physician's written consent and training guidelines, these individuals may effectively participate in appropriately modified muscle building

Table 5.8 Body Composition Changes for Subjects Performing Endurance Exercise Only and for Subjects Performing Both Endurance and Strength Exercise

Change	Number of subjects	Weight change	Fat change	Muscle change
Endurance exercise only	22	–3.5 pounds	–3.0 pounds	–0.5 pounds
Endurance and strength exercise	50	–8.0 pounds	–10.0 pounds	+2.0 pounds

programs. For those not confined to wheelchairs, it is usually possible to train most of the major muscle groups in a conventional manner. Free-weights may offer greater versatility and freedom of movement, whereas resistance machines may provide better support and operational efficiency.

For those who must remain in their wheelchairs, some excellent resistance devices are available. In most cases, the participant moves onto a training platform, secures the wheelchair, and performs a variety of exercises for the arms and upper body using cables attached to a preselected resistance. The major concern with wheelchair strength training participants is stabilizing their torsos so they can safely and successfully perform the desired exercise movement. Although this may be accomplished by strapping the torso to the seatback, better stability and performance are usually obtained when the instructor holds the participant in place.

Because each person's disability is different, it is difficult to present a specific strength training protocol. The YMCA recommends that staff collaborate with local agencies and their medical community to effectively plan and implement programs for individuals with special needs. Once medical clearance and support are obtained, the major emphasis should be providing progressive resistance exercise to all of the functional muscle groups. Participant feedback is perhaps the best means for determining if this objective is achieved.

Strength Training for Pregnant Women

The few studies that have examined strength training during pregnancy have demonstrated a desirable increase in muscular strength and an absence of adverse effects. Nonetheless, certain precautions should be taken when training pregnant women. All pregnant women should obtain their physician's written approval and any specific guidelines for participation in all YMCA exercise programs, including resistance exercise programs. The participants should complete a health screening and fitness testing to determine an appropriate exercise starting point taking into account any specific guidelines recommended by their physician.

The American College of Obstetricians and Gynecologists provides the following general exercise guidelines:

- Exercise at least three times per week.
- Don't exercise on your back after the first trimester.
- Modify your intensity; listen to your body.
- Don't jeopardize your balance.
- Avoid activities with the potential for even mild abdominal trauma.
- Be careful not to overheat, especially in the first trimester.
- Warm up and cool down every time you exercise.
- Exercise on a resilient floor.
- Don't flex your joints excessively or stretch to your limit.
- Eat enough calories for the extra energy you need for both your pregnancy and exercise.
- Don't rotate your trunk while your hips or spine are flexed.

It is advisable to train with moderate resistance and movement range to reduce stress on lax connective tissue caused by the release of relaxin and other hormones. It is helpful to drink cold water throughout the exercise session to replace fluids and to cool body temperature. Exercise should be stopped and medical assistance attained in response to the following events:

- Pain (chest, back, abdomen, hip)
- Vaginal bleeding
- Dizziness or weakness
- Headache or nausea
- Decreased fetal activity
- Uterine contractions
- Generalized edema

The goal of strength training for women during pregnancy should be to continue with an ongoing program to maintain muscular strength, not to begin a new program. For more information, refer to the YMCA of the USA's *Prenatal Exercise Instructor Manual* and related Medical Advisory Committee recommendation.

Strength Training Myths

A number of myths have developed over the years related to strength training. Here are some of those myths, with the facts to refute them.

• **Strength training increases blood pressure**—Although it is strongly recommended that all adults over age 40 see their physician before beginning an exercise program, there is no reason for healthy men and women to avoid sensible strength training. The studies reviewed previously in this chapter revealed acceptable blood pressure responses in normal adults during and after sensible strength exercise. Sensible strength training is characterized by the following:

-Weightloads that can be lifted for 8 to 12 repetitions in good form

-Continuous breathing throughout each exercise set

-Controlled muscle movement throughout each exercise set

-Loose handgrips

When these guidelines are observed, strength training appears to be a safe physical activity that provides important benefits to our musculoskeletal system.

• **To gain muscle size, free-weights, not weight machines, must be used**—The relationship between muscle gain and the exclusive use of free-weights has been a misconception since the rise in popularity of resistance type machines. Many believe that the only way to gain muscle size is to train with free-weights. Although many free weight enthusiasts believe that this is the best method, the type of equipment is, in fact, not the significant variable in muscle hypertrophy. It is rather the level of intensity and whether an overload is placed on the muscle that creates the response. As a case in point, in 1999, 20 of the National Football League (NFL) teams trained predominantly with free-weights, whereas 10 of the NFL teams trained almost exclusively with machines. Obviously, players on all of the teams have developed extremely high levels of strength and muscularity. It is not the type of equipment used but the progressive overload training that is responsible for the athletes' muscular development. Results are also determined by the individual genetic potential; no matter the type of equipment used, large gains in muscle hypertrophy may not be possible for some people.

• **Strength training decreases flexibility and range of motion**—A properly performed dynamic weight training program does not impair flexibility and can possibly increase range of motion in some muscle joints.

• **Older adults do not benefit from strength training**—A program of resistance exercise can be safely carried out by both male and female older adults. Such a program significantly increases muscle strength due, at least in part, to muscle hypertrophy.

• **Weight belts should be worn at all times**—During movements in which the stress on the lumbar spine is low, little is gained in wearing a tightly cinched weightlifting belt, which may needlessly restrict natural breathing.

• **Protein supplementation is required to increase muscle mass**—The American Dietetic Association states that athletes may require more protein than the Recommended Dietary Allowance (RDA) of 0.8 g/kg body weight. However, the increased requirement for protein appears to be small. Research suggests that the quantity of dietary protein needed to achieve maximal protein deposition is between 1.0 to 1.5 g/kg body weight. Researchers have found that the limiting factor for protein deposition is energy intake, not protein. Athletes who wish to increase muscle mass should meet their energy requirements first, through an adequate intake of carbohydrates, and then check that they have met their protein needs. A range of 1.0 to 1.5 g protein per kilogram of body weight may be a more appropriate guide for intake than protein as a percentage of total energy.

Even the highest protein requirements can be met easily with a balanced diet that includes a variety of foods. Therefore, excessive protein intake, through either consumption of high-protein foods or protein/amino-acid supplements, is unnecessary, does not contribute to athletic performance or increase muscle mass, and actually may be detrimental to health and athletic performance.

• **One set is not productive**—ACSM strength training guidelines are based on research that shows that significant strength gains result from one set of exercises. Whether the participant uses free-weights, machines, or manual resistance, one set of 8 to 12 repetitions seems to be a good starting point for strength development.

• **When you quit strength training, your muscle turns to fat**—As an individual regularly participates in a resistance training program, the common result is additional muscle weight in the form of muscle hypertrophy. This additional muscle combined with the effect of regular exercise sessions increases the body's ability to burn calories and body fat. The result is a lean, well-defined individual. If the individual continues to participate in the program, his or her chance of maintaining leanness is very good. There is much confusion among fitness enthusiasts as to what happens when strength training is stopped. Some believe that the muscle turns to fat. Because muscle and fat are two different substances, it is impossible to change one into the other. The result of any detraining is muscle atrophy, the same as in any disuse situation. At the same time, calorie expenditure is significantly reduced due to lack of activity. Because this caloric consumption is no longer available to the body, fat increase may result at the same time that muscle atrophy is occurring, creating the perception of muscle turning to fat.

- **Weight training will stunt growth**—Numerous research studies concluded that a sensibly designed, supervised program of strength training is safe and beneficial for a child's physical growth.

Performing Strength Exercises

Participants who perform strength exercises need to know the procedures for doing them safely and effectively. They particularly need to be cautious when performing exercises for the low back, knees, and neck. Participants who are knowledgeable about strength training equipment can exercise more safely and comfortably; they also can choose to exercise either alternating limbs or using both at the same time. Finally, they often can avoid injuries by using free-weights for certain exercises only when spotters are present and by following guidelines for safe use of weight machines.

Exercise Procedures

Following are some general procedures for performing strength training exercises:

- All movements should be performed in a controlled manner, without jerking or bouncing.
- There should be a slight pause—a momentary hold—between concentric (positive) and eccentric (negative) contractions.
- Do not hesitate or rest between repetitions, and on machine exercises, do not let the weight stacks touch while performing a set.
- Perform the lowering or negative phase of each exercise more slowly than the initial or positive phase of the exercise, for example, two to three seconds in the positive movement and four to six seconds in the negative portion. Perform the lowering motion in a controlled manner and do not allow gravity to simply "drop" the weight back to the starting position, as many inexperienced lifters do.
- Use a full range of movement during each exercise.
- Do not hold the breath while performing any strength exercises. Exhale on the positive (when raising the weight) when possible.

Strengthening the Low Back, Knees, and Neck

Three areas of the body that typically need strengthening are the low back, knees, and neck. However, these areas are particularly susceptible to injury, so strength training must be performed with certain precautions.

Low Back

It is estimated that over 80 percent of all people in the United States have experienced some level of low back pain, the vast majority of which is not spinal or other related structural damage. Most low back problems are associated with muscular weakness or imbalance. Low back muscles help the body to maintain proper posture and body carriage. Along with the abdominal muscles on the front of the body and the oblique muscles on both sides, the muscles of the low back provide a "girdle" of support for the entire midsection of the body and form a base of support for the spine. Strong low back muscles are needed to help people move easily and safely through everyday life, as well as provide support in their daily activities, athletic endeavors, or in emergency situations.

Unfortunately, because many people report back problems, some fitness staff shied away from including the low back area in exercise routines. However, with guidance from medical specialists, the majority of people with low back problems can effectively exercise their low back muscles, thereby increasing strength and flexibility.

People who have no known back problem should be encouraged to include exercises in their routine to develop and maintain strength and flexibility of the low back muscles. This can be done, in most cases, under the guidance of a certified YMCA Personal Training Instructor.

Following are guidelines for individuals with low back problems:

- All members who are experiencing low back problems should obtain a physician release before participating in a strength training program.
- YMCA staff should incorporate physician and therapist recommendations into the member's strength training program.
- Refer individuals who indicate low back difficulties and have no personal physician to the care of a qualified medical practitioner.
- Do not recommend any exercises that might prove harmful/detrimental to persons indicating back problems (i.e., squats, leg presses, overhead pressing movements, twisting movements, side-bending exercises, and any exercise movements that take the body into an unsupported position of leaning either forward or backward).
- Develop a local Medical Advisory Committee at your YMCA to address program guidelines for individuals with special needs.
- Begin a YMCA Healthy Back program for individuals who are unable to perform strength training.

Knees

Exercise involving the knee, when performed correctly, can help prevent injury associated with daily and leisure time activity. Exercises performed incorrectly can, themselves, cause injury.

During squatting activities, caution must be taken to avoid bending the knee beyond 90 degrees and locking the knee during leg pressing actions. People with current knee pain should consult their physician before performing any type of leg exercises. When performing exercises that involve the knee, it is important not to project the knee beyond the toes in any weight-bearing exercises (i.e., squats, lunges, etc.).

Neck

The neck is one of the most neglected yet most used muscles of the body. The muscles of the neck hold up a 15-pound head all day long, which can lead to muscle fatigue and strain after several hours. Scientific evidence shows that weak neck muscles can cause headaches, migraines, and poor posture.

Strengthening the neck can help to prevent this strain and the accompanying pain. As the neck is a very sensitive area to exercise, proper execution and care must be taken to prevent injury. Caution must be used to prevent sudden, excessive, or inconsistent application of force while performing neck exercises. Neck muscles should be worked last in any exercise session. They are supportively involved in all exercise movements and to fatigue them early inhibits their ability to be supportive in any exercises later in the session.

Free-Weight Equipment

The following are descriptions of some common free-weight equipment. The exercises mentioned in the Application sections can be found at the end of this chapter.

EASY CURL BAR

Purpose

Takes pressure off wrists and elbows by allowing for a natural grip angle. Provides a variety of muscle tension angles depending on grip.

Application

Barbell curls, triceps extensions, upright row, preacher bench curls.

WEIGHT BELTS

Purpose

Provide back and internal support by increasing abdominal wall pressure; may be useful in working with heavier weightloads.

Application

Squats, deadlift, overhead press, standing arm curl.

Note: For a belt to provide support, it must be worn as tight as possible, which may make taking a deep breath difficult. Tightening a belt in this manner increases intra-abdominal pressure, causing an air pocket to form, which provides an inner support for the spinal erector muscles. This, combined with the support of the belt externally, neutralizes the stress of lifting. Belts not worn properly may leave the person at risk of injury.

In some instances, weight belts are overused. Exercises such as the squat, deadlift, overhead lifts, and standing curls with heavier weightloads performed for a low number of repetitions may require the use of a weight belt. Using the belt for other exercises may give the person psychological benefit but is not needed for injury prevention. There is also the possibility that using the belt may prevent strength increases in the spinal erectors because the musculature becomes dependent on the belt to support the spinal column.

HAND STRAPS

Purpose

Provide additional bar-holding ability during heavy lifting movements.

Application

Pull-ups, pulley pull-downs, shrugs, curls, cable rows, dumbbell row, deadlifts.

GLOVES

Purpose

Provide extra bar-holding ability, protect hands, increase overall comfort of lifting.

Application

Used for all strength training activities as needed or desired.

WRIST SUPPORTS

Purpose

Provide extra support, improve lifting comfort.

Application

Can be used during all strength training as needed or desired.

KNEEWRAPS

Purpose

Provide additional support and protection during certain weight training exercises with heavy weights. For the healthy knee, knee wraps are not generally recommended or needed. If knee wraps are required because of an injury, the participant should consult with his or her physician or physical therapist for correct application and wrapping procedures.

Application

Squats, lunges.

WEIGHTLIFTING SHOES

Purpose

Provide safety and improve functional ability in certain exercises. Special shoes with additional heel lift for squats and lunges. Especially recommended for powerlifting and/or Olympic lifting.

BOARDS (2 × 4 INCHES AND 18 TO 24 INCHES IN LENGTH)

Purpose

When placed under the heels, provide additional support and range of movement during certain exercises. Useful with beginners as a teaching tool and for beginners with limited range of motion and flexibility in the Achilles tendons.

Application

Squats, heel raise. Participant should take care not to become dependent on the board for exercises requiring good flexibility. Use of the board is not a substitute for increasing flexibility as part of a natural exercise progression.

CHALK (CARBONATE OF MAGNESIA)

Purpose

Increases bar-holding ability and decreases the likelihood of calluses.

Application

Used commonly by Olympic free-weight lifters. Used to inhibit moisture on the hands, which can impact bar-holding ability.

Alternating Versus Concomitant Exercise

Exercises can be done either alternating arms or sides or using both arms or sides at the same time (concomitant exercise). Alternating arms or sides has the advantage of increasing ability to concentrate on an individual muscle or side.

It also has these disadvantages:

- Causes greater forearm fatigue
- Takes longer to perform the exercise
- Requires a higher level of aerobic endurance

Using both arms or sides (concomitant exercise) has these benefits:

- Causes less forearm fatigue
- Requires less balance and coordination
- Takes less time to perform an exercise
- Is less confusing for beginners

However, it also has the disadvantages of decreasing ability to concentrate on an individual muscle or side.

Spotting During Strength Training

The use of a partner to provide safety, assistance, and motivation is recommended during certain strength training exercises. An effective spotter should

- know how to properly execute the exercise and the appropriate assistance methods;
- focus entirely on the exerciser, and be prepared at all times;
- check bar for even and proper loading;
- be aware of how many repetitions will be attempted;
- decide prior to lift how lifter and spotter will communicate;
- assist with lift off and racking of the weight as requested;
- always use two hands to ensure balance and safety;
- give exerciser feedback on form;
- provide motivation and encouragement for the exerciser, but not carry on a dialogue with the lifter or anyone else;
- strongly encourage the use of collars;
- have a solid stance;
- keep hands off of the bench's uprights; and
- above all, use common sense.

The following are some spotting techniques:

- **Barbell bench press/incline press**—The spotter stands directly behind the lifter in a ready position. Feet should be planted securely, shoulder-width apart, and arms should be extended in front, palms up, ready to grab the bar if necessary. The moment the barbell stops its upward movement, the spotter grasps the barbell with an overhand grip. Using the arms and the legs, the spotter provides enough assistance to complete the lift and return the barbell to the standards.
- **Barbell squats**—The spotter stands directly behind the lifter and moves up and down in tandem with the lifter. The moment the lifter stops the upward movement, the spotter wraps his or her arms around the lifter's upper torso or puts his or her arms under the lifter's arms. Using the legs, the spotter provides enough assistance to complete the lift and return the barbell to the standards.
- **Dumbbell exercises**—The spotter applies assistance directly in line with the resistance force. For example, during the final repetition of the dumbbell bench press, the spotter may best assist by lifting at the exerciser's wrists.

Guidelines for Using Strength Training Machines

Selectorized strength training equipment (weight stack machines with pins used to select a given weight) is popular with a great many adults seeking to develop and maintain muscular strength and endurance. However, some exercises on certain types of equipment cannot be executed in proper form by every participant. This is because the machines' dimensions cannot match the differing limb lengths and adjustments needed by many participants, especially youth, women, and older adults. Some general considerations are listed below; additionally, participants should be coached to suggest other adjustments needed to their trainer. This particularly applies to those participants requiring rehabilitation, those with disabilities, and those with other special or medical circumstances.

- Use each machine in the manner the manufacturer recommends. Do not try alternative applications for which the machine is not intended.
- Use belts and straps if provided by the manufacturer.
- Adjust seat heights to ensure proper body alignment on all machines by aligning the machine's axis of rotation or cam center with the participant's joint axis.
- For best results, do not allow the moving weight stack to touch the stationary weight stack during the exercise.
- Do not let participants drop weight plates or allow them to slam onto the weight stack.
- Use the appropriate pin in all selectorized machines.
- Teach participants that proper exercise form is more important than the amount of weight lifted.
- Use additional seat pads for people whose limb lengths and/or body size do not fit the machine dimensions.
- Instruct participants to grasp exercise handles lightly and not use excessive grip force.
- Teach participants to concentrate on performing each exercise with the prime mover muscle and not engage assisting muscles.
- Instruct participants to use as full a range of motion as comfortably possible.
- Regularly check equipment to make sure machines are working correctly, and teach members to report repair needs.

Recommended Strength Training Exercises

This section lists strength exercises for each major muscle group of the body, using both free weights and machines. Generic descriptions of exercise machines are used because a wide variety of brands are available for use. The exercises listed were chosen based on the types of equipment commonly found in YMCAs, and to best match the needs of the majority of YMCA members. The use of other equipment and exercises can be found in other strength training resources.

Descriptions and photographs of the strength training exercises in table 5.9 can be found at the end of this chapter. They are listed by body part.

Choosing the Right Exercises

The challenge for YMCA Personal Training Instructors is appropriately selecting from all of these exercise choices to design a strength training program that covers all of the major muscle groups without exhausting or injuring the member. Table 5.10 is a sample basic workout that will be appropriate for most adults seeking to develop overall muscular fitness and conditioning.

Strength Training Effectiveness and Efficiency

When designing strength training programs, keep in mind that the exercises should work effectively for participants and should be efficient enough to fit participants' time constraints.

Effectiveness

Once training safety has been established, the next concern is effectiveness. Although any system of progressive resistance exercise will produce at least minimum strength gains, some programs are more effective than others. Basically, strength development depends on application of the strength training principles discussed earlier. However, many individuals and equipment manufacturers believe that the type of exercise equipment plays a more significant role in training effectiveness than it actually does. For example, some people prefer free-weights to machines and vice versa. Of the machine advocates, some prefer weight stacks whereas others favor compressed air, hydraulic, or electronic resistance. For the majority of participants, the type of resistance has less influence on muscle response than the way resistance is applied. A prime consideration is the degree to which the resistance force matches the muscle force throughout the movement range.

Table 5.9 Strength Training Exercises

Exercise	Muscles involved
	Upper leg
Barbell squat	Quadriceps, hamstrings, gluteus maximus
Dumbbell squat	Quadriceps, hamstrings, gluteus maximus
Dumbbell lunge	Quadriceps, hamstrings, gluteus maximus
Leg extension machine	Quadriceps
Leg press machine	Quadriceps, hamstrings, gluteus maximus
Leg curl machine	Hamstrings
Low cable crossover adduction	Hip adductors
Ankle weights adduction	Hip adductors
Hip adduction machine	Hip adductors
Low cable crossover abduction	Hip abductors
Ankle weight abduction	Hip abductors
Hip abduction machine	Hip abductors
	Buttocks
Low cable hip extension	Gluteus maximus, hamstrings
	Lower leg
Weighted toe raise	Anterior tibialis
Low cable dorsiflexion	Anterior tibialis
Supported single leg-dumbbell heel raise	Gastrocnemius, soleus
Seated calf apparatus	Soleus, gastrocnemius
Standing calf apparatus	Gastrocnemius, soleus
Calf press using leg press machine	Gastrocnemius, soleus
	Chest
Barbell bench press	Pectoralis major, anterior deltoids, triceps
Dumbbell bench press	Pectoralis major, anterior deltoids, triceps
Incline barbell press	Upper pectoralis major, triceps, anterior deltoids
Incline dumbbell press	Upper pectoralis major, triceps, anterior deltoids
Dumbbell flys	Pectoralis major, anterior deltoids
Chest press machine	Pectoralis major, anterior deltoids, triceps
Chest cross machine	Pectoralis major, anterior deltoids
Incline press machine	Pectoralis major, anterior deltoids, triceps
	Middle back
Dumbbell bent row	Latissimus dorsi, teres major, middle trapezius, posterior deltoids, rhomboids, biceps
Lat pull-down	Latissimus dorsi, biceps
Chin-up	Latissimus dorsi, biceps
Pullover machine	Latissimus dorsi, teres major
Seated rowing machine	Rhomboids, posterior deltoids, latissimus dorsi, teres major, middle trapezius
Pull-down machine	Latissimus dorsi, teres major, biceps
	Upper back
Barbell shrug	Upper trapezius, levator scapulae
Dumbbell shrug	Upper trapezius, levator scapulae
Shoulder shrug machine	Upper trapezius, levator scapulae

(continued)

Table 5.9 (continued)

Shoulders	
Dumbbell lateral raise	Middle deltoids
Dumbbell shoulder press	Anterior deltoids, middle deltoids, triceps, upper trapezius
Barbell shoulder press	Medial deltoids, anterior deltoids, triceps, upper trapezius
Dumbbell front raise	Anterior deltoids
Lateral raise machine	Deltoids
Shoulder press machine	Anterior and middle deltoids, triceps, superior trapezius
Upper arm	
Dumbbell curl	Biceps
Barbell curl	Biceps
Incline dumbbell curl	Biceps
Standing cable curl	Biceps
Biceps machine	Biceps
Pulley pressdown	Triceps
Dumbbell kickback	Triceps
Seated dumbbell triceps extension	Triceps
Triceps machine	Triceps
Seated dip machine	Triceps, pectoralis major, anterior deltoids
Lower arm	
Reverse forearm curl	Forearm extensors
Weighted forearm roll	Forearm flexors, forearm extensors
Reverse cable forearm curl	Forearm extensors
Cable forearm curl	Forearm flexors
Forearm curl	Forearm flexors
Midsection	
Trunk curl (unweighted/weighted)	Rectus abdominis
Hip flexor apparatus	Hip flexors
Abdominal machine	Rectus abdominis
Twisting trunk curl (unweighted/weighted)	Obliques, rectus abdominis
Cable/dumbbell side bends	Obliques
Rotary torso machine	Obliques
Back	
Seated low pulley back extension	Erector spinae, hip extensors
Floor back extension	Erector spinae
Low back machine	Erector spinae
Neck	
Supine weighted neck flexion	Sternocleidomastoid
Prone weighted neck extension	Upper trapezius, levator scapulae
Neck machine	Upper trapezius, levator scapulae
Shoulder rotator cuff	
Cable internal rotation	Pectoralis major, latissimus dorsi, subscapularis
Cable external rotation	Infraspinatus, teres minor, posterior deltoid
Dumbbell abduction	Supraspinatus, deltoid

Table 5.10 General Strength Training Program for Adults

Muscle groups	Free-weight exercise	Machine exercise
Quadriceps, hamstrings	Squat, lunge	Leg press
Calves	Heel raise	Heel raise on leg press
Pectoralis major, triceps, latissimus dorsi	Bench press	Bench press
Latissimus dorsi, biceps	Dumbbell bent row	Pull-down
Deltoids, triceps	Dumbbell press	Lateral raise
Biceps	Dumbbell curl	Bicep
Triceps	Dumbbell kickback	Tricep
Abdominals	Trunk curl	Abdominal
Erector spinae	Back extension	Back

Select either free-weight or machine exercises, or combine.

For example, dumbbell flies are intended to strengthen the chest muscles, and they are reasonably effective for this purpose. However, dumbbell flies do not match resistance force and muscle force very closely throughout the entire movement range. Due to leverage factors, the bottom position is characterized by relatively high resistance force and relatively low muscle force. Conversely, the top position is characterized by relatively low resistance force and relatively high muscle force. In contrast, some variable resistance exercise machines match resistance forces and muscle forces better by means of a counter leverage system. Through a system of cams or levers, the resistance is reduced in positions of low muscle force and increased in positions of high muscle force, resulting in what some would argue to be a more effective exercise.

Another consideration with respect to exercise effectiveness is external friction. Although free-weights have virtually no external friction, machines provide varying levels of frictional force due to the movement of chains, cams, and the weight stack. It is therefore essential to keep all exercise as friction-free as possible, by cleaning weight stack guiderods for example. Guiderods that are not smooth produce more friction, making it harder to lift the weightstack (concentric movement) and easier to lower the weightstack (eccentric movement). This is opposite to muscle force output, which is lower during concentric contractions and higher during eccentric contractions. All sprockets, chains, pulleys, and cables should also function as smoothly as possible to reduce external friction.

Efficiency

For many people, strength training is a viable fitness activity only when it can be accomplished in a time-efficient manner. Training two hours a day may be acceptable for athletes but is impractical for most adults. Normally sedentary people are more likely to participate in a strength training program when it requires less than 30 minutes per session, three times per week. Fortunately, in the area of strength development, training effectiveness and training efficiency go hand in hand. Whereas cardiorespiratory endurance is best developed through exercise of low intensity and long duration, muscular strength is best developed through exercise of high intensity and short duration. In addition, research has demonstrated that brief strength training sessions can significantly improve body composition. Studies have shown a three-pound muscle gain and a three-pound fat loss after two months of strength training for 30 minutes per session, three sessions per week.

Successful bodybuilders perform many sets of different exercises, but few of us have either the ability or the time to train in this manner. Although numerous training protocols provide an efficient workout, there are two basic exercise formats that work for most people (table 5.11).

When training a beginner, it is particularly advisable to use an efficient exercise program. This simplifies the learning process and facilitates recovery. When the participant desires a more comprehensive training program, it is then easier to build on the solid foundation of basic exercises previously developed.

Table 5.11 Sample Exercise Circuits

Single Muscle Exercises	
Leg extension	Quadriceps
Leg curl	Hamstrings
Chest cross	Pectoralis major
Pullover	Latissimus dorsi
Lateral raise	Deltoid
Biceps curl	Biceps
Triceps extension	Triceps
Trunk curl	Rectus abdominis
Back extension	Erector spinea
Neck flexion	Sternocleidomastoid
Neck extension	Levator scapulae, upper trapezius
Multiple Muscle Exercises	
Squat	Quadriceps, hamstrings, and gluteus maximus
Bench press	Pectoralis major, triceps, and deltoids
Pull-down	Latissimus, dorsi, and biceps
Shoulder press	Deltoid and triceps
Weighted trunk curl	Rectus abdominis and sternocleidomastoid

The exerciser performs one set of 10 to 12 single muscle exercises.
The exerciser performs three sets of 4 to 5 multiple muscle exercises.

Advanced Strength Training Principles and Techniques

After participants have performed the same strength training exercises for a while, they probably will reach a plateau, at which point progression ceases. Some of the techniques described in this section can be utilized to help participants get past these plateaus to make further progress.

Some participants may also become interested in the competitive sports of bodybuilding or weightlifting. Some of the basics of these sports and how they differ from general strength training are explained here.

Strength Plateaus

During the first few weeks of strength training, progress occurs relatively rapidly with noticeable strength improvement occurring almost every exercise session. However, the rate of strength gain typically slows during the second and third months of training as strength levels off and little additional progress is observed. This is referred to as a *strength plateau,* and it indicates that the training program needs to be modified to facilitate further progress.

Strength plateaus appear to be a normal result of continued training and should not be cause for discouragement. Every strength training program eventually becomes stale if it remains unchanged. Sensible and systematic changes in the training program should help overcome the strength plateau and achieve further muscle development.

Following are suggested modifications that can be made to a strength training routine when a plateau is reached:

- **Change training exercises**—The first training modification probably should be to select different exercises. As muscles become accustomed to performing the same exercises, the stimulus-response pattern becomes less and less effective. Basically, the same muscle fibers are activated in the same recruitment pattern, which becomes routine and unproductive.

By changing the training exercises periodically, different muscle fibers are activated in different recruitment patterns, which fosters positive stimulus-response adaptations. For example, after six weeks of standing barbell curls, the biceps muscles' response to this exercise is lessened. When a new biceps exercise is substituted, such as incline dumbbell curls, different muscle fibers are stimulated in a different recruitment order, and positive adaptations are likely to occur. When the muscles become accustomed to incline dumbbell curls, a return to standing barbell curls or another biceps exercise should avoid another plateau and continue progress.

- **Change training frequency**—As muscles become stronger and use heavier resistance, they may require longer recovery and building periods between training sessions. For example, if training each muscle group every other day ceases to be productive, it may be necessary to switch to training every third day. One example of such a program is to perform back and biceps exercises on Mondays and Thursdays, chest and triceps exercises on Tuesdays and Fridays, and leg and shoulder exercises on Wednesdays and Saturdays. In this manner, each major muscle group is trained twice a week with at least three days of recovery and building time between workouts.

- **Change training sets**—The number of sets performed per exercise is a significant factor in muscle development and strength gains. Persons who perform multiple sets per exercise may gain little additional strength but experience much muscle fatigue from the high-volume training. They may obtain better results by cutting down the number of sets and training with greater intensity. On the other hand, single-set training may not produce maximum benefits for many people. For those who have difficulty training in a high-intensity manner, less weight and/or less repetitions may be beneficial. Generally, the more exercises performed, the fewer sets performed per exercise.

- **Change training repetitions**—There is an inverse relationship between repetitions and resistance. More resistance allows for fewer repetitions, and less resistance allows for more repetitions. Periodically changing the repetition/resistance relationship may produce further strength development. For example, performing 8 repetitions with 160 pounds provides a different muscle stimulus than completing 12 repetitions with 140 pounds. It is therefore advisable to consider occasional repetition variations to overcome both physical and mental staleness.

Another effective way to address strength plateaus is to use various techniques to increase training intensity. An exercise can be made harder to perform in several ways, but some techniques carry a high risk of injury. The following high-intensity training methods—breakdown training, assisted training, super-slow training, super-set training, and negative training—are safe and effective when used properly. They can help participants move beyond strength plateaus.

A safety note: when increased resistance is used, the role of the spotter becomes even more important. When using methods such as assisted training or negative training, the spotter is crucial to the success, safety, and motivation of the lifter.

Breakdown Training

Let's assume that Dan has 100 fibers in his biceps muscles and that each fiber can produce 1 pound of force. Theoretically, he could curl a maximum weight of 100 pounds. If he trains with 75 pounds, he may complete 10 repetitions before the weight exceeds his muscle force and he must stop. At this point he has fatigued at least 26 of his 100 muscle fibers, and there are not enough fresh fibers to lift the weightload. If he rests for about two minutes, most of the fatigued muscle fibers will recover and he can perform a second set of 9 or 10 curls. He will again fatigue the same 26 muscle fibers, at which point he must terminate the exercise set. In this manner, his biceps muscles are pushed to the limit once during each exercise set.

Suppose that at the completion of Dan's last repetition with 75 pounds, a training partner reduces the weightload by 10 pounds. Because Dan still has 74 functioning muscle fibers and only 65 pounds of resistance, he can complete two or three additional repetitions and fatigue 10 more muscle fibers before stopping the set of exercise. Perhaps more importantly, his biceps muscles are pushed to the limit twice during the extended exercise set.

This type of high-intensity exercise is referred to as breakdown training, because the starting weightload is "broken down" to permit more repetitions. This is a demanding training technique that causes temporary discomfort and requires additional recovery and building time. An example of breakdown training is to perform 10 repetitions to failure in a given exercise, let's say 100 pounds in the leg extension exercise. Immediately after completing the final repetition, the lifter reduces the weightload by about 15 percent (85 pounds) and performs as many additional repetitions as possible. The additional two or three repetitions make a big difference in the fatigue level and the strength-building stimulus.

Breakdown training is effective for stimulating muscle development, as long as it is not overdone. It is not usually advisable to break down the weightload more than once per exercise or to perform breakdown training more than once per week for a particular muscle group.

Assisted Training

Like breakdown training, assisted training involves a small reduction in exercise resistance at the point of muscle fatigue. Unlike breakdown training, the resistance is reduced only during the lifting (concentric) phase of the exercise. Let's assume Karen has performed 10 repetitions in the leg curl, and her hamstring muscles are unable to complete another lift. Her training partner assists her just enough to lift the weightload but allows her to lower the weightload on her own, because her eccentric force output is greater than her concentric force output. Assisted training allows her to perform additional repetitions that would not be possible otherwise.

Generally, two to four assisted repetitions are sufficient to stimulate the desired muscle response. Like breakdown training, this is a demanding form of exercise that should not be overdone. One assisted training session per week is probably enough for a given muscle group.

Super-Slow Training

Slow exercise movements are utilized to minimize the role of momentum and produce increased muscle tension. Simply slowing down the exercise speed is therefore a highly effective means for increasing the training stimulus. Super-slow training is usually conducted with a 10-second lifting movement and a 5-second lowering movement. At 15 seconds per repetition, four to six super-slow reps require 60 to 90 seconds of continuous muscle tension. This may be the most demanding and productive form of high-intensity training. It is also a very safe exercise technique as long as the exerciser breathes continuously.

Super-Set Training

Performing two or more sets of the same biceps exercise activates the same muscle fibers in the same recruitment pattern. Performing two or more sets of different biceps exercises activates different muscle fibers in different recruitment patterns, and is referred to as super-set training. This becomes particularly effective when the exercises are performed in close succession.

For example, a set of barbell curls could be followed immediately by a set of incline dumbbell curls. Both exercises target the biceps muscles but require different muscle fiber recruitment patterns. Involving different muscle fibers in a different activation order seems to enhance the training stimulus. Once again, it is not advisable to carry super-set training to extremes, as overtraining problems may result. One super-set session per week per muscle group is a reasonable high-intensity training technique.

Negative Training

As indicated under Assisted Training, emphasizing the negative (eccentric) movement is an excellent means for stimulating muscle development. Generally, a person can lower (negative movement) about 40 percent more weight than she or he can lift (positive movement), producing a highly effective muscle stimulus. Unfortunately, for the same reason, negative training also carries a high risk of tissue injury.

The safest method of negative exercise is assisted training in which the exerciser works to fatigue, then receives help on the lifting movements but not on the lowering movement. The most risky method of negative exercise requires a training partner to lift a heavier resistance than the exerciser can manage. The exerciser then lowers the resistance slowly to emphasize eccentric muscle contraction. If the exerciser fatigues midway through the lowering movement, muscle tissues may be damaged.

Negative training can be a useful technique for exercises using one's body weight, such as chin-ups and bar dips. For example, after five chin-ups, Susan can no longer lift her body to the bar. However, she can use a prop to step up to the top position and then slowly lower her body. The lowering (negative) movement uses the same muscles as the lifting (positive) movement and provides an excellent training stimulus. Be aware that forceful negative exercise typically produces delayed onset muscle soreness a day or two after the exercise session. This is not necessarily bad, but it underscores the need to utilize negative training prudently. A little negative training goes a long way and should never be overdone or performed carelessly. One negative training session per muscle group per week should be sufficient.

Strength Training for Competitive Purposes

Many individuals pursue strength training for the purpose of becoming a competitive bodybuilder or weightlifter. Although this may be an admirable goal, for most it is unrealistic, because very few people possess the genetic potential to develop really large and strong muscles. One's basic body type, predominant muscle fiber (fast twitch, slow twitch), skeletal structure (small frame, large frame), biomechanical advantage (tendon insertion points), relative muscle length (short, medium, long), and hormone balance (testosterone level) all affect the capacity to become big and strong. For every bodybuilder featured in a magazine, there are thousands of dedicated strength trainers who achieve very modest results by comparison. Too often, they believe that training harder and longer will produce the physique they desire. Unfortunately, this typically leads to overuse injuries, frustration, and discontinuation of their exercise programs.

Although there is nothing wrong with pursuing a bodybuilding or weightlifting program, one should be aware of the genetic factors and time commitment necessary to achieve competitive success in these sports. If someone understands these requirements and still wants to pursue a competitive goal, it is advisable to begin with a well-balanced training program that is substantially less demanding than those of competitive athletes. If the initial results are positive, then more exercises, more sets, and more resistance may be progressively added. If the initial results do not justify the time and effort, if there is undue fatigue and muscle soreness, or if there is high incidence of injury, then perhaps the exercise routine should be modified and scaled down.

Both bodybuilders and weightlifters exhibit large and strong muscles. However, bodybuilders train primarily for muscle size and typically look strong because of increased muscle definition. Conversely, weightlifters train primarily for muscle strength and usually are stronger than they look. Although they both train with weights for two or more hours per day, there are important differences in their exercise routines. Training specialization is most evident in the amount of rest bodybuilders and weightlifters take between exercise sets.

Bodybuilders use a variety of techniques to achieve their goals. A common technique is for the bodybuilder to take very brief breaks (15 to 45 seconds) between sets to achieve "pumped-up" muscles. The muscle pump is actually a temporary increase in muscle size as a result of blood accumulation. By quickly repeating the exercise sets, fluid is trapped in the muscle tissue, thereby producing the pumped-up look. Because short rests allow only partial muscle recovery, bodybuilders must train with relatively low percentages of their maximum resistance. For example, a bodybuilder who is able to bench press 400 pounds may perform six sets of 10 reps with 250 pounds during a given workout. The short recovery periods force him to train with about 65 percent of his maximum resistance.

Weightlifters, on the other hand, take relatively long rest periods (three to six minutes) between sets to permit the use of heavy weightloads. The longer rest interval enhances muscle recovery between sets and allows them to train with relatively high percentages of their maximum resistance. For example, a powerlifter who is able to bench press 400 pounds may perform a pyramid workout such as the following:

150 pounds × 8 reps
200 pounds × 7 reps
250 pounds × 6 reps
300 pounds × 5 reps
350 pounds × 3 reps
350 pounds × 3 reps
350 pounds × 3 reps

The long recovery periods permit the powerlifter to train with about 90 percent of his maximum resistance.

Although bodybuilders and weightlifters train for over two hours per workout, bodybuilders complete a much greater volume of work during each exercise session. Table 5.12 provides typical training protocols for bodybuilders and weightlifters.

Few activities are as physically demanding as bodybuilding and weightlifting. However, successful bodybuilders and weightlifters appear to have two genetically related training advantages: they tolerate stressful workouts with relatively few injuries, and they respond to training stimuli with greater muscle size and strength than the average person. Persons interested in bodybuilding or weightlifting should work with trained instructors to develop a sound and systematic approach to attaining their competitive goals.

Educating Participants About Strength Training

Member education is an ongoing process that begins with an orientation program and continues with trained, knowledgeable instructors, and involves the development of a planned member communication strategy.

Strength Training Orientation

This section provides guidelines on how to provide strength training participants with a thorough orientation if they are not working with a personal training instructor. Each YMCA should recommend that all members participate in a strength training orientation prior to beginning an exercise program, regardless of their previous experience with strength training. Here are some ideas for designing orientations appropriate for beginning, intermediate, and advanced participants.

Orientation for Beginning Participants

The first step is to screen for people with various health risks. People who have arthritis, heart disease, lower back pain, knee pain or injury, or high blood pressure; who are pregnant; or who have recently undergone surgery should not participate without a physician's permission. If they do participate, they may need to follow their physician's recommendations for safe participation.

Recommend performing one or two sets every other day, the number of sets depending on the type of equipment used. Suggest 8 to 12 reps for each set, although more may be necessary (with lower resistance) as they first learn how to perform the exercise. If the training intensity and pace are right, the last two reps of each set should be hard to do, as the participant nears muscle failure.

Select specific exercises and equipment according to what is available, the participant's previous experience with weights, and his or her body weight. Design a workout that has one exercise for each major muscle group. Start participants with a submaximal weight that they can lift for 8 to 12 reps. Beginners should not do more than 12 exercises during a session.

Tour beginning participants through the strength training facility, showing them the various equipment and stations. Teach beginners how to perform exercises using the correct technique and form. It is often helpful if beginning participants have a support partner, someone who counsels them and ensures that they perform correctly. In many cases this function can be performed by facility staff.

Table 5.12 Typical Training Protocols for Bodybuilders and Weightlifters

	Bodybuilders (Muscle size)	Weightlifters (Muscle strength)
Exercises	3 to 5 per muscle group	1 to 2 per muscle group
Sets	4 to 6 per exercise	6 to 8 per exercise
Repetitions	6 to 15 per set	2 to 8 per set
Resistance	60 to 75 percent maximum	80 to 95 percent maximum
Rest between sets	15 to 45 seconds	3 to 6 minutes

Check each person's progress once every 4 to 6 weeks. Examine each of the following check points:

- Heart rate
- Measurements
- Body composition
- Blood pressure
- Appearance
- Strength increase, measured by retesting

After checking, acknowledge any progress that has been made, and suggest appropriate modification to their program. This type of support can make him feel good about himself and the YMCA.

Orientation for Intermediate Participants

Briefly discuss any items in the beginners program that need review. At the intermediate level, participants can still benefit from having a training partner, someone who counsels them, watches to see that they perform correctly, and perhaps also trains with them. This could be another knowledgeable strength training participant or an instructor. Review the following techniques for intermediate level participants to try:

- *Strict reps* are reps performed in a way that isolates the muscle so that no assistance is supplied by any other body part or muscle group.
- *Forced reps* are reps done with a training partner manually assisting the participant in moving through a desired range of motion when the participant is unable to do it alone.
- *Negative training,* which emphasized the eccentric contraction, is the lowering of resistance against gravity through a desired range of motion.
- *Breakdown training* is doing a set at a given weight to muscle failure, then having the weight immediately reduced by 15 to 20 percent by a training partner, and performing another two or three additional reps.
- *Isolation* is much like strict reps; it is emphasizing a specific body part or muscle group without any assistance from any other part of the body. It is usually done with dumbbells or cable exercises.
- *Pyramiding* is increasing weight and decreasing repetitions in successive sets.

Following are two systems for designing intermediate-level workouts:

- *Super sets* are sets in which a compound movement is done for a particular muscle group and then followed by an isolated exercise for muscles in that same group. For example, with barbells, arm curls would be followed by concentration curls.
- *Split routines* are workout schedules that emphasize particular muscle groups on certain days. For example, the chest and shoulders would be exercised on Mondays and Wednesdays and the legs and back on Tuesdays and Thursdays.

Orientation for Advanced Participants

Briefly discuss any items in the orientation programs for beginners and intermediate participants that need review. Following are some techniques you may wish to teach advanced participants:

- *Priority training* emphasizes conditioning programs for a specific or immediate need, such as for a particular sport. For example, off-season and in-season sports training will differ.
- *Advanced isolation* is doing two exercises instead of one for a particular body part.
- *Continuous tension* means that the resistance remains the same throughout the complete range of motion during an exercise.
- *Preexhaustion* is exercising a muscle with a single isolated muscle movement before a compound movement that uses the same muscle group.
- A *varied tempo* means adjusting the speed at which the participant progresses from exercise to exercise.
- *Cycling* (periodization) is gradually increasing resistance in a series of exercises over an extended period of time. Note that it is sometimes necessary to decrease repetitions as the resistance is increased.

The following are three training methods to teach advanced level participants:

- *Diminishing sets* are a method of performing three sets of a specific exercise for a particular muscle or muscle group. The sets are done as follows: A set of 10 reps is completed. Then 20 to 25 percent of the weight is removed and a second set of 4 to 6 reps is performed. Again, 20 to 25 percent of the weight is removed, and a third set of 4 to 6 reps is done.

- *Compound sets* are groups of two or three exercises for the same body part in which each is performed for 8 to 12 reps. Up to two minutes of recovery time is allowed between exercises. For example, for the chest, the exercises can be the bench press, dumbbell flies, and dips.

- *Trisets* are compound sets in which there is no rest between exercises. This is a more intense effort.

On-Going Member Education

Few areas are in greater need of our educational efforts than strength training. There is a general lack of understanding regarding strength training benefits and a widespread misunderstanding regarding strength training principles. This is partly due to the large number of bodybuilding magazines that promote an almost unlimited number of championship training routines.

Strength training education should therefore be one of our professional priorities. One thing we can do to better educate our members is provide well-written strength training materials, using information from this textbook and appropriate article reprints. A frequently updated strength training bulletin board is also helpful. Another effective means for sharing information is through strength training seminars and workshops. These should be conducted regularly for both instructors and members. Better understanding leads to better training, which leads to better results. When members learn and practice the strength training principles, they become models for other participants, and the cause of sensible strength training is advanced.

UPPER LEG

BARBELL SQUAT

Muscle Group

Quadriceps, hamstrings, gluteus maximus

Begin with barbell supported across upper back. Hands should have a firm overhand grip. Feet should be shoulder-width apart and toes pointed slightly outward as if sitting down into a chair. Lower hips until thighs are parallel to the floor (or as far as comfortable without going beyond parallel). Keep the head up and torso erect. Raise hips to standing position and repeat.

Note: Do not let knees extend beyond the toes.

The barbell squat should be performed with a spotter who wraps his or her arms around the lifter's torso and helps the lifter stand up, if necessary.

DUMBBELL SQUAT

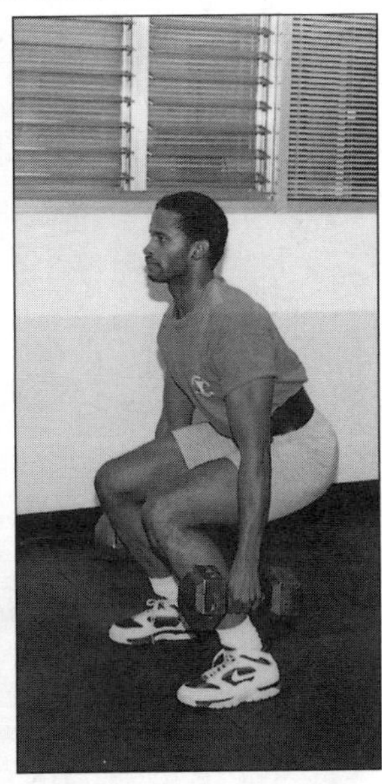

Muscle Group

Quadriceps, hamstrings, gluteus maximus

Begin by holding dumbbells at the sides. Hands should have a firm overhand grip. Feet should be shoulder-width apart and toes pointed slightly outward as if sitting down into a chair. Lower hips until thighs are parallel to the floor (or as far as comfortable without going beyond parallel). Keep the head up and torso erect. Raise hips to standing position and repeat.

Note: Do not let knees extend beyond the toes.

DUMBBELL LUNGE

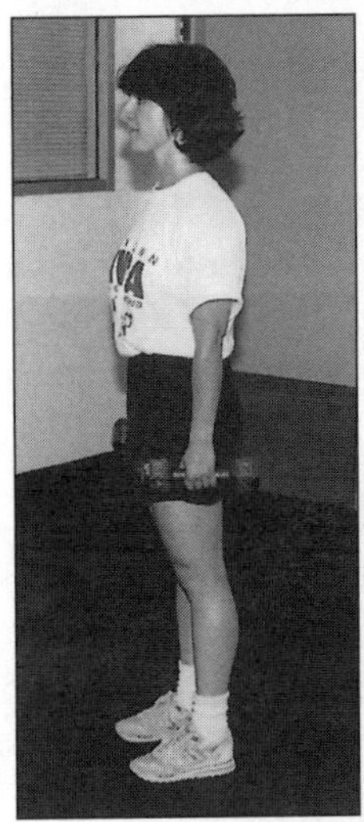

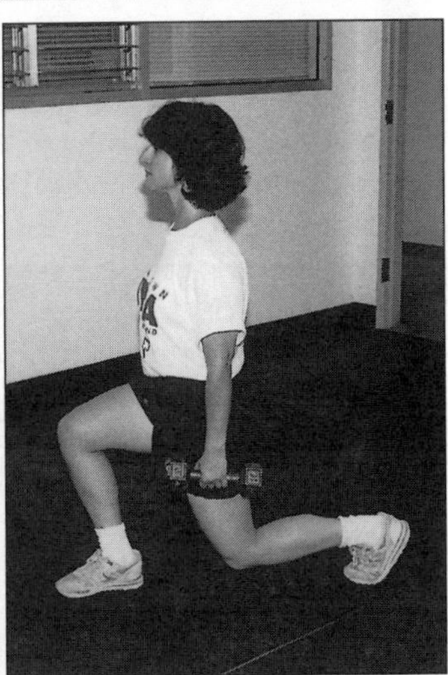

Muscle Group

Quadriceps, hamstrings, gluteus maximus

Begin by holding dumbbells at the sides, feet hip-width apart. Take a large step forward with one leg landing heel first. Bend the forward leg until the knee is directly over the foot and the rear knee is close to the floor. Pause. Push up to the starting position, keeping head up and torso erect. Repeat. Continue exercise with other leg.

Note: Move in a controlled manner to reduce landing forces and joint stress.

LEG EXTENSION MACHINE

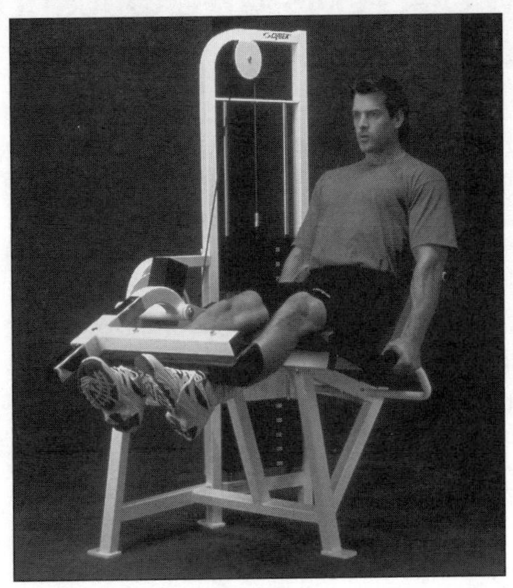

Muscle Group

Quadriceps

Sit on machine with low back touching back support pad. The bend of the knee should fall at the end of the seat and the knee joint should line up with the machine axis of rotation. The rollers or pads should touch just above the ankle. Extend the lower leg to a fully extended horizontal position. Pause and return to the starting position. Repeat.

Note: Keep constant tension on the muscle. Do not allow the weightstacks to touch during the exercise.

LEG PRESS MACHINE

Muscle Group

Quadriceps, hamstrings, gluteus maximus

Adjust seat to allow for a 90 degree angle of knee. Place full foot on foot pedals. Press both feet forward, stopping just short of knee lock or straight leg. Bend knee again and return to starting position. Repeat. Do not allow gluteals to raise off seat.

LEG CURL MACHINE

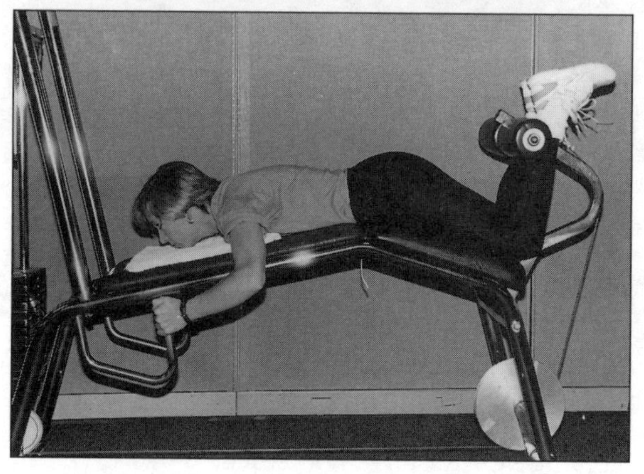

Muscle Group

Hamstrings

Lying face down, place heels under pads or rollers. Align knees with the point of rotation of the machine's resistance arm (the point where the arm holding the pads for the ankle and the machine connect and rotate).

Move the heels toward the buttocks, keeping the upper leg stationary (hips may rise slightly off the pads). Grasp the handles below the bench for stability only. Avoid excessively squeezing the handles.

Stop leg flexion with heels one to two inches from buttocks. Pause and return to starting position. Repeat.

Note: Feet should remain at right angles to lower leg.

LOW CABLE CROSSOVER ADDUCTION

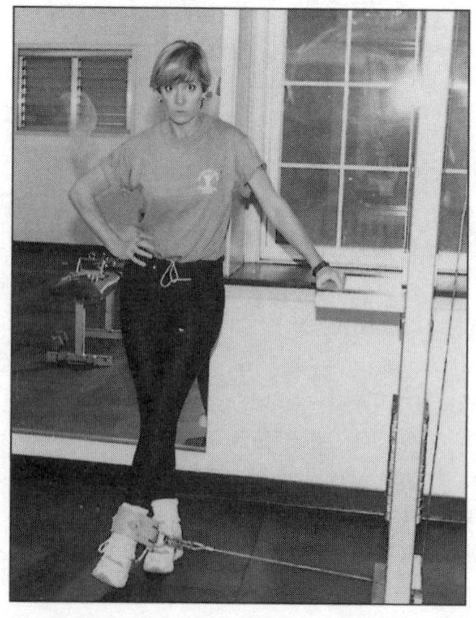

Muscle Group

Hip adductors

Sit or stand sideways with ankles in line with pulley, legs straight, and feet 12 to 18 inches apart. Place strap over ankle nearest pulley and move strapped ankle toward other ankle. Pause and return to starting position. Repeat.

Note: Keep torso in neutral position. Avoid shifting or twisting movements.

ANKLE WEIGHTS ADDUCTION

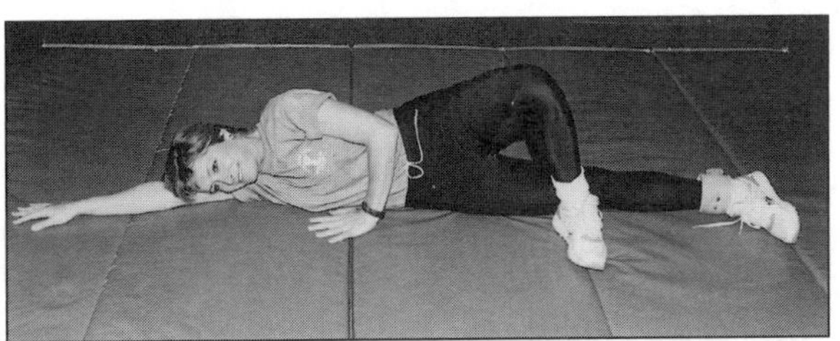

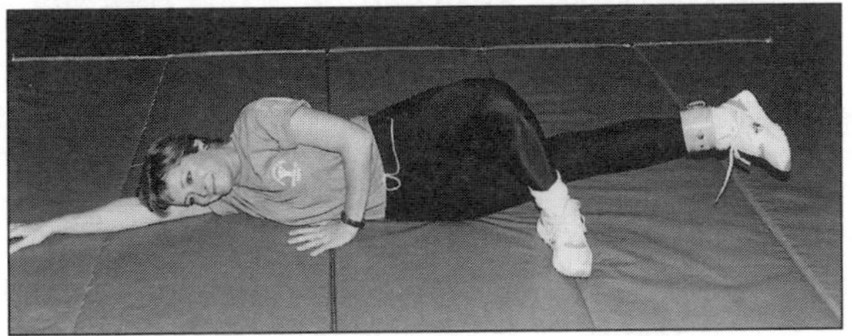

Muscle Group

Hip adductors

Place ankle weight on right ankle, and lie on right side. Cross left leg over right, placing left foot flat on floor and in front of right knee. Place left hand on floor in front of body for support. Move right leg upward with straight knee, and pause in fully contracted position. Return to starting position and repeat. Continue exercise with left leg.

HIP ADDUCTION MACHINE

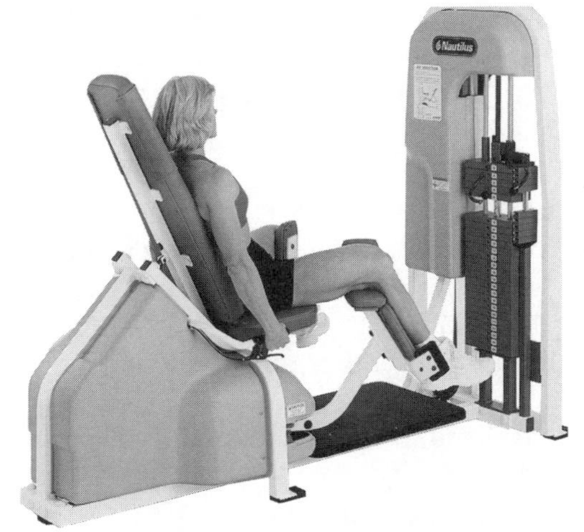

Muscle Group

Hip adductors

Adjust machine so that legs are as far apart as comfortably possible. Place machine pads slightly above and on inside of knees and ankles. Lean back into seat. Squeeze thighs together until machine arms touch. Pause. Return to stretch position. Repeat.

Note: Keep lower legs relaxed throughout the movement.

LOW CABLE CROSSOVER ABDUCTION

Muscle Group

Hip abductors

Sit or stand sideways with ankles in line with pulley, legs straight, and feet together. Place strap over ankle farthest from pulley and move strapped ankle away from pulley to the fully contracted position. Pause and return to starting position. Repeat.

Note: Keep torso in neutral position. Avoid shifting or twisting movements.

ANKLE WEIGHT ABDUCTION

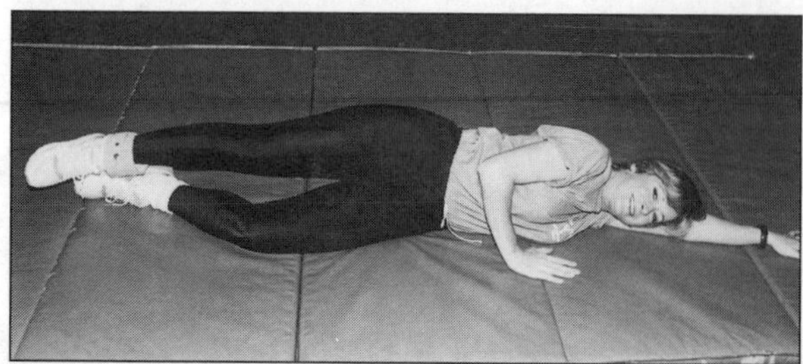

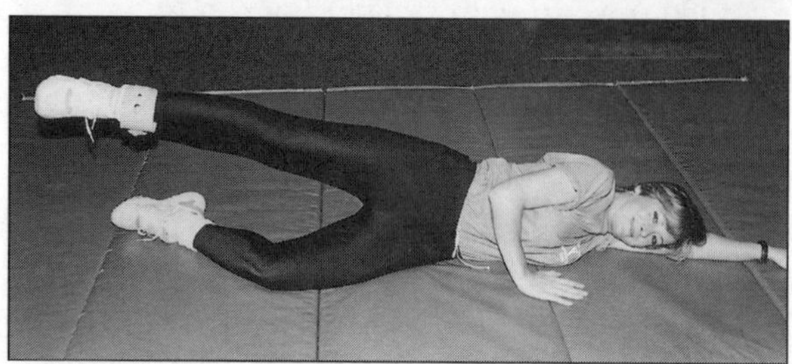

Muscle Group

Hip abductors

Place ankle weight on right ankle, and lie on left side. With left leg slightly bent, move right leg upward with straight knee to a maximum of 30 to 40 degrees, and pause in fully contracted position. Return to starting position and repeat. Continue exercise with left leg.

HIP ABDUCTION MACHINE

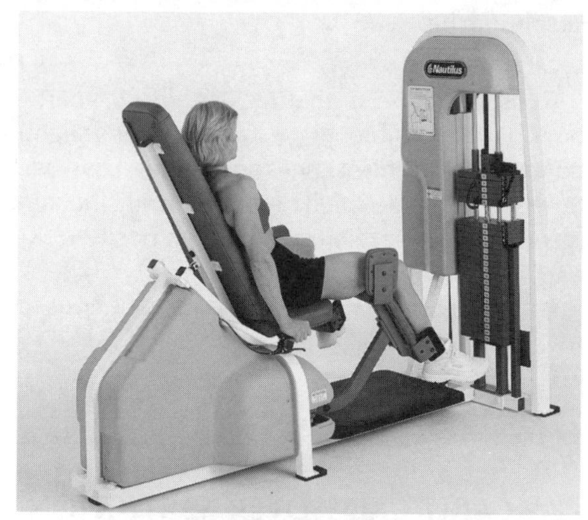

Muscle Group

Hip abductors

Begin exercise with legs together, machine pads on and just above the outside of knees and ankles. Lean back into seat. Push thighs apart as far as possible. Pause and return to starting position. Repeat.

Note: Keep lower legs relaxed throughout the movement.

4-Way Hip Type

Align hip joints with machine's axis of rotation (only on machines with adjustable platform). Adjust lever arm so that pad is just above and on the inside of knee. Raise lever arm to a position slightly lower than horizontal to the floor (to the right side). Stand facing the axis of rotation with feet hip-width apart. Lightly grasp handles for stability. Place right leg over lever arm pad. Bring right leg to left leg. Pause. Return to starting position. Repeat. Repeat repetitions on left leg.

Note: Avoid leaning or twisting the trunk throughout the exercise.

BUTTOCKS

LOW CABLE HIP EXTENSION

Muscle Group

Gluteus maximus, hamstrings

Place strap over right ankle and stand facing weightstack. Using arms for support, move right leg backward (straight, not locked) to fully contracted position. Keep back in neutral position. Pause and return to starting position. Repeat. Continue exercise with left leg.

Note: Avoid shifting or twisting motion. Keep back in neutral position.

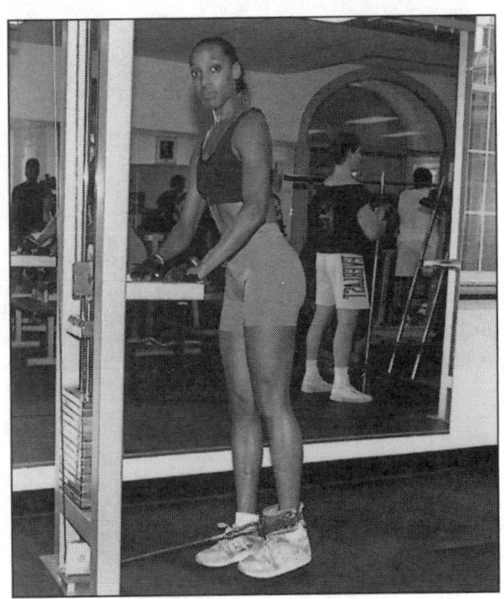

LOWER LEG

WEIGHTED TOE RAISE

Muscle Group

Anterior tibialis

Place weight plate carefully on toes. Raise toes toward shin and pause in fully contracted position. Slowly lower toes to floor and repeat.

Note: For an enhanced range of motion, elevate the heels with a board.

LOW CABLE DORSIFLEXION

Muscle Group

Anterior tibialis

Place strap on toes. Move toes toward shin and pause in fully contracted position. Pause and return to starting position. Repeat.

Note: Place a wooden block under heel to allow full movement range.

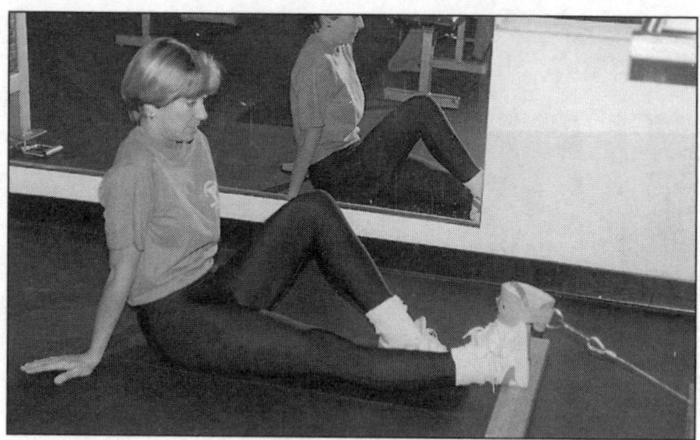

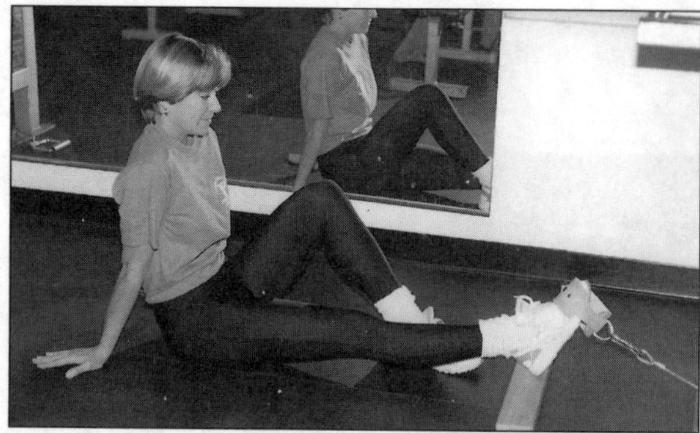

LOWER LEG

SUPPORTED SINGLE-LEG DUMBBELL HEEL RAISE

Muscle Group

Gastrocnemius, soleus

Place one foot on a 2 inch × 4 inch board with the other foot crossed behind the ankle of the supporting leg. Hold dumbbell on the supporting leg side, and use other hand for balance. Raise the heel upward until calf muscles are fully contracted. Pause. Slowly lower heel to floor and repeat. Continue exercise with other leg.

Note: Keep knee straight (not locked) throughout the exercise.

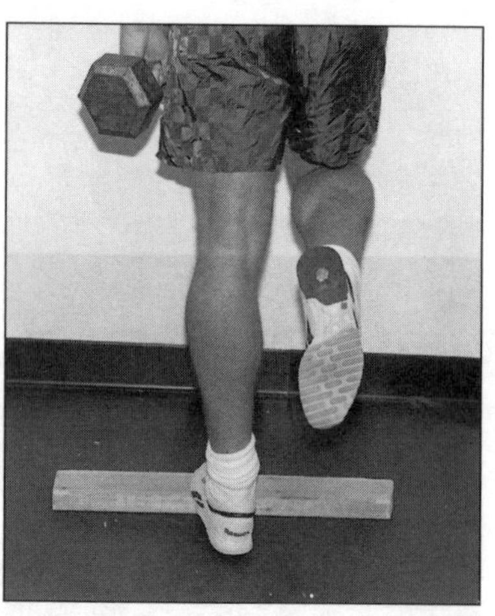

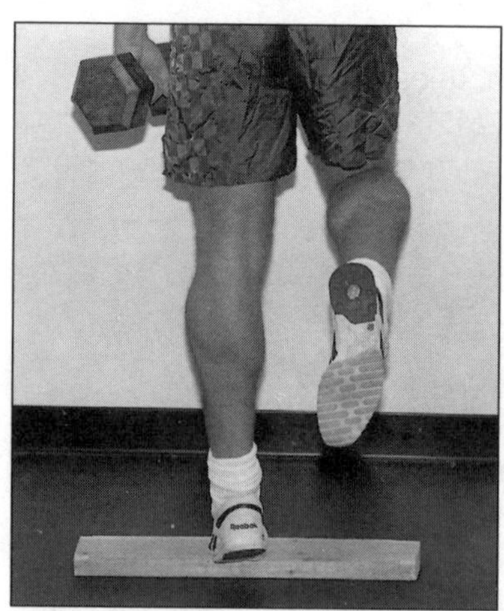

SEATED CALF APPARATUS

Muscle Group

Soleus, gastrocnemius

Sit on apparatus and adjust loading pad for full movement range by placing pad above knee joint. Keeping toes on platform, lower heels until calf muscles are fully stretched. Raise onto toes until calf muscles are fully contracted. Pause. Slowly return to starting position and repeat.

STANDING CALF APPARATUS

Muscle Group

Gastrocnemius, soleus

Stand with toes on platform and adjust loading pad for full movement range. Keeping toes on platform, lower heels until calf muscles are fully stretched. Raise onto toes until calf muscles are fully contracted. Pause. Slowly return to starting position and repeat.

CALF PRESS USING LEG PRESS MACHINE

Muscle Group

Gastrocnemius, soleus

Using the leg press machine, adjust seat to allow for full range of motion of the ankle. Place balls of feet on bottom of foot pedal(s) and fully extend legs (do not lock knees). Begin exercise by pushing out with toes as far as possible. Pause and bring toes back toward body, allowing for a full stretch. Repeat.

CHEST

BARBELL BENCH PRESS

Muscle Group

Pectoralis major, anterior deltoids, triceps

Lie face up with head, shoulders, and hips on bench and feet flat on floor or support stand. Remove barbell from standards and hold above shoulders. Lower barbell slowly to thickest part of chest and pause. Press barbell to full elbow extension (do not lock) and repeat. After final repetition, replace barbell on standards.

Note: Grasp bar with secure (thumb-around) grip, a little wider than shoulders such that forearms become perpendicular to the floor when the bar is at the chest position. Distance between hands will be different for each person.

This exercise should always be performed with a spotter who helps lift the barbell from and to the standards and assists whenever the lifter experiences difficulty.

DUMBBELL BENCH PRESS

Muscle Group

Pectoralis major, anterior deltoids, triceps

Sit on end of bench with dumbbells resting on thighs. Carefully lie back, placing head and shoulders on bench while shifting dumbbells to shoulder level. Feet should be flat on floor or support stand. Press dumbbells to full elbow extension (do not lock). Slowly lower to starting position.

Note: Grasp dumbbells with secure (thumb-around) grip and with palms facing the feet.

At completion of exercise, tuck elbows to body and lower dumbbells to floor by straightening elbows. Be sure there are no dumbbells or plates around the bench.

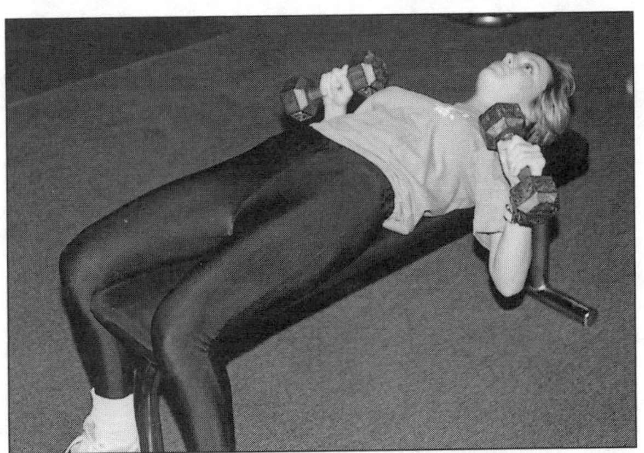

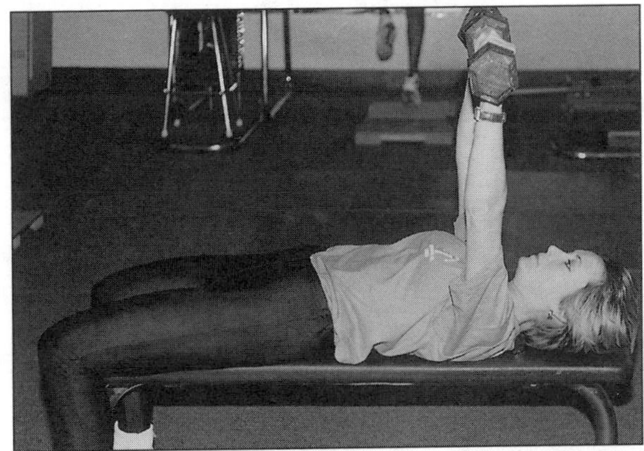

INCLINE BARBELL PRESS

Muscle Group

Upper pectoralis major, triceps, anterior deltoids

Lean back with head, shoulders, and hips on bench and feet flat on floor or support stand. Remove barbell from standards and hold above chin. Lower barbell slowly to top part of chest (slightly lower than collarbone). Press barbell to full elbow extension (do not lock) and repeat. After final repetition, replace barbell on standards.

Note: Grasp bar with secure (thumb-around) grip, a little wider than shoulders such that forearms become perpendicular to the floor when the bar is at the chest position. This position will be different for each person.

When possible, this exercise should be performed with a spotter who helps lift the barbell from and to the standards and assists whenever the lifter experiences difficulty.

INCLINE DUMBBELL PRESS

Muscle Group

Upper pectoralis major, triceps, anterior deltoids

Sit on end of bench with dumbbells resting on thighs. Carefully lean back, placing head and shoulders on bench while shifting dumbbells to shoulder level. Feet should be flat on floor or support stand. Press dumbbells to full elbow extension (do not lock). Slowly lower to starting position.

Note: Grasp dumbbells with secure (thumb-around) grip, palms facing the feet.

At completion of exercise, tuck elbows to body and lower dumbbells to floor by straightening elbows. Be sure there are no dumbbells or plates around the bench.

DUMBBELL FLYS

Muscle Group

Pectoralis major

Lie face up on a flat bench. Start with arms extended and dumbbells directly above the shoulders with elbows slightly bent. With slow and controlled movement, lower arms to the side until they are in a parallel position. Slowly raise the dumbbells to the starting position. Pause. Repeat.

CHEST PRESS MACHINE

Muscle Group

Pectoralis major, anterior deltoids, triceps

Adjust the machine to fit each person. Use belts if provided by machine manufacturer. Position the midchest in alignment with the movement arm or handles. Grasp handles lightly while pushing the movement arm away from you to full extension (do not lock elbow). Pause. Slowly lower the movement arm. Repeat.

CHEST CROSS MACHINE

Muscle Group

Pectoralis major

Adjust the seat so that the arms are parallel to the ground when the hands grasp the handles and the forearm is at a 90 degree angle at the elbow. Push the handles forward and together in front of the chest. Pause and return to a stretched position. Repeat.

Note: Keep back pressed firmly against back pad and head in a neutral position during entire movement.

INCLINE PRESS MACHINE

Muscle Group

Pectoralis major, anterior deltoids, triceps

Sit on machine with seat adjusted so that handles are at chest level. Grip handles and prress them forward until arms are nearly extended.

Pause and return slowly until hands are by chest. Repeat.

Caution: To avoid excessive stress on the shoulder joint, do not allow hands to move too far backward.

MIDDLE BACK

DUMBBELL BENT ROW

Muscle Group

Latissimus dorsi, teres major, medial trapezius, posterior deltoids, rhomboids, biceps

Support the body with one hand or one hand and knee on a bench. Hold the dumbbell with the opposite hand. Bend the elbow, lifting the weight close to the side to approximately shoulder height. Pause. Slowly return to starting position. Repeat. Repeat exercise on opposite side.

Note: Keep pelvis square to the floor throughout movement. The further the elbow is from the side of the body, the more the posterior deltoid is involved.

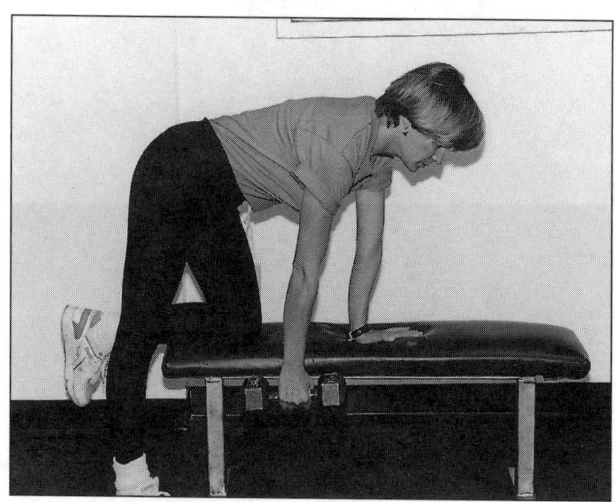

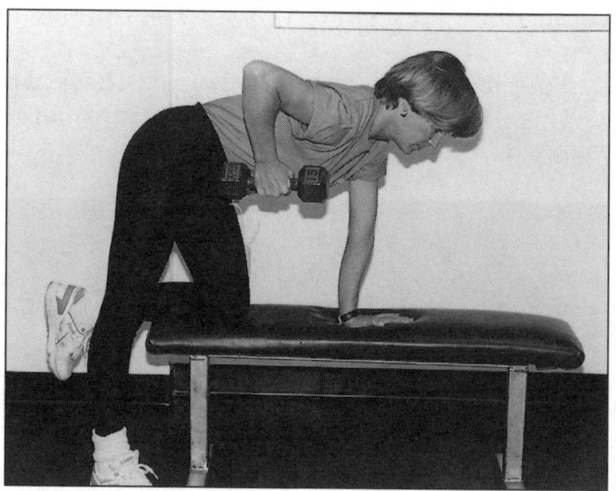

LAT PULL-DOWN

Muscle Group

Latissimus dorsi, biceps

Hand positions may vary from palms in, out, or facing each other. For palms-in position, use a shoulder-width grip. For palms-out position, use a slightly wider than shoulder-width grip. For palms facing each other, use a grip approximately shoulder-width apart. Grip the bar above the head. Slowly and with control, pull the bar in front of the head to the chest. (palms in, palms out, or palms facing each other). Pause. Return the bar to the extended position, allowing for a slight bend in the elbow. Repeat.

Note: On machines equipped with an adjustable knee pad, adjust to body size.

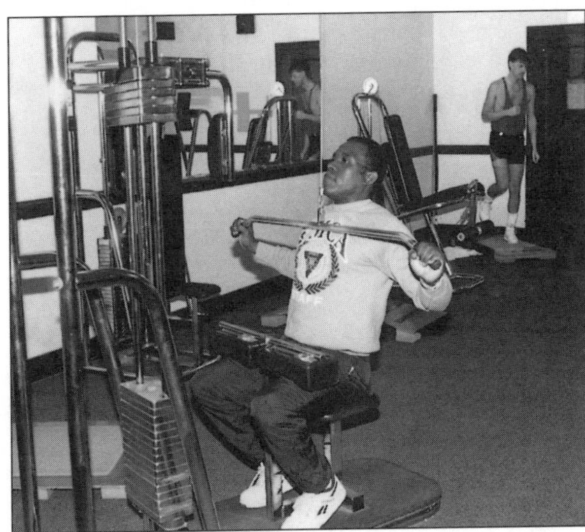

CHIN-UP

Muscle Group

Latissimus dorsi, biceps

Hand positions may vary from palms in or palms out. Using a stationary bar suspended above arm's length, grasp the bar. For palms-in position, use a shoulder-width grip. Lift feet to suspend body from bar. Pull chin or back of neck to the bar. Pause. Lower and repeat. For palms-out position, use a slightly wider than shoulder-width grip. Lift feet to suspend body from bar. Pull chin or back of neck to the bar. Pause. Lower and repeat.

PULLOVER MACHINE

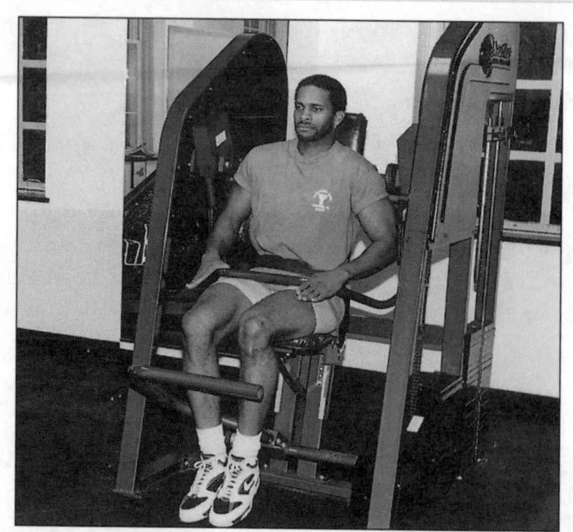

Muscle Group

Latissimus dorsi, teres major

Sitting upright, align the shoulder joint with the machine's axis of rotation by raising or lowering the seat. Place elbows on pads and keep hands relaxed. Pushing with the elbows, bring the machine arm down and into abdominal area. Pause and return arms overhead to a full stretch position while keeping lower back pressed firmly against seatback. Repeat.

Note: Keep head in a neutral position and avoid shrugging shoulders.

SEATED ROWING MACHINE

Muscle Group

Rhomboids, posterior deltoids, latissimus dorsi, teres major, middle trapezius

Adjust seat so that the shoulders and machine handles are at the same height and the handles are just within reach. Grasp handles and pull toward you while bending the elbows. Pull toward you as far as possible while keeping the chest against the supporting pad. Pause, slowly return to starting position. Repeat.

PULL-DOWN MACHINE

Muscle Group

Latissimus dorsi, teres major, biceps

Adjust seat height so that the movement bar or handles are just within reach, or adjust the knee pad to fit body size, ensuring a full range of movement. Use seat belts if provided by manufacturer. Grasp movement bar or handles with both hands. Place both feet on the floor or crossed at the ankles underneath the seat. Pull the movement bar or handles to the back of the neck or chin level. Pause. Slowly return to the fully stretched position. (Do not lock elbows.) Repeat.

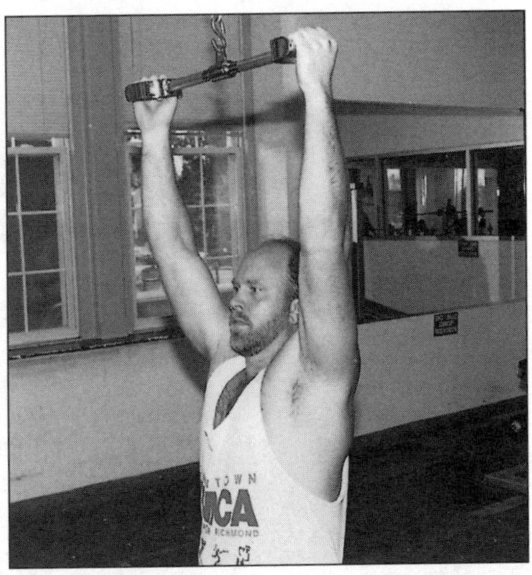

UPPER BACK

BARBELL SHRUG

Muscle Group

Superior trapezius, levator scapulae

Stand with bar resting on the thigh with an overhand or underhand grip. Keep the arms straight and elevate the bar by raising the shoulders up as high as possible toward the ears. Pause and lower to the starting position. Repeat.

DUMBBELL SHRUG

Muscle Group

Superior trapezius, levator scapulae

Stand with the dumbbells at sides, palms facing body. Keep the arms straight and elevate the dumbbells by raising the shoulders up as high as possible toward the ears. Pause and lower. Repeat.

SHOULDER SHRUG MACHINE

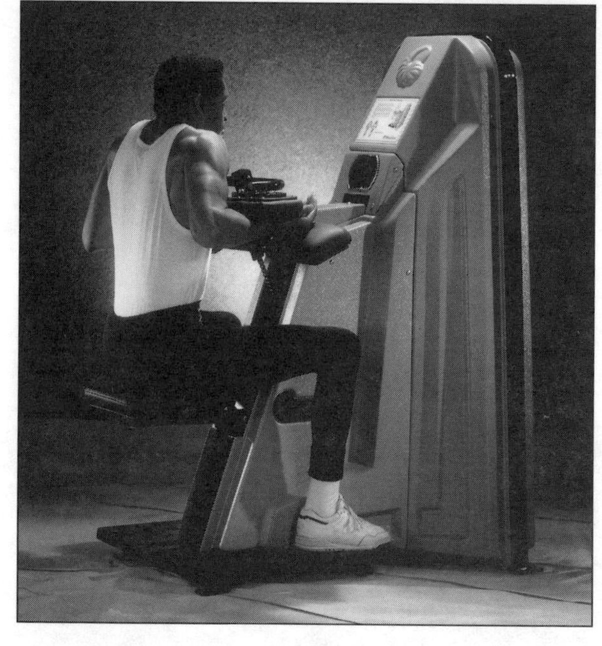

Muscle Group

Superior trapezius, levator scapulae

Sit on machine with feet flat on floor. Place forearms between resistance pads with palms facing up. Without changing arm position, shrug shoulders upward as high as possible. Keep head in a neutral position. Pause and slowly return to starting position. Repeat.

Note: Keep elbows fixed at a right angle throughout the exercise.

SHOULDERS

DUMBBELL LATERAL RAISE

Muscle Group

Middle deltoids

Sit or stand with a dumbbell at each side, palms facing the body. Raise the dumbbells directly sideways to shoulder height, keeping the arms slightly bent throughout. Hold at the top position for a second. Lower and repeat.

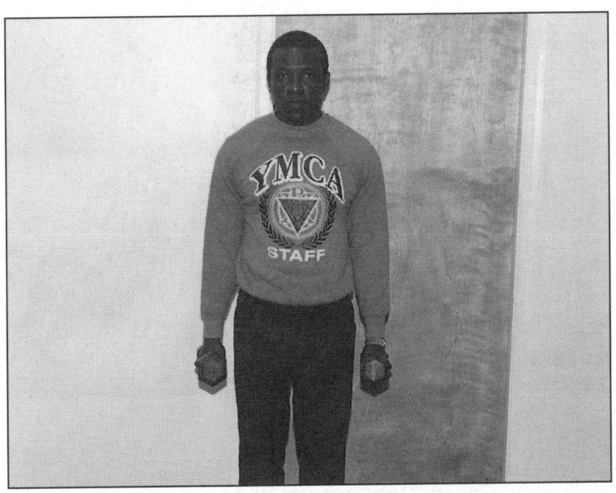

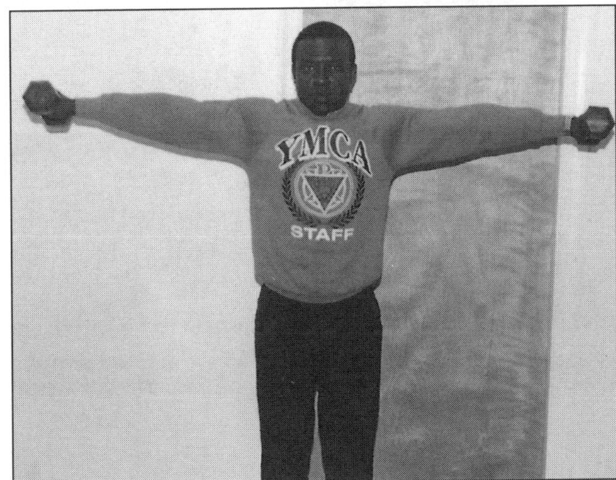

DUMBBELL SHOULDER PRESS

Muscle Group

Anterior deltoids, middle deltoids, triceps, superior trapezius

Sit with dumbbells at shoulder level with palms facing forward (overhand grip). The dumbbells should start at the corners of the shoulders and travel overhead to a point where the dumbbells almost touch when pressed overhead. Return to starting position and repeat.

Note: Keep the back straight and shoulders back.

BARBELL SHOULDER PRESS

Muscle Group

Medial deltoids, anterior deltoids, triceps, upper trapezius

Sit with back pressed against chair, palms facing forward (overhand grip), and bar resting on top of chest. With hands shoulder-width apart, press bar overhead to full extension. Return to starting position and repeat.

DUMBBELL FRONT RAISE

Muscle Group

Anterior deltoids

Stand with a dumbbell at thigh level with palms facing thighs. Raise dumbbells alternately with wrist slightly flexed and elbow slightly bent. Raise dumbbell to eye level, hold for a second, lower, and repeat alternately with other arm.

LATERAL RAISE MACHINE

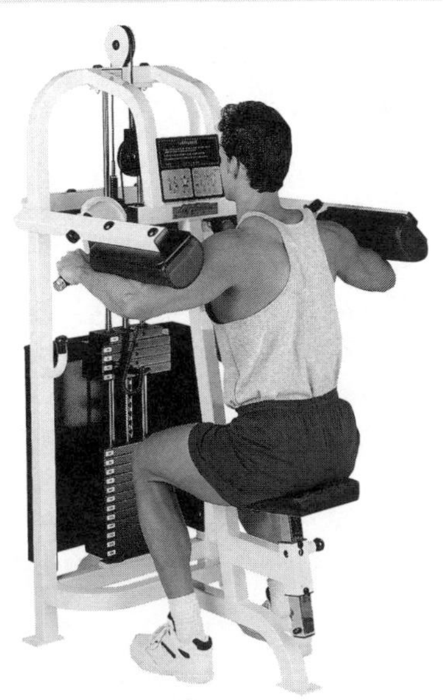

Muscle Group

Deltoids

Sit on machine and align shoulder joint with the machine's axis of rotation. Adjust seat height to accommodate. Flex elbows to 90 degrees and place against arm pads. Lightly grasp handles and raise arms, bringing elbows to shoulder height. Pause. Lower to starting position. Repeat.

SHOULDER PRESS MACHINE

Muscle Group

Anterior and middle deltoids, triceps, superior trapezius

Position body in the machine so that the seat height allows for a full range of movement. This is accomplished when the movement arms are allowed to stop just before touching the shoulders and when the weightstacks do not touch. Lightly grasping the movement handles and keeping the back flat against the supporting pad, slowly press the movement arms directly overhead to full arm length. Do not lock elbows. Pause. Slowly lower to the starting position. Repeat.

UPPER ARM

DUMBBELL CURL

Muscle Group

Biceps

Sit or stand using underhand grip, keeping a neutral back, and holding elbows close to sides. Alternately raise dumbbell toward the shoulder. Pause at the top of the movement. Lower and repeat with other arm.

Note: Keep upper arm in vertical position close to sides through full range of movement.

BARBELL CURL

Muscle Group

Biceps

Stand using an underhand grip with the bar at thigh level. Keep the elbows close to the sides with the upper arm in vertical position and parallel to the floor through the full range of motion. Raise the bar toward the shoulder. Pause at the top of the movement. Lower and repeat.

INCLINE DUMBBELL CURL

Muscle Group

Biceps

With a dumbbell in each hand, palms facing forward, lean back on an incline bench, allowing arms to hang freely toward the floor while slightly bent. Keeping the upper arms perpendicular to the floor, bring the dumbbell toward the shoulders. Pause at the top of the movement and return to starting position. Repeat.

STANDING CABLE CURL

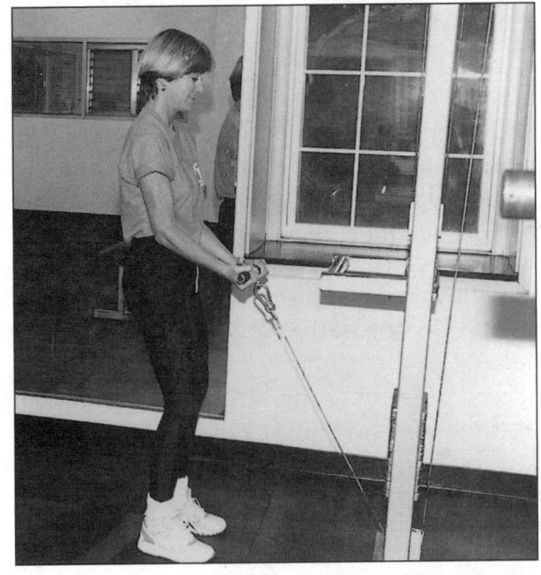

Muscle Group

Biceps

Using an underhand grip and with arms at full length, lean slightly back, making sure that the arms are in line with cable. Bring hands toward shoulders, keeping upper arm stationary. Pause at top of movement and return to starting position. Repeat.

BICEPS MACHINE

Muscle Group

Biceps

Adjust seat so that elbow joints align with machine's axis of rotation, and so that elbows, when resting on pad, are even with shoulders. Extend forearms and lightly grasp machine handles. Pull hands toward shoulders as far as possible. Pause and return to starting position. Repeat.

Note: Wrist should remain in neutral position throughout movement. Elbows higher than shoulder may cause hyperextension.

PULLEY PRESSDOWN

Muscle Group

Triceps

Grasp cable bar with close-spaced (6 to 8 inches apart) overhand grip, feet shoulder-width apart, knees slightly bent. Begin with hands at chest level. Keeping elbows firmly pressed against sides and wrists in neutral position, push cable bar down until elbows are fully extended (do not lock). Pause and return slowly to the starting position. Repeat.

Note: Do not let the cable bar go above chest level.

Using a V-bar or ropes instead of a straight bar places the wrists in a less stressful position and may allow for a slightly greater range of motion. Wrists should be kept in a neutral position.

DUMBBELL KICKBACK

Muscle Group

Triceps

Support the body with one hand or one hand and knee on a bench. Hold dumbbell in other hand, palm facing body, upper arm tight to the side and parallel to floor. Extend forearm until arm is straight. Pause and return to starting position. Repeat.

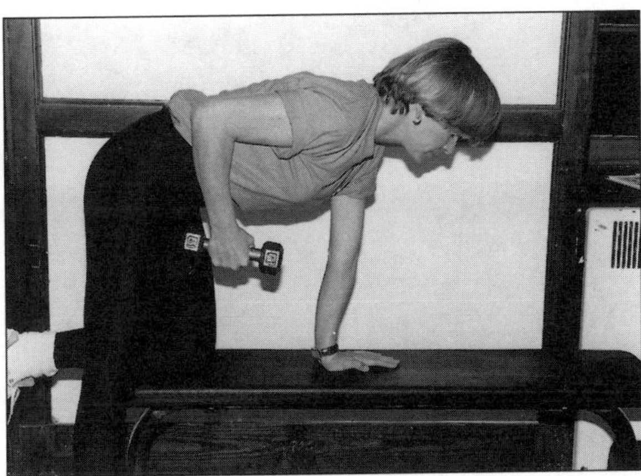

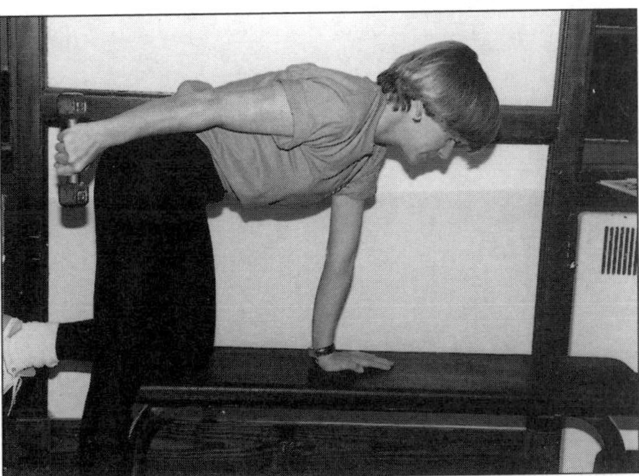

SEATED DUMBBELL TRICEPS EXTENSION

Muscle Group

Triceps

From a seated position, hold a dumbbell in both hands and extend arms straight overhead (palm facing in). Keeping upper arm stationary, lower dumbbell to a point immediately behind the head. Pause at bottom of movement, and extend elbows to a straight arm position (do not lock joints). Lower and repeat movement.

TRICEPS MACHINE

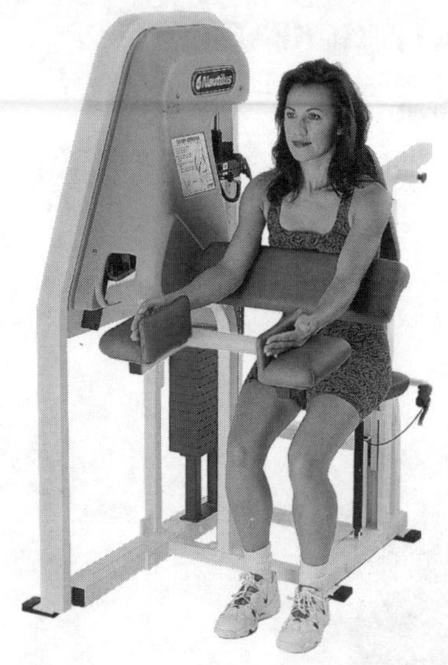

Muscle Group

Triceps

Adjust seat so that elbows align with machine's axis of rotation. Keep elbows in and palms facing each other. Fully extend arms. Pause. Return to starting position. Repeat.

TRICEPS PRESS DOWN

Muscle Group

Triceps, pectoralis major, anterior deltoids

Sit on machine with seat adjusted so that hands are at chest level and feet are crossed. Fasten seat belt to provide stability. Place hands on resistance handles and press downward, keeping elbows pointed backward until arms are extended. (Do not lock elbows.) Pause and slowly return to starting position. Repeat.

Note: A slight forward torso lean is acceptable in this exercise.

Caution: To avoid excessive stress on the shoulder joint, do not allow the hands to raise above chest level.

LOWER ARM

REVERSE FOREARM CURL

Muscle Group

Forearm extensors

Sit on the end of a flat bench holding a barbell or dumbbell with an overhand grip. Rest forearms against thighs with wrists extended slightly beyond the knees. Curl the barbell slowly, bringing the backs of hands and knuckles toward the forearms. Keep the forearms in contact with the thighs. Pause. Slowly return to starting position. Repeat.

WEIGHTED FOREARM ROLL

Muscle Group

Forearm flexors, forearm extensors

Grasp a weighted wrist roll bar in an overhand grip with both hands. Extend arms to full length, parallel to floor, with the weight hanging at full length near the floor. Slowly roll the bar toward you, bringing the weight up until it touches the bar. Pause. Reverse the action by slowly rolling the bar in the opposite direction, lowering the weight back to the starting position. Repeat. Pause. Repeat.

REVERSE CABLE FOREARM CURL

Muscle Group

Forearm extensors

Sit facing a low pulley weight station. Grasp both handles in an overhand position and rest the forearms on the top of the thighs. Keep the elbows close to the body. Bring the back of hands and knuckles toward the forearms, trying not to raise the forearms off the thighs. Pause. Slowly return to starting position. Repeat.

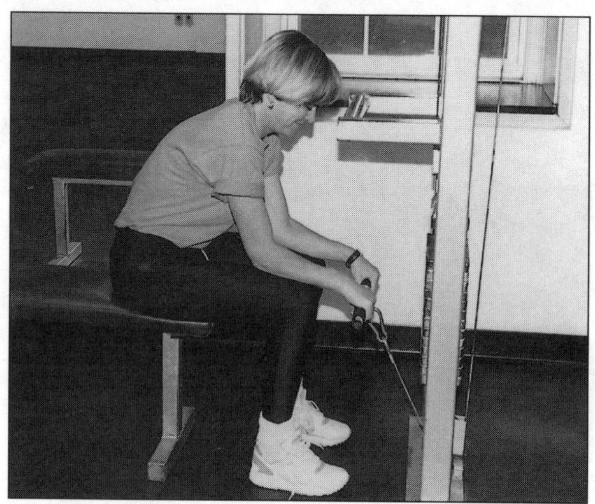

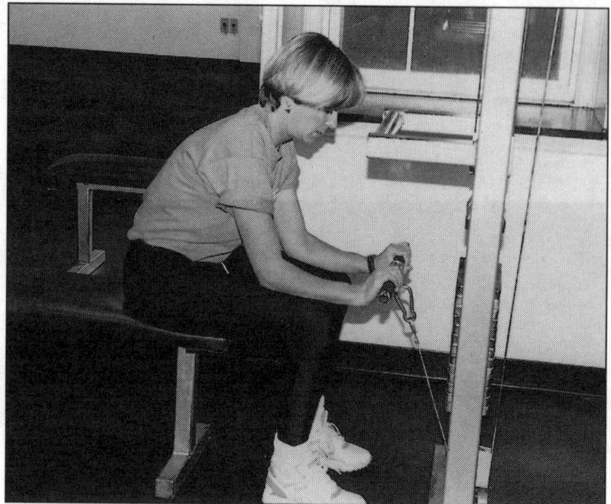

CABLE FOREARM CURL

Muscle Group

Forearm flexors

Sit facing a low pulley weight station. Grasp both handles in an underhand position and rest the forearms on the top of the thighs. Keep the elbows close to the body. Curl the palms of the hands toward the forearms as far as possible, trying not to raise the forearms off the thighs. Pause. Slowly return to starting position. Repeat.

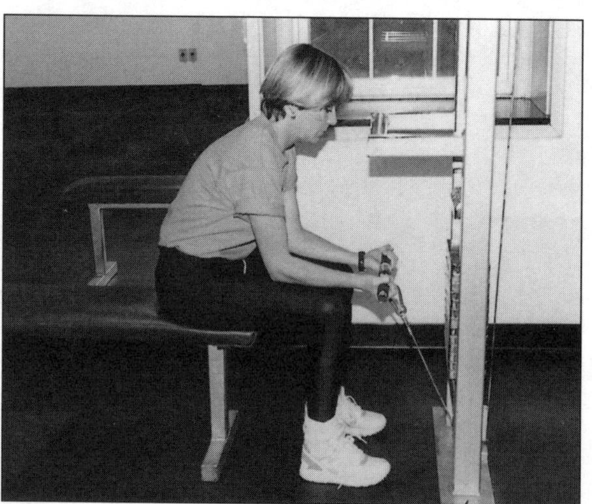

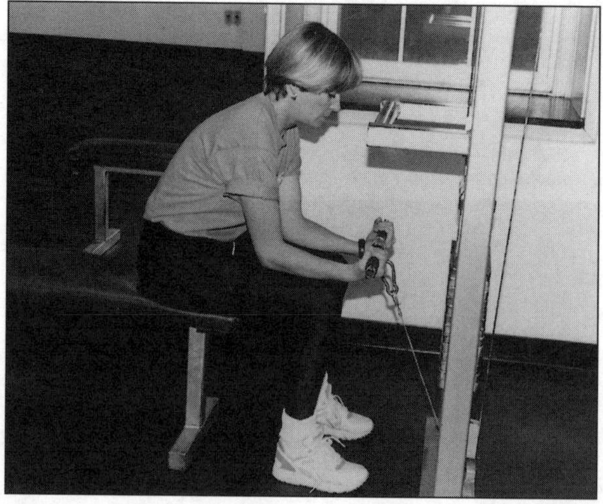

FOREARM CURL

Muscle Group

Forearm flexors

Sit on the end of a flat bench holding a barbell or dumbbell in an underhand position. Rest forearms against thighs with wrists extended slightly beyond the knees. Lower the back of the hands/knuckles as close to the lower leg as possible. Slowly curl the barbell upward toward the forearms as far as possible. Pause. Slowly return to starting position. Repeat.

MIDSECTION

TRUNK CURL (UNWEIGHTED/WEIGHTED)

Muscle Group

Rectus abdominis

Lie in a supine position. Place both feet flat on the floor with knees bent. Carefully place a weight plate on the chest (optional). Cross both arms over the chest. Slowly curl the head, neck, and shoulders up off the floor, keeping the lower back in contact with the floor at all times. Pause. Lower slowly to the starting position, attempting to keep the head from touching the floor. Pause. Repeat.

Note: Keep the head and neck in a neutral position throughout the exercise.

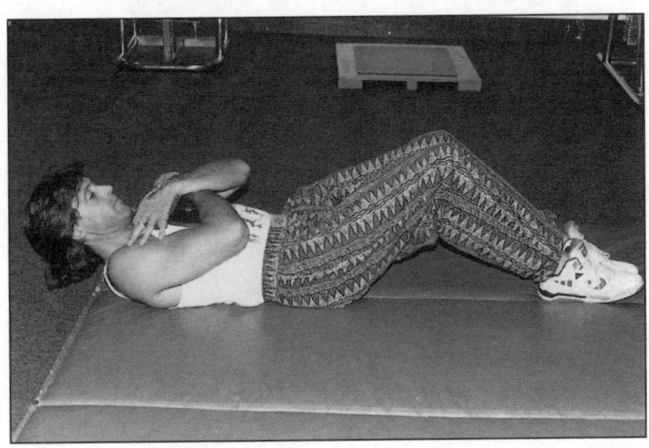

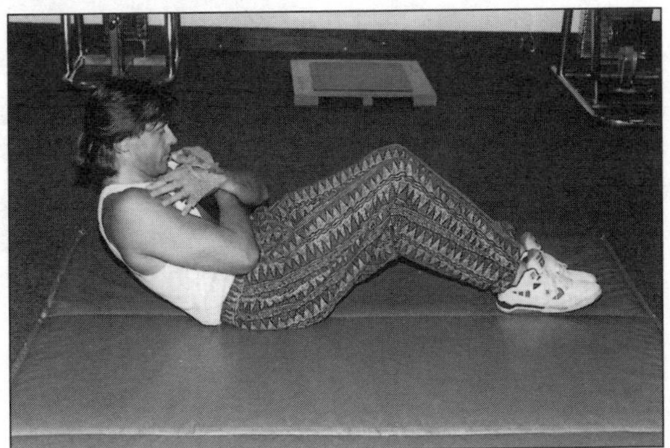

HIP FLEXOR APPARATUS

Muscle Group

Hip flexors

Place elbows on pads and grasp handles, supporting the body with the forearms and elbows. Move body into an upright full-length position. Bending both knees, bring them slowly upward as high as possible. Pause. Lower both legs slowly to full length. Repeat.

Note: Maintain contact between the back and the back support pad at all times.

ABDOMINAL MACHINE

Muscle Group

Rectus abdominis

Adjust the seat height so that the navel or midsection of the body is aligned with the machine's axis of rotation.

Overhead Handle Type Machines

Adjust machine so that handles are just above ear level. Grasp handles, and using the abdominals, bring the head, neck, and shoulders forward and down toward the thighs until in a fully contracted position. Pause. Slowly return to starting position. Repeat.

Chest Pad Type Machines (see photo)

Position pad(s) to rest firmly against upper chest. Use seat belt as indicated. Grasp handles, keeping hands relaxed. Space feet evenly and place them underneath the foot bar/pad. Using the abdominals, bring the head, neck, and shoulders forward and down toward the thighs until in a fully contracted position. Pause. Slowly return to the starting position. Repeat.

Note: Avoid attempting to handle too much weight. Concentrate on using the abdominal muscle to initiate and control the entire movement slowly and steadily. The hips should never leave or pull to the front of the seat pad.

TWISTING TRUNK CURL (UNWEIGHTED/WEIGHTED)

Muscle Group

Obliques, rectus abdominis

Lie on the back. Place both feet flat on the floor, with the knees bent. Cross both arms over the chest. Carefully place a weight plate on chest (optional). Slowly curl the head, neck, and shoulders up off the floor while twisting the upper trunk to one side (i.e., pull the right shoulder toward the left knee). Pause.

Slowly lower to the floor, attempting to keep the head from touching the floor. Immediately curl the trunk forward/upward once again, this time alternating the twisting movement toward the opposite side of the body (i.e., pull the left elbow toward the right knee). Pause. Lower slowly to the floor. Repeat, alternating sides on each repetition.

Note: Keep the head and neck in a neutral position throughout the exercise.

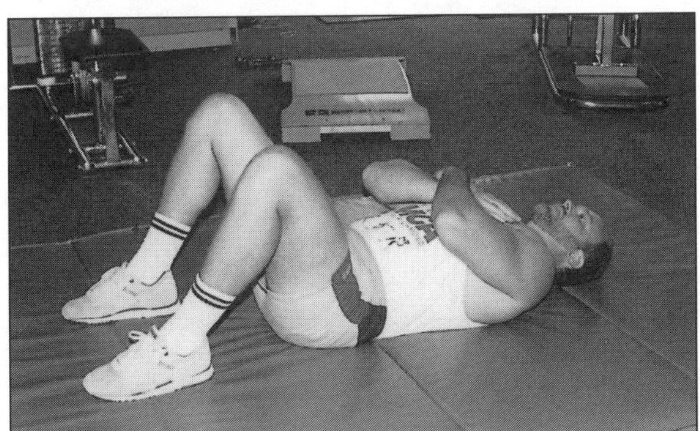

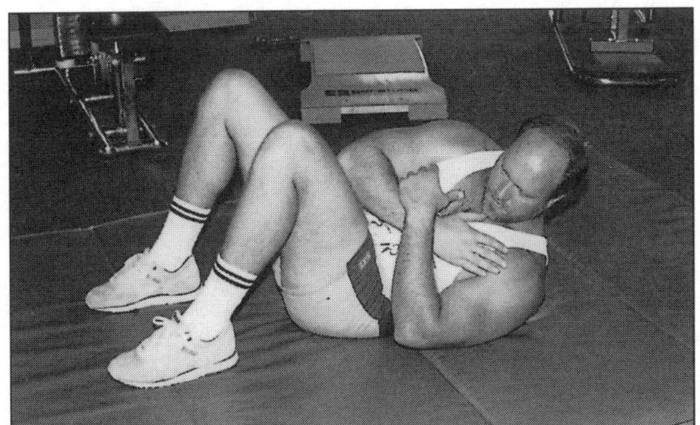

CABLE/DUMBBELL SIDE BENDS

Muscle Group

Obliques

Stand with one side of the body facing a low pulley station. Grasp the pulley station handle or dumbbell securely. Place the opposite hand/palm against the back of the head. Slowly bend the body sideways, toward the weight station or dumbbell, as far as possible without compromising the direct sideways movement (i.e., do not lean the body forward or backward). Slowly return to the starting position, allowing for a full range of motion to stretch the oblique area, which has just been contracted.

Pause. Repeat. Change weight or pulley station handle to opposite side and repeat. Start leaning toward resistance and move to upright position.

ROTARY TORSO MACHINE

Muscle Group

Obliques

Sit on machine and align spine with machine axis of rotation. Position feet appropriately and place arms behind or in front of resistance pads depending on type of machine. Without moving hips, turn to the right a short distance until obliques are fully contracted. Pause and return to starting position. Repeat. Continue exercise, turning to left.

Note: The movement range of the oblique muscles is very short.

BACK

SEATED LOW PULLEY BACK EXTENSION

Muscle Group

Hip extensors, erector spinae

Sit on the floor facing a low pulley station. Grasp both handles firmly. Place the bottoms of the feet against the base of the weight station (or a box/platform). Keeping the knees slightly bent and arms straight, lean backward to near full extension, pausing just before the low back area touches the floor. Slowly return to the starting position, pausing before the weights touch the weightstack. Repeat.

Note: Keep the back and spine in their neutral positions throughout the exercise.

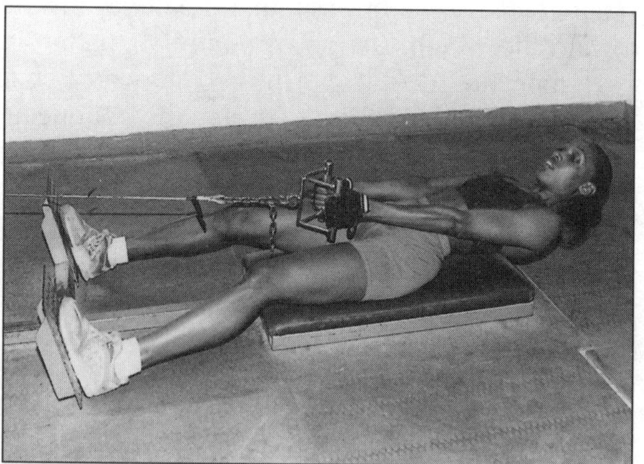

FLOOR BACK EXTENSION

Muscle Group

Erector spinae

Starting Position

Lie on a mat in a full length facedown position, chin resting on the mat.

Basic Movement

Place both hands palms down on the mat with the fingertips in line with the tops of the shoulders. Slowly, lift the head, neck, and shoulders up off the mat until the rib cage is free from the mat. Push with the hands as needed. Keep the legs and feet on the floor. Pause. Lower slowly to the starting position. Repeat.

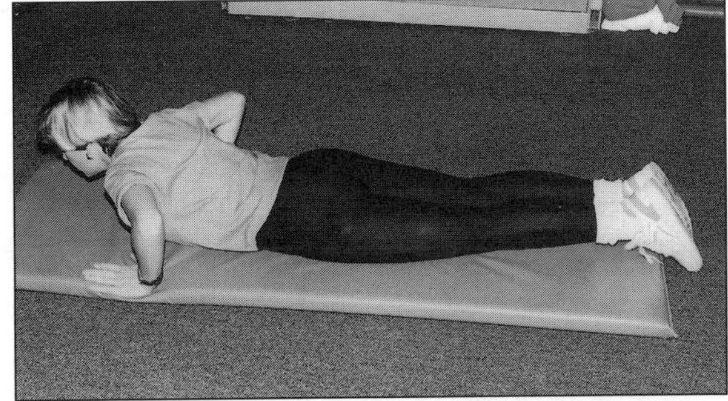

Intermediate Movement

Place both arms full length alongside body, palms down. Slowly lift the head, neck, and shoulders off the mat until the rib cage is free from the mat. Keep the legs and the feet on the mat. Pause. Slowly lower to the starting position. Repeat.

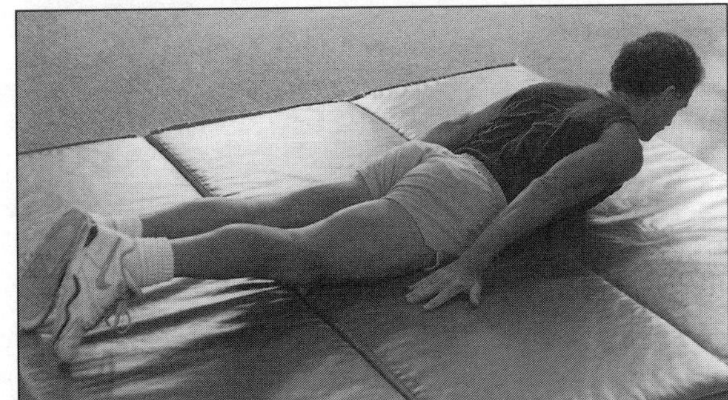

Intermediate-Advanced Movement

Place both hands on the small of the back. Lift the head, neck, and shoulders off the mat until the rib cage area is free from the mat. Pause. Slowly lower to the starting position. Repeat.

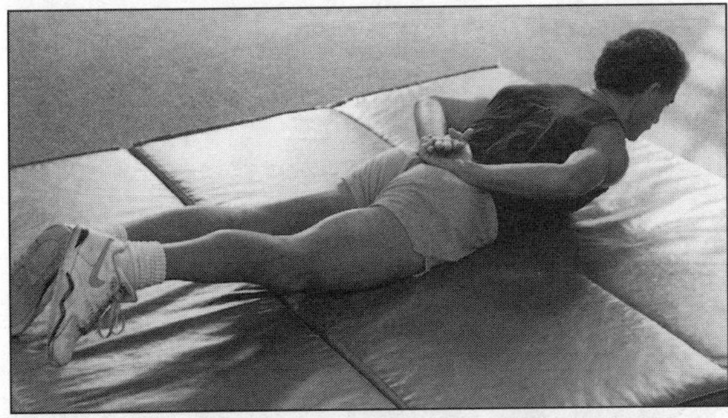

Advanced Movement

Place both hands behind the head/neck, elbows pointing out to the sides. Slowly, lift the head, neck, and shoulders off the mat until the rib cage area is free from the mat. Pause. Slowly lower the upper body to the starting position. Repeat.

Note: Always keep the neck and spine in their natural or neutral position, and do not hold the breath.

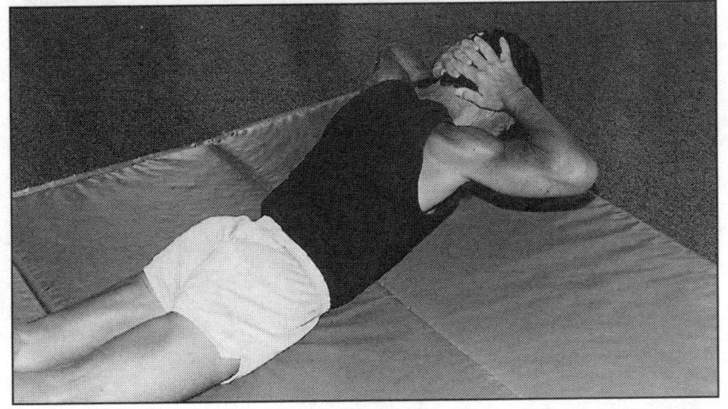

LOW BACK MACHINE

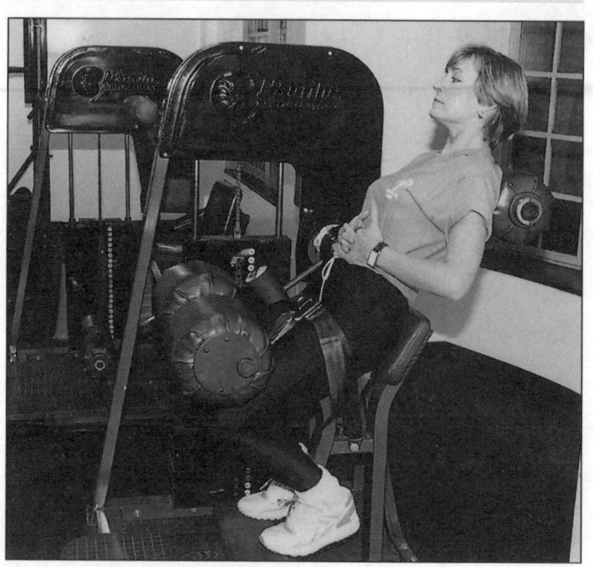

Muscle Group

Erector spinae

Place upper back against pad (on machines with adjustable pads, align pad with shoulder blades). Lock upper legs into place with leg pads (on Nautilus-type equipment), or put belt on. Place arms across chest. Keeping head in a neutral position, push back until hips, knees, and shoulders are in a straight line. Pause, return to starting position. Repeat.

NECK

SUPINE WEIGHTED NECK FLEXION

Muscle Group

Sternocleidomastoid

Lie in a supine position with the head and neck extended off one end of a flat bench. Hold the neck in a flexed position (chin to chest). Carefully place a weight plate against the forehead. Holding the weight firmly with both hands, slowly lower the head to a neutral position. Exhaling, bring the head forward and upward toward the chest until the chin comes close to or touches the chest. Pause. Slowly return to starting position. Repeat.

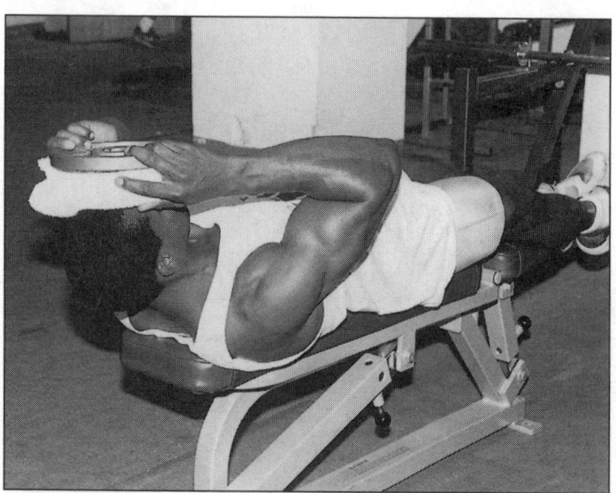

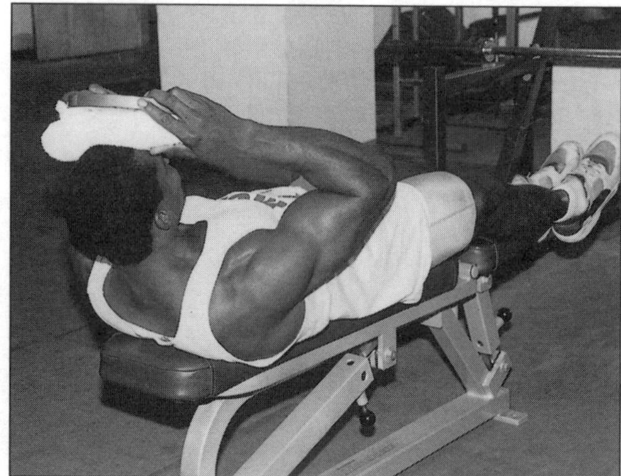

PRONE WEIGHTED NECK EXTENSION

Muscle Group

Superior trapezius, levator scapulae

Lie in a prone position with the head and neck extended off one end of a flat bench. Carefully place a weight plate against the back of the head. Holding the weight plate firmly with both hands, lower the head to a fully stretched position. Exhale and bring the back of the head toward the upper back and shoulders to a neutral position. Pause. Slowly return to starting position. Repeat.

NECK MACHINE

Muscle Group

Extension: Superior trapezius, levator scapulae
Flexion: Sternocleidomastoid

Sit on machine with seat adjusted so that rear head (extension) or face (flexion) fits comfortably against resistance pad. Place feet on floor and grasp stabilizer handles with hands. Slowly move resistance pad backward and downward until neck extensors or flexors are fully contracted. Slowly return to neutral position. Pause. Repeat.

Caution: Persons with neck pain or injuries should consult with a physician before performing neck exercises.

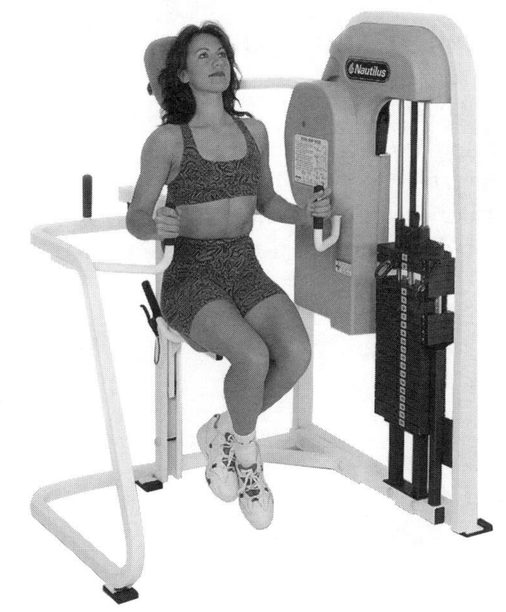

SHOULDER ROTATOR CUFF

CABLE INTERNAL ROTATION

Muscle Group

Pectoralis major, latissimus dorsi, subscapularis, anterior deltoid

Stand with right side to cable resistance and grasp cable handle with right hand. With upper arm vertical against side, allow lower arm to rotate backward horizontal to floor. Slowly move lower arm forward as far as comfortable (internal rotation). Pause, slowly return to starting position, and repeat.

Note: Perform the same exercise with the upper arm horizontal and the lower arm moving forward in the vertical plane. Continue exercise with left arm.

CABLE EXTERNAL ROTATION

Muscle Group

Infraspinatus, teres minor, posterior deltoid

Stand with left side to cable resistance and grasp cable handle with right hand. With upper arm vertical against side, allow lower arm to rotate forward horizontal to floor. Slowly move lower arm backward as far as comfortable (external rotation). Pause, slowly return to starting position, and repeat. Continue exercise with left arm.

Note: Perform the same exercise with the upper arm horizontal and the lower arm moving backward in the vertical plane.

DUMBBELL ABDUCTION

Muscle Group

Supraspinatus deltoid

Stand with feet shoulder-width apart. Hold dumbbells vertical, with upper arms along sides and lower arms horizontal to the front. Leading with the elbows, abduct the arms upward until the ends of the dumbbell change positions. Pause, slowly lower to starting position, and repeat.

6

Flexibility Training

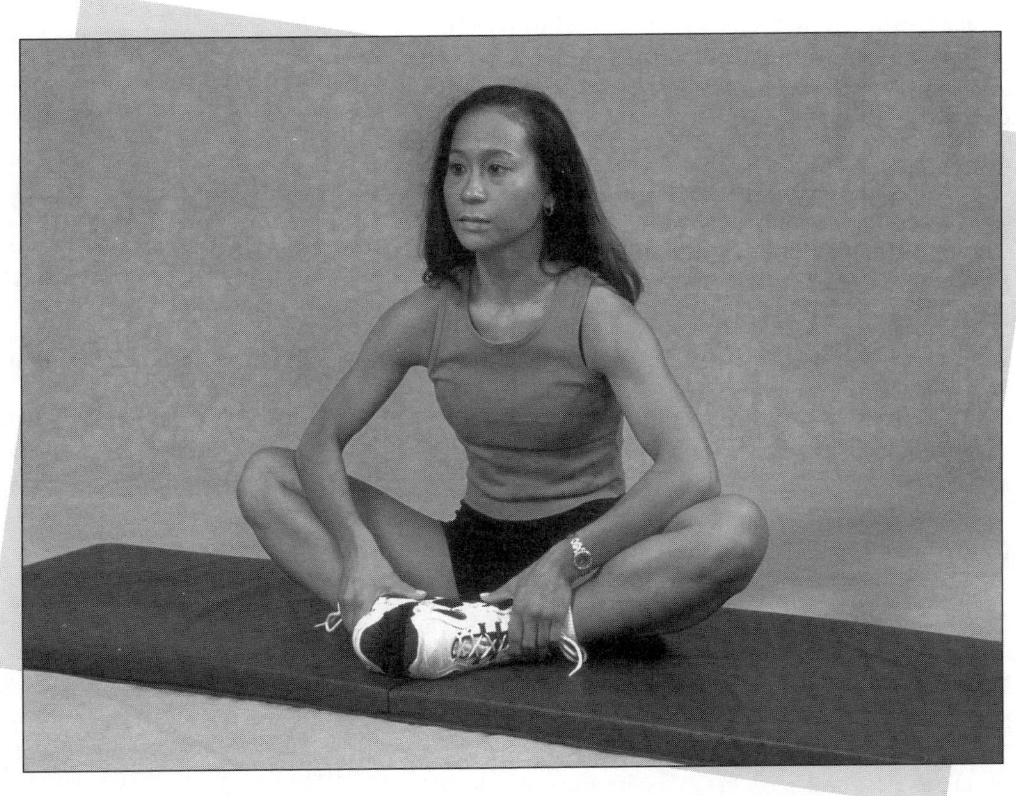

Flexibility is one of the three primary components of physical fitness, along with cardiorespiratory endurance and muscular strength and endurance. Developing a healthy range of flexibility allows an individual to move with greater extent of motion. It also keeps muscles supple and responsive to the demands of daily life activities, including leisure-time sports and exercise. Stretching to increase flexibility is a key component of a comprehensive personal training program.

Conditioning programs today usually emphasize cardiovascular training and resistance training. Current programs, equipment, and facilities do a good job of addressing the needs of most individuals in these two areas. However, the third fitness factor—flexibility—is often overlooked and is sometimes referred to as the "missing fitness link." There is an ever-increasing awareness of the benefits of flexibility training, as evidenced by the increasing prevalence of stretching and yoga programs in fitness centers and on home videos. As an instructor, you need to understand the basic science and principles of flexibility in order to develop safe and effective ways for participants to stretch the major muscle groups, particularly those that are typically tight.

The information contained in this chapter will help you recommend specific stretching exercises and incorporate effective flexibility exercises in programs for members. We start with a definition of flexibility and describe the benefits of flexibility training. Then we discuss the science of flexibility, the anatomy and physiology, as they relate to training. After reviewing the factors that affect flexibility, we talk about stretching techniques and training guidelines, along with some teaching tips. We conclude the chapter with some sample flexibility exercises.

A Definition of Flexibility

The term *flexibility* is defined as the ability to move joints and use muscles through their full normal range of motion. Flexibility training is broadly accepted as a means of increasing joint mobility and reducing injuries. Flexibility differs from joint to joint and involves not only the muscles but several other components of the musculoskeletal system.

There is no one way to assess an individual's total flexibility, because flexibility at one joint cannot be used to validly predict the range of motion in another body area. The type of movement that a person typically performs often dictates the range of flexibility at that particular joint. For example, trained dancers may have much more flexibility in their lower extremities, whereas baseball pitchers may have more flexibility of the shoulder joint. Although research has shown that different stretching methods will improve joint flexibility, it should be noted that inappropriate stretching can cause injury and impair joint stability. The goal of stretching should be to optimize joint mobility while maintaining joint stability. Recently, exercise researchers have promoted the concept of *functional range of motion*. This refers to developing the flexibility necessary for a specific activity or sport without compromising joint stability, and it can be useful to you in effectively designing exercises to meet the specific needs of participants.

Benefits of Flexibility Training

As a personal training instructor, you can be a valuable resource to members by educating them about the benefits of flexibility training. Following is a list of those benefits:

- Helps maintain or increase joint mobility
- Reduces muscle tension
- Helps prevent injuries
- Alleviates muscle soreness after exercise
- Delays the onset of muscle fatigue
- Contributes to enhanced performance in daily life, sports, or other physical activity
- Provides better equilibrium to maintain balance and joint stability
- Improves posture and coordination
- Enhances feeling of well-being
- Promotes mental relaxation
- Adds variety, enjoyment, and sense of satisfaction with exercise program

The Science of Flexibility

In order to set up a flexibility program properly, you need to understand something about the anatomy of joints and how physiology affects the development of flexibility.

Anatomy of a Joint

The nature of flexibility is complex and is influenced by many factors. Flexibility differs from joint to joint and involves not only the muscles but several soft-tissue components of the musculoskeletal system at the joints. The properties of the soft tissues—the ligaments, tendons, cartilage, and muscles and their covering are important in determining the contribution of each to the flexibility of a particular joint. Those tissues and their properties are as follows:

- **Ligaments**—Ligaments contain connective tissue fiber arranged in parallel lines packed closely together; they are inelastic and therefore not stretchable.
- **Tendons**—Like ligaments, tendons contain connective tissue fiber arranged in parallel lines packed closely together; they are inelastic and therefore not stretchable.
- **Cartilage**—This tissue contains more elastic fibers to facilitate its shock-absorbing function.
- **Muscle and muscle fascia**—Muscles are extensible and can be stretched to about 150 percent of their resting length. The fascia is a

sheath that holds the muscle fibers together and is modifiable by stretching.

Several physiological factors can limit an individual's functional range of motion around any particular joint. Those factors include

- skin, scar tissue, and excessive fat;
- the structure of the bone and type of joint;
- tight ligaments and tendons around the joint; and
- tight muscle tissue.

Physiology of Flexibility

Two concepts you'll need to know when teaching flexibility exercises are the *stretch reflex* and *reciprocal innervation.*

Stretch Reflex

A phenomenon known as the *stretch reflex* occurs when a signal is sent by motor receptors in the muscle being stretched to the spinal cord, which sends a motor response back to generate a reflex action causing the muscle to contract against the stretch. This natural action protects the joint and muscles from injury, but it also can limit stretch effectiveness. The force of the reflex contraction is directly related to the force generated by the stretch. If a stretch is performed slowly and gently, the stretch reflex is minimal, if invoked at all. This provides an explanation of why slow, static stretches are the recommended technique to ensure safe and effective stretching. The components of the muscle tissue involved in the stretch reflex are these:

- **Muscle spindle**—This is a sensory motor receptor in the muscle that regulates changes in the length and tension of the muscle's fibers. It sends the signal to the spinal cord that invokes the stretch reflex.
- **Golgi tendon organ (GTO)**—This is another sensory motor receptor, located in the muscle-tendon junction of a joint. When stimulated by excessive tension caused by a stretch or contraction, GTO receptors invoke an inhibitory reflex on the muscle, causing it to relax. This is called an *inverse stretch reflex*. The amount of force required to stimulate the GTO is much greater than the force required to stimulate the muscle spindles. A slow, long stretch will elicit a significant response from the GTO that causes the muscle to relax and stretch easily without injury.

Reciprocal Innervation

Muscles usually operate in pairs, so that when one set of muscles (agonists) contract, the opposing muscles (antagonists) relax. Without this organization, known as *reciprocal innervation*, coordinated muscular activity would be impossible. This phenomenon can be used to induce relaxation in the muscles you want to stretch by contracting the opposing muscle group.

Factors Influencing Flexibility

You will find that the degree of flexibility in members with whom you work will vary greatly. In addition to the physiological factors of the joint and muscle anatomy as previously discussed, a number of other factors influence an individual's flexibility. You must take all of these factors into consideration when prescribing flexibility exercises. Those factors include the following:

- **Age**—Muscle connective tissues have a natural tendency to shorten with aging, as evidenced in the stiffness of older people. Contractility remains while elasticity is lost, resulting in tighter, stiffer muscles. Muscles must be regularly stretched to minimize the effect of natural muscle shortening.
- **Gender**—Several studies have shown that females tend to be more flexible than males.
- **Exercise history**—It appears that active people tend to be more flexible than inactive people. Engaging in regular exercise can delay and even reverse the normal loss of flexibility due to aging.
- **Temperature**—An increase in intramuscular temperature results in a decrease in intramuscular resistance, which translates into an increase in range of motion in associated joints. This points to the need to warm up prior to stretching.
- **Body type**—There is no indication that body type is a factor in determining one's flexibility.
- **Resistance training**—Proper strength training, in which exercises are performed to the full range of motion, probably enhances flexibility.

Stretching Techniques and Methods

Types of stretches commonly used are classified by the following three techniques:

- **Static**—A low-force, high-duration stretch where the muscle is held at the greatest possible length for up to 30 seconds.
- **Ballistic**—A high-force, short-duration stretch using rapid bouncing motions.
- **Proprioceptive neuromuscular facilitation (PNF)**—A static stretch of a muscle immediately after maximally contracting it. There are two types of PNF stretches:

  –**Contract-relax:** an isometric contraction of the muscle, followed by relaxing, then stretching to the point of limitation.

  –**Contract-relax-agonist contract:** an isometric contraction of the muscle, followed by relaxing, stretching to the point of limitation, then contracting the agonist muscle, followed by a stretch to the point of limitation.

The two most accepted techniques for improving flexibility are static and PNF stretching. Ballistic stretching was popular in the early years of the fitness boom, but its use is discouraged today because of a greater risk of injury and less efficiency than other techniques. Static and PNF stretching both operate on the premise that to increase flexibility and prevent injury, the muscle being stretched should be as relaxed as possible. Static stretching is probably the most widely used technique and is very safe and effective. This technique involves gradually stretching a muscle or muscle group to the point of limitation, then holding that position for 15–30 seconds.

PNF stretching techniques are also effective and safe for increasing flexibility. Developed in the 1950s as therapy for patients with paralysis and muscular diseases, they have been modified for use by fitness instructors and trainers. PNF techniques are based on the theory of *reciprocal inhibition,* which states that when the flexors of a joint (agonists) are voluntarily contracted, the extensors of that joint (antagonists) are automatically deactivated, and vice versa. The result is that after an isometric contraction of a selected muscle, there is a more profound reflexive relaxation in that muscle, thus facilitating a greater stretch.

The two methods for stretching are *active* and *passive*. Active stretching is most common, as it involves an individual's body movement causing a stretch. Passive stretching is usually performed with a towel, prop, or a partner who applies a stretch to a relaxed joint. Partner stretching requires close communication and an even and slow application of the stretch. Because working with a partner presents a number of safety factors that need to be controlled, these techniques have limited application.

Flexibility Training Guidelines

Few standard guidelines exist that prescribe the type, duration, and number of repetitions of any given stretching technique. Techniques continue to evolve, and ongoing research will continue to provide information in this regard.

One principle underlying each of the flexibility techniques is the principle of *specific adaptations to imposed demands* (*SAID*). When related to stretching techniques, the SAID principle dictates that to bring about an increase in flexibility, one must slowly and progressively stretch the muscle to the point of limitation, but not to the point of tearing.

Given that a participant's fitness level, flexibility-limiting factors, and goals will factor into the design of a safe and effective flexibility program, nonetheless there are some training guidelines to follow.

- Prescribe exercises that will stretch all of the major muscle groups.
- Design a program that will assess and improve one's flexibility weakness.
- Recommend daily stretching exercises.
- Suggest wearing clothing that will not constrict movement.
- Teach participants to

  –warm up before stretching to increase the body temperature and range of motion.

  –make sure to stretch opposing muscle groups equally.

  –focus on the muscles involved in the stretch, minimizing the movement of other body parts.

  –hold stretches between 15 and 30 seconds. Recent research suggests that four sets of 15 to 20 seconds per stretch will result in optimal gains (Taylor et al., 1990).

–stretch to the limit of movement, not to the point of pain.

–keep the breathing slow and rhythmical while holding the stretches.

–stretch the muscles in various positions, as stretching in different places may enhance muscle relaxation and improve overall range of motion at the joint.

–relax the target muscle before going into the stretch.

–stretch after each vigorous workout to reduce the potential of delayed-onset muscle soreness and to encourage mind and body relaxation.

–discontinue exercising in any position that causes unusual discomfort or pain. It may be necessary to correct technique or try another position or stretch variation for the target muscles.

Flexibility Teaching Tips

You will need to make a number of leadership decisions in order to effectively teach flexibility training, including such factors as what to teach, when to stretch, what the training program format should be, how to address safety concerns, and how to communicate the correct technique. Following are some tips that will be useful when you are teaching stretching exercises.

- To answer the question "When to stretch?," first determine the goal:

  –If the goal is to help prepare the muscles for a workout, incorporate mild static stretches during warm-up, being sure that each stretch is performed gradually and lasts no more than 10 seconds. Intersperse the stretches with rhythmic limbering movements, keeping in mind the purpose of a warm-up.

  –If the goal is to increase range of motion, stretch right after the cardiorespiratory cool-down or after the muscle strengthening section of the class. The muscles are still warm and are more likely to respond with an increase in flexibility.

  –For stretching-only workouts, perform a short warm-up of rhythmic limbering movements for all major muscle groups prior to stretching.

- Remember that all stretches are not appropriate for all people. Certain exercises need to be modified or adjusted to correctly accommodate an individual's particular needs. Be especially aware of this when working with different population groups, such as athletes, older adults, the inactive, youth, and pregnant women.

- Keep in mind that the following muscles are typically tight in the general population:

  –Upper Trapezius

  –Shoulder Protractors

  –Trunk Extensors

  –Hip Flexors

  –Hamstrings

  –Gastrocnemius

- It is best to avoid stretching when the following situations are apparent:

  –When the muscles are in the area of a recent fracture

  –When there is evidence of a recent sprain or strain

  –If osteoporosis is present or suspected (recommend a consultation with physician)

  –If pain occurs in the joint or muscle

  –If the area is infected or inflamed

- Verbally explain and physically demonstrate proper posture and positioning.

- Each stretch should begin gently and progress gradually to the more advanced static stretch.

- The sequence of exercises should work progressively through the entire body and be specific to each joint and/or muscle group.

- Selection of an exercise should depend on its effectiveness versus a possible risk of injury. The stretch should be performed in the most effective and safest way possible.

- Monitor participants for proper technique, form, and posture.

- Assist members when they are having difficulty with a stretch by gently guiding them through a movement.

Sample Flexibility Exercises

Here are a few sample flexibility exercises for the main areas of the body that require such training.

Neck

Head Tilt—Tilt head to one side relaxing muscles along side of neck.

Variation: Place hand on head; lift or tuck chin while tilting.

Chin Tuck—Gently drop chin and retract to stretch back of the neck.

Side to Side—Look to side keeping shoulders pressed down.

Variation: Retract chin and depress opposite shoulder.

Arms/Shoulders

Overhead Elbow Hold—With one arm straight up over the head, bend the elbow so the hand is behind head, hold elbow with opposite hand as you try to walk fingers down your back.

Variation: Hold wrist, gently pull down behind your back.

Shoulder—Cross one arm in front of chest, hold elbow with opposite hand, gently press shoulders down.

Forearm—Extend arm forward (or side), flex hands and hold, then point fists down and hold.

Variation: Extended forward, pull fingers back gently with opposite hand.

Wrap & Hug—Both arms wrap around and grab the shoulders, gently press shoulders down.

Upper Trapezius—Lace fingers, press palms to overhead, then lower forward to shoulder level as you press shoulders down.

Upper Torso

Pectoral—Place fingertips behind head, gently press elbows back to open the chest. Seated, place hands behind your back on floor close to buttock, pull shoulders back, contracting rhomboids.Hook thumbs behind your waist with elbows pulled back.

Variation: Place palms on lower back. Lace fingers behind your back and lift arms up gently.

Lats—Standing, lift one arm overhead, bending slightly, opposite hand on thigh for support. Tailor sit and side bend toward feet lifting one arm overhead, other hand on floor for support.

Obliques

Torso Twist—In a bent-leg straddle position; flip knees to one side as you twist upper torso to face toward the rear, keeping back straight, shoulders down.

Variation: Tailor sit, loose butterfly, standing.

Supine—Lying on your back with legs tucked into chest, slowly roll legs to side and rest on the floor. Extend arms out to sides for support.

Abdominals

Supine—Full-body stretch with arms overhead.

Beginner: legs bent, feet on floor.

Advanced: natural arch in back.

Prone—Face down, forehead on hands; lift chest and head as one unit off the floor.

Lower Back

Cat Stretch—Hands and knees on floor; contract abdominals and gluteals, rounding spine, then release to neutral position.

Caution: Not recommended if wrist or knee problems are present.

Supine—Lying on your back; tuck your knees into chest, grabbing behind thighs with hands. Pull thighs into chest, lifting tailbone off the floor. Seated tailor sit; walk hands forward on floor.

Variation: Loose butterfly.

Standing—With feet apart, place hands on thighs, bending knees, rounding spine as you tuck your tailbone down and forward.

Hip Abductors

Supine—Cross ankle on the opposite thigh, lift both legs into chest. Hands reach through and hold thigh. Pretzel tailor sit; lift top leg to place foot on floor alongside opposite thigh. With buttocks on floor, lean forward.

Seated—From tailor sit, move one leg behind so that both legs are bent in the same direction. Place hands apart on the floor in front, lean forward from the hip.

Variation: Extend rear leg.

Half Straddle—Seated with one leg extended to side, other leg bent so that foot is at midline of body. Hold from foot with hands as you lean forward from the hip.

Long Sit—Position one leg crossed over and tucked in close to the torso. Wrap opposite arm around tucked leg, pulling knee toward underarm. Spinal twist upper body toward tucked leg. Sit straight.

Adductors

Standing Lateral—Feet wide apart, lunge to one side. Make sure foot is pointed in the direction of the lunge and knee is above ankle, not extended over toes. Use hand support on thigh, reaching other arm over head.

Variation: Use elbow support.

Butterfly Sit—Seated with soles of shoes together; place hands on ankles as you gently press knees toward floor.

Variation: Place hands on floor behind hips (close to body).

Butterfly PNF—Seated with soles of shoes together; place hands on knees and gently press toward floor; at the same time try to press knees up against the resistance. Release, perform the Butterfly Sit stretch. Repeat twice.

Butterfly Supine—On your back with legs tucked, toes together, knees apart; grab ankles with hands, pull them in close to body.

Straddle Supine—On your back; open legs to straddle position; placing hands on top of thighs.

Variation: Do one leg at a time.

Straddle Sit—Seated with legs extended in straddle position; place hands behind hips to press hips forward. Replace hands close to buttocks and press again.

Quadriceps/Hip Flexors

Runner's Stretch—Keep front leg 90 degrees while extending other leg back. Front leg should be hugging your chest, foot flat on floor, straight line from heel up to knee. Rear leg should be extended, with knee off the floor.

Variation: With rear knee on the floor.

Quad Sit—Seated with both legs bent and resting on floor in the same direction; lean to elbow support, posterior pelvic tilt. Avoid hyperextending the spine.

Quad Lift—Seated with both legs bent and resting on floor in the same direction; place hands on floor behind your hips, lift hips off the floor and posterior pelvic tilt.

Standing Quad—Shift weight to one foot, lift other foot to buttock. Grab foot with same hand as you gently press heel toward buttock. Keep hips even, thighs parallel.

Variation: Press foot into hand, lifting knee backward slightly.

Modified Standing Quad—Stride position with rear heel off the floor, leg bent. Rotate hips to posterior pelvic tilt. Bend both knees slightly.

Hamstring/Gluteals

Standing Hamstring—Extend one leg forward with foot flexed, heel resting on floor. Place hands on rear thigh for support and bend support (rear) leg. Now lean forward from the hip, keeping your back straight as you tip the tailbone up (anterior pelvic tilt).

Kneeling Hamstring—Kneel on one knee, extending other leg forward. Lean forward to place hands alongside front leg. Keep your back straight and do anterior pelvic tilt.

Caution: Not recommended for bad knees.

Long Sit Hamstring—Seated with both legs extended forward; bend one leg, placing foot next to calf of extended leg. Lean forward from the hip, place hands alongside extended leg.

Side-Lying Hamstring—From tailor sit, roll down to side lying as you extend top leg overhead. Hold leg with free hand to pull toward chest.

Tuck and Extend Sit—Seated, tuck one leg into chest, grab ankle or foot to extend up to ceiling.

Variation: Wrap arms around thigh and hug to chest.

Supine Hamstring—On your back, tuck leg to chest, unfold leg to extend to ceiling.

Variation: Lower leg bent, foot on floor or lower leg extended on floor. Hands hold ankle, calf, thigh, or "shoestrings."

Hamstring PNF—Supine, extend one leg overhead for an easy stretch; grab thigh with both hands & pull toward chest at the same time try to press entire leg away, toward floor; relax; then execute a hamstring stretch overhead without pulling with hands. Repeat twice.

Calf/Achilles Tendon

Standing—Stride position with both feet pointing in same direction, front leg bent, rear leg straight; press rear heel to floor.

Variation: Lace fingers, press palms overhead in line with rear leg.

Kneebend Hold—Feet pigeon-toed; bend legs, keeping heels on floor.

Kneeing—Kneeling on both knees hands on floor in front; extend one leg to rear, curl toes under and press heel to floor.

Supine—On your back with legs extended up; relax knees, flex feet, and press heels to the ceiling.

Variation: Alternate point/flex, emphasizing the flexion.

Soleus—Stride position; bend both legs, keeping heels on the floor.

Variation: Rear leg bent, front leg straight.

Achilles Tendon—Seated with one leg tucked; grab toes of shoe, keeping heel on floor, pull toes toward the shin bone.

Variation: Rotate inward/outward.

7

Screening and Assessment

Personal training is by definition an individual activity that requires a personalized approach to help ensure safe and effective results. Health screening is the vital first step in the development of any personal training program. It gives you essential information that will ensure safe and effective programming, and it also educates the participant as to possible risks and realistic goals. The testing and assessment of a participant using the YMCA's fitness test battery offers an opportunity to gather information related to the participant's current level of physical fitness. This information is essential in designing appropriate exercise programs and helping members develop exercise goals. Test results also can be used as a baseline for evaluating your program's effectiveness over time. Finally, an individual's exercise history must be taken into account when a personal training program is developed.

Screening

The initial step for developing an individual exercise plan is screening for medical contraindications and coronary risk factors. The YMCA has established a series of forms and screening guidelines that are designed to assist staff in establishing a safe and effective program for members. YMCAs are strongly encouraged to administer the screening forms when participants enter a program and yearly thereafter. You should record, file, and use member forms when developing a personal exercise plan, always erring on the side of caution. The forms and their use are described in the following paragraphs, and copies of the forms are located in appendix B. They can be reproduced and used as needed for your YMCA personal training programs.

- **Health Screen Form (PAR-Q & You).** The PAR-Q is designed to obtain general information about the participant's physical condition and to identify major risk factors. The YMCA recommends that this form be completed by all members and program participants prior to taking part in any activity. Individuals with affirmative answers to the questions on the form should obtain medical clearance from a physician before being allowed to participate in YMCA fitness testing or exercise programs.
- **Medical Clearance Form.** The medical clearance form is used by the participant's physician to report any restrictions that should be placed on the participant during fitness testing or exercise programs. The physician should see both the form to be signed and the description of fitness testing and exercise programs. The description explains the general character of YMCA fitness testing and exercise programs and the risks associated with each.
- **Informed Consent for Fitness Testing.** This form ensures that the participant is aware of the risks involved in the fitness testing procedures. It documents that a description of the testing procedures has been read and that all questions concerning those procedures have been answered satisfactorily.
- **Informed Consent for Exercise Participation.** This form ensures that the participant is aware of the risks involved in exercise. It documents that the description of the exercise program has been read and all questions concerning the exercise program have been answered to the participant's satisfaction. It is recommended that this form be reviewed by each YMCA's legal counsel to determine its effectiveness based on state laws.

The health screen form should be completed before a participant starts any program. The information obtained in these forms is valuable for educating participants on potential health and cardiorespiratory risk. Note that these forms are not intended to be a substitute for a medical exam but simply a means to obtain key health information. If a potential participant requires medical clearance prior to exercise participation, have his/her physician complete and sign the medical clearance form.

The informed consent forms are designed to notify participants of the inherent risks of fitness testing and exercise programs. They should be read and signed by participants prior to fitness testing and/or participation in any exercise program.

Physical Fitness Assessment

When members are seeking information regarding their fitness status, or when staff feel it is appropriate, a physical fitness assessment can be administered to determine each participant's current fitness level. The YMCA Fitness Testing and Assessment Battery includes measurements in four key areas of physical fitness: body composition, cardiorespiratory endurance, flexibility, and muscular strength and endurance

Individual results are compared to norm tables that are age- and gender-specific and are used in a variety of ways:

- A fitness profile is educational in that it provides feedback to the participant on current strengths and weaknesses. By comparing the test results to norms, the individual may be motivated to improve the weak areas of fitness.

- Staff can use test results in setting realistic short- and long-term goals and to assess the individual's progress over time. The setting of goals and the subsequent reassessment can be effective motivational tools.
- Fitness test results can be used as the basis for prescribing exercise. This may prevent the individual from initiating an exercise program at too high a level, which might cause injury and/or discouragement; or too low a level, which might not produce fitness benefits.

Although you may not be directly involved in performing fitness assessments, you should have a basic understanding of what the testing process is all about, which tests are generally conducted, how they are performed, and what test results will tell both participant and trainer. In the following section we briefly describe the standard YMCA fitness tests.

Measuring of Cardiorespiratory Fitness

YMCAs may administer any of three kinds of cardiorespiratory tests: the cycle ergometer test, the bench step test, and the one-mile walking test. Details on these tests can be found in the *YMCA Fitness Testing and Assessment Manual* and in the *YMCA Walk Reebok Instructor Manual.*

Cycle Ergometer Test

In this test the participant pedals a calibrated cycle ergometer at increasing workloads. This submaximal test is designed to be safely administered by nonmedical personnel. Submaximal tests estimate aerobic capacity rather than actually measuring the maximum level. The person's heart-rate response to the final two workloads is used to estimate maximum capacity.

An advantage to testing with the bike is that the participant's body weight is supported by the cycle, which makes the exercise easier on the body's joints than walking, jogging, running on the treadmill, or doing the bench step test. A disadvantage to the cycle ergometer test is that those who are not accustomed to cycling may find that their thigh muscles fatigue rapidly. This may result in a spurious response of the heart rate and may reduce the accuracy of the test results.

Bench Step Test

The three-minute bench step test is also a safe submaximal test of cardiorespiratory fitness. The test, developed by Kasch and Boyer (1968), requires stepping in an established cadence up and down on a bench. The recovery heart rate from the test is used to determine the level of fitness. Although the bench step test is easy to administer, especially to a group, the participant's body weight must be carried up and down with each step. Overweight individuals or those with joint problems may have pain associated with the repetitive jarring of up-and-down motion and may have difficulty in completing the test.

One-Mile Walking Test

Fitness walking tests are a safe, easy way to assess cardiorespiratory fitness. The participant walks one mile as fast as possible and then takes his or her heart rate at the end of the test. The time in which the walk is completed and the heart rate are then converted to the appropriate fitness level rating. The YMCA uses the one-mile walking test developed by The Cooper Institute for Aerobics Research. See the *YMCA Walk Reebok Instructor Manual* for more information on this test.

Measuring Body Composition

Body composition refers to lean body weight plus fat weight, which together make up total body weight. Fat weight is calculated by multiplying the total body weight by the percentage of body fat. The percentage of body fat is estimated from skinfold measurements taken as described in the *YMCA Fitness Testing and Assessment Manual.*

Measuring Flexibility

No general test accurately reflects total body flexibility. However, because of the marked incidence of lower back pain and disability among participants, the YMCA uses the trunk-flexion sit-and-reach test to measure the flexibility of the hip and back along with the elasticity of the hamstring muscle group (at the back of the upper leg).

Measuring Muscular Strength and Endurance

The bench press and the one-minute timed half–sit-up tests assess muscular strength and endurance. The latter is particularly important because it assesses abdominal strength and endurance, and the fitness status of abdominal muscles is related to correct posture and alignment of the pelvis. Weak abdominal muscles are often related to lower back problems because of tilting of the pelvis.

Results from all tests performed can be summarized on a fitness profile summary sheet for each participant. This efficient and attractive form can be quickly scanned for strengths and weaknesses.

Information on Test Use

For a detailed explanation of these assessments, refer to the *YMCA Fitness Testing and Assessment Manual,* available from the YMCA Program Store. The YMCA of the USA strongly recommends that assessments be performed by a certified YMCA Fitness Specialist. To be trained and certified to administer the test battery, staff must attend a YMCA Fitness Specialist certification course. This 40-hour training is available at selected YMCA of the USA Program Schools and other training sites across the country. Refer to the current YMCA of the USA Training Course Catalog or contact the YMCA of the USA for specific dates, locations, and the name of a contact person.

Consultation and Development of Training Goals

After the health screening and fitness assessment have been completed, discuss the results and the implications for a training program with the participant. Although it is important to address all of the fitness parameters (body composition, muscular strength, cardiorespiratory endurance, and joint flexibility), each person may have specific training objectives.

For example, some participants may desire weight loss, and others may desire weight gain. Some may be more concerned with muscular strength, and others may be more concerned with cardiorespiratory endurance. Some may prefer upper-body conditioning, and others may prefer lower-body conditioning. Some may be more interested in physical appearance, and others may be more interested in athletic performance.

In addition to training objectives, the participant's exercise preferences and time constraints should be carefully considered when designing the fitness program. For example, some may prefer free-weights, and others may prefer machines. Some may schedule 90-minute training sessions, and others may schedule 30-minute training sessions. Staff should be sensitive to these needs. A well-designed program will have no benefit if it can't be successfully fit into the member's schedule.

Exercise History

Another factor that you should consider prior to establishing an individual's personal training program is his or her previous exercise experience. Persons who have never exercised need to be introduced to training gradually. Even more caution should be observed with former athletes who have not exercised for several years, because they tend to train more intensely than they should. At the other extreme, endurance exercise enthusiasts who already train two hours a day should be counseled into a more balanced program of physical activity. Sensible training is especially useful for endurance athletes to reduce their risk of overuse injuries. A sample Exercise History Form is included on the next two pages.

Exercise History Form/Past and Present

1. Name ______________________ Date ______________

2. Address ______________________________________

3. Phone Number (home) ___________________________

4. Age ______________________ Sex: M______ F______

5. Height ______________________________________

6. Occupation: Physical ______ Non-Physical ______

7. Are you presently exercising: Yes ______ No ______

   If you answered yes:

   How long have you been exercising? ____________

   Briefly describe your program:

   ____

   ____

   ____

   ____

8. Rate yourself on a scale of 1 to 5 (1 indicating the lowest value and 5 the highest) circling the number that applies most closely:

   a. Daily stress level:

      1 2 3 4 5

   b. Competitive personality (pertaining to physical activity)

      1 2 3 4 5

   c. Aerobic (endurance) fitness level:

      1 2 3 4 5

(continued)

Figure 7.1 Exercise history form.
Reprinted, by permission, from the *YMCA Exercise Instructor Manual,* © YMCA of the USA, 1995, Human Kinetics.

d. Muscular (strength) level:

1 2 3 4 5

e. Flexibility level:

1 2 3 4 5

9. Check the description below which most closely describes your diet:

_____ High fat, high sodium, low carbohydrate

_____ Low fat, low sodium, high carbohydrate

_____ Moderate fat, moderate sodium, moderate carbohydrate

_____ Other: briefly describe your average dietary habits:

____

____

____

____

10. Are you currently on a calorie restrictive diet?

Yes _____ No _____

11. How much time can you comfortably allocate per workout session based on your lifestyle? Check the answer that most closely applies:

_____ 45 min or less

_____ 45-60 min

_____ 60-90 min

12. Briefly describe the goal(s) you have set to attain from your exercise program:

____

____

____

____

Figure 7.1 *(continued)*

8

Designing Individual Exercise Programs

As a personal training instructor, you have the unique opportunity to develop individualized exercise programs to meet the fitness needs of YMCA members. In developing programs that best meet the expectations of the members in a safe and effective manner, you must always keep the members' distinctive goals, interests, health and fitness status, age, and motivation in mind.

A comprehensive personal training program involves the following three components:

- Aerobic exercise to enhance cardiorespiratory endurance, typically by means of sustained large-muscle activity (such as walking, running, swimming, cycling, stairclimbing, or rowing).
- Strength training exercise to develop all of the major muscle groups.
- Stretching exercises to increase flexibility in the major joint structures, particularly the injury-prone hip, trunk, and shoulder areas.

In this chapter we discuss how to design programs using appropriate guidelines for exercise prescription, as well as how to implement such programs and to alter them in a progression over time. We conclude with some recommendations on how to orient new participants and how to work with participants effectively.

Program Design

Every fitness program should be designed to include comprehensive physical conditioning based on sound exercise principles and personal training preferences. This approach reduces the risk of injury, increases the rate of compliance, and facilitates the desired fitness results. Previous chapters of this book have presented information on health screening, fitness assessment, and training components of cardiorespiratory fitness, muscular strength and endurance, and flexibility. This chapter discusses how these components can be combined to provide a comprehensive exercise program for each of your participants. There are three steps in designing a comprehensive personal training program for a participant: health screening, physical fitness assessment, and design of specific training components (cardiorespiratory, strength, and flexibility).

Guidelines for Exercise Prescription

Conducting the health screening and physical fitness assessments are the first two steps in the process of engaging an individual in physical activity. The third step is using that information to design an exercise program for the person that will meet his or her needs and goals and that he or she will be able to follow and enjoy for a long time. The term *exercise prescription* has become common in the field of exercise science to describe the process of developing a personalized plan for someone to follow by a trained, certified professional with special knowledge of fitness and exercise. When used appropriately by fitness professionals, the term is a good term, defined by the American College of Sports Medicine as "the process whereby a person's recommended regimen of physical activity is designed in a systematic and individualized manner" (ACSM, 1995).

Once a person's fitness capacity has been determined through assessment, health status known through questionnaires and/or clearances, and interests and goals expressed, you can give an individualized exercise prescription. To be effective, a prescription must be based on all three of these factors. You can then develop specific guidelines for the intensity, duration, frequency, type, and progression of exercise—the integral components of a sound exercise prescription. Because the reasons for exercising can vary greatly among individuals of all different fitness levels, the need for precision in prescribing exercise will also vary. Whereas performance athletes and persons limited by disease may need careful and precise prescriptions, average, apparently healthy adults rarely need precision, and general principles of exercise and training are usually adequate. Most such people will select activities that they enjoy or that allow them to have social and recreational interaction. The important point to remember is that the same principles of training apply to everyone. Modifications are usually associated with the absence or presence of medical contraindications, types of activities to be avoided, the initial level of fitness, the intensity of participation, and the rate of improvement expected.

The following discussion focuses on the five primary factors that should be considered in developing fitness prescriptions for apparently healthy adults: frequency, intensity, duration, mode of activity, and rate of progression. These five factors will be discussed for the three primary components of physical fitness: cardiorespiratory conditioning, muscle strength and endurance, and flexibility. This information is based on the American College of Sports Medicine's position paper on exercise prescription, which includes recommendations concerning the quantity and quality of exercise training for healthy adults (1998).

Cardiorespiratory Conditioning

1. **Frequency of training:** Three to five days per week.
2. **Intensity:** 55/65 to 90 percent of maximal heart rate. Note that exercise of low and moderate intensity may provide important health benefits and may result in increased levels of fitness in the sedentary and low-fitness-level populations.
3. **Duration of training:** 20 to 60 minutes of continuous aerobic activity. The actual length of time spent exercising aerobically is dependent on the relative intensity level of the activity. For example, activities of a lower intensity should be conducted over a longer period of time, particularly early on in training.
4. **Mode of activity:** An appropriate modality for developing cardiorespiratory fitness is any activity that uses the large muscle groups, can be maintained at submaximal levels continuously, and is rhythmical in nature. Examples are walking, jogging, running, bicycling, swimming, aerobic dancing, machine-based stair climbing, rowing, or cross-country skiing. It should be noted that activities such as walking, jogging, or cycling are particularly good activities to start out with as an individual begins an exercise program.
5. **Rate of progression:** Because of the body's ability to adapt to the stresses placed upon it (referred to as the *training effect*), individuals are able to gradually increase the total work they can do over time. With cardiorespiratory exercise, increasing the work performed can be achieved by increasing the intensity of the exercise, the duration of the exercise, or by some combination of the two. The most significant training effects are typically observed during the first six to eight weeks of an exercise program. The individual's exercise prescription can be adjusted as these conditioning effects occur. The extent of the adjustment depends on the individual involved and his or her performance during exercise sessions.

Muscle Strength and Endurance

1. **Frequency of training:** Minimum of two days per week.
2. **Intensity:** Moderate intensity resistance training, sufficient to develop and maintain lean body tissue.
3. **Duration of training:** One set of 8–12 repetitions of each exercise.
4. **Mode of activity:** 8–10 exercises that train the major muscle groups of the body.
5. **Rate of progression:**
   - Adhere to the specific techniques for performing each exercise
   - Exercise to the point of momentary muscular fatigue
   - Perform each exercise through a full range of motion
   - Exercise antagonist muscle groups
   - Perform both lifting and lowering movements in a controlled manner
   - Be conscious of not holding the breath while strength training

Flexibility

1. **Frequency of training:** Minimum of two to three days a week.
2. **Intensity:** To a position of mild discomfort.
3. **Duration of training:** 10 to 30 seconds for each stretch.
4. **Mode of activity:** Stretching should include appropriate static and/or dynamic techniques with an emphasis on the low back and hamstring area because of the prevalence of low back pain.
5. **Rate of progression:** 2–6 for each stretch.

Developing an Appropriate Exercise Prescription

Remember that desirable fitness outcomes for members can be attained with exercise programs that vary considerably in terms of mode, frequency, intensity, and duration. In addition, remember that some individuals achieve a faster and/or greater rate of improvement than others.

For example, members who have been relatively sedentary for years should be counseled to progress more slowly. They should begin exercising at a level that they can successfully complete and then gradually increase the amount of work performed. This slow progression not only reduces the potential for injury, it ensures appropriate adaptations in previously unused or underused muscles. On the other hand, active individuals may progress more rapidly and they are ready to be challenged physically. As a skilled personal trainer, recognize how individuals are adapting to an exercise routine and make necessary and appropriate adjustments to prescriptions.

Physical activity can be a valuable tool in improving the health and fitness levels of YMCA members. To assist them in receiving the maximum benefits of exercise you must analyze their personal needs, interests, health status, and current fitness level. Using that information, you can establish a personal plan for exercise that will meet the member's unique requirements. Remember that all exercise prescriptions should closely adhere to the primary prescription variables for a sound exercise regimen. With periodic adjustments as appropriate, you will help give each member a prescription for a lifetime of health and fitness.

Program Implementation

Put individual programs in writing on a form like the one shown in figure 8.1, a workout card, or a log book for each participant. Examples of workout cards are included at the end of the chapter (see figures 8.2 to 8.4 on pages 160-162). Once the program is established on paper, implement it in a persistent and progressive manner.

The first step in implementing a program is a training orientation. This step is essential to the safety and success of the individual's program. Unless there is a contraindication, the initial program should be followed for about four to eight weeks. This allows the participant time to establish a familiar exercise routine, to develop a degree of training consistency, and to obtain observable results from the fitness program.

Progression Rate and Program Redesign

Because the human body tends to adapt to a given exercise program, the training protocol should be changed periodically. The rate of progression in any exercise program is dependent on many factors, including the participant's initial fitness and health status, age, motivation, and the frequency and intensity of training. Many beginning exercisers will make greater measurable gains during the first three to six months of an exercise program than will current exercisers, relatively speaking. The following three progression stages in an exercise program is based on The American College of Sports Medicine's guidelines (1995):

1. **Initial conditioning stage**—This stage typically lasts four to six weeks. The ACSM recommends that the intensity, duration, and frequency of exercise sessions be at the low end of the training range during this stage, to minimize muscle soreness, injury, discomfort, and discouragement. Gradual progression is urged to help ensure that members feel successful in modifying their lifestyles.

2. **Improvement conditioning stage**—This stage usually lasts 12 to 20 weeks, with a more rapid rate of progression. Intensity, duration, and frequency all should be gradually increased to at least the middle of the recommended training ranges. Retesting of all fitness components should take place about three months after the program starts and every three months thereafter, to help members maintain interest and motivation. Fitness objectives can be altered after each retesting session to help members aim for higher goals or to maintain goals already attained.

3. **Maintenance conditioning stage**—Once the desired level of fitness is reached, the maintenance stage of an exercise program is reached. This stage usually begins five to six months after the start of training and can last for a lifetime. To ensure compliance, the program should be enjoyable, fit into the member's daily schedule, meet his or her personal needs and goals, and be adaptable to changes in location.

Numerous research studies have shown that physical activity must be continued on a regular basis in order for benefits to be maintained. Stopping exercise training will unfortunately result in a rapid decrease in both cardiorespiratory and muscular conditioning. However, maintaining physical fitness is achievable even if the amount of training is lessened, as long as the intensity is maintained. It takes a lot of work to achieve desirable fitness levels, and once the habits have been established, maintaining levels becomes a bit easier. Recognize, however, that many members need continual help in maintaining the motivation that will enable them to continue to enjoy the fitness benefits they have worked so hard to attain.

The YMCA Exercise Program Design Form

Warm-Up

Purpose: To gradually elevate the heart rate and increase body temperature by engaging in 5–10 minutes of low-intensity activity.

Cardiorespiratory Fitness

Purpose: To improve one's cardiorespiratory system by continuous, rhythmic, and vigorous exercise for 20–30 minutes, 3 times a week.

Frequency: Days a week of exercise: Mon. Tues. Wed. Thurs. Fri. Sat. Sun.

Intensity: % of heart rate: Max. HR – Age × 55% = Low end of training HR Range

_______ _______ _______ _______________

Intensity: % of heart rate: Max. HR – Age × 90% = Upper end of training HR Range

_______ _______ _______ _______________

Duration—No. of minutes per session: 10–20 20–30 30–45

Mode—select activity: ______________________________

Cool-Down

Purpose: To gradually decrease the heart rate by slowing the intensity and pace of the activity for 5–10 minutes.

Muscle Strength and Endurance

Purpose: To develop muscular strength and endurance using various calisthenics and weight training exercises for 10–20 minutes.

Exercises:

Muscle: ______________ Exercise: ______________ Resistance: _____ Repetitions: _____

Muscle: ______________ Exercise: ______________ Resistance: _____ Repetitions: _____

Muscle: ______________ Exercise: ______________ Resistance: _____ Repetitions: _____

Muscle: ______________ Exercise: ______________ Resistance: _____ Repetitions: _____

Muscle: ______________ Exercise: ______________ Resistance: _____ Repetitions: _____

Muscle: ______________ Exercise: ______________ Resistance: _____ Repetitions: _____

Muscle: ______________ Exercise: ______________ Resistance: _____ Repetitions: _____

Flexibility:

Purpose: To stretch the major muscles and joints using static stretching techniques for 5–10 minutes.

Exercises: ______________________________

____

____

____

Figure 8.1 Sample program form.

Reprinted, by permission, from *YMCA Strength Training,* © YMCA of the USA, 1994, Human Kinetics.

Recommended First Session Guidelines

The first session with new members is critical to making them feel comfortable with you and in the training environment. When teaching members their new training programs, cover some basic information about each piece of equipment or each exercise.

- **Explain the equipment.** Demonstrate the correct way to position oneself on the equipment (either cardio or strength) and to operate the machine.
- **Demonstrate the exercise.** Demonstrate the exercise, showing proper form and technique.
- **Adjust the equipment.** Have the member position him- or herself on the equipment and make any necessary adjustments for size. Explain that this procedure will ensure that they have proper positioning on the equipment. Write all of the adjustments down on the member's workout card.
- **Have the member perform the exercise.** First have him or her do a trial exercise at a slow speed and/or with little resistance. As the member attempts the exercise, provide verbal cues about form, body alignment, and exercise technique. Cover the following points at this time:
  - –Major muscle group used
  - –Proper starting position
  - –Description of movement
  - –Breathing
  - –Speed of movement
  - –Proper grip for strength exercises
- **Set the starting level.** Cardiorespiratory conditioning should begin at a pace and duration that can be comfortably handled by the member. Use caution; do not have him or her attempt to do too much too soon. As a general guideline for strength training, start members with the highest weight they can lift for 8 to 12 repetitions. Document the weight on the member's workout card. Beginners should perform 12 repetitions in order to learn the exercise.
- **Discuss the progression.** Explain that they should perform at the starting level and gradually progress in intensity and duration. For example, strength exercise should progress to where 12 repetitions can be accomplished comfortably; then the weight can be increased by 5 percent.
- **Answer questions.** Ask if there are any questions. Review the notes on the workout card. Review equipment adjustments.
- **Set a schedule.** Discuss with the member the days of the week and times that he or she will be working out. New exercisers generally need to set a specific schedule, which helps them adhere to a routine in the beginning stages of an exercise program.

Being an Effective Personal Trainer

Establishing an exercise prescription and program for a member and then supporting the process for the long term is not a simple task. Not only must you be knowledgeable and skillful in exercise science and technique, you must have the communications skills and personality traits required of a good consultant.

Provide the proper environment for self-growth by motivating and challenging members, giving them responsibility, and providing encouragement along the way. An effective personal trainer develops warm, personal relationships with each member he or she works with and regards everyone as worthy of respect, concern, and personal attention. Traits of a good instructor/counselor include the following:

- **Empathy**—having the ability to put yourself in the member's position and communicate that you understand her or his concerns and feelings.
- **Respect**—possessing genuine appreciation of the worth of each individual.
- **Genuineness**—being freely yourself, not just playing a role.
- **Honesty**—being truthful in all of your dealings and relationships with each member.
- **Concern**—exhibiting a warmth that communicates your concern for each member.

In many respects, developing a personal, caring relationship with each member will go further in helping them be successful at exercise and maintain a program than possessing all of the technical knowledge available about exercise. Chapter 10 will discuss participant motivation in more detail.

Table 8.1 Sample Training Outline

Warm-Up Activity	5 minutes
Cardiorespiratory Exercise Examples	20 minutes—choose one or cross-train Running Swimming Cycling Stairclimbing Rowing Walking Cross-country skiing Basketball Racquetball Group aerobics
Strength Exercise Examples	20 minutes—all major muscle groups Leg extension (quadriceps) Leg curl (hamstrings) Chest cross (chest) Pullover (upper back) Lateral raise (shoulders) Arm extension (triceps) Arm curl (biceps) Trunk extension (lower back) Trunk flexion (abdominals) Neck extension (neck extensors) Neck flexion (neck flexors)
Flexibility and Cool-Down Activity	15 minutes

Reprinted, by permission, from the *YMCA Exercise Instructor Manual,* © YMCA of the USA, 1995, Human Kinetics.

Name __________ THR __________

Date	**Seat Height**											
Leg Extension												
Leg Curl												
Leg Press												
Chest Cross												
Chest Press												
Row												
Overhead Press												
Biceps												
Triceps												
Low Back												
Abdominal												
Neck Flexion												
Neck Extension												
Treadmill												
Stepper												
Cycle												

Figure 8.2 Sample workout card 1.

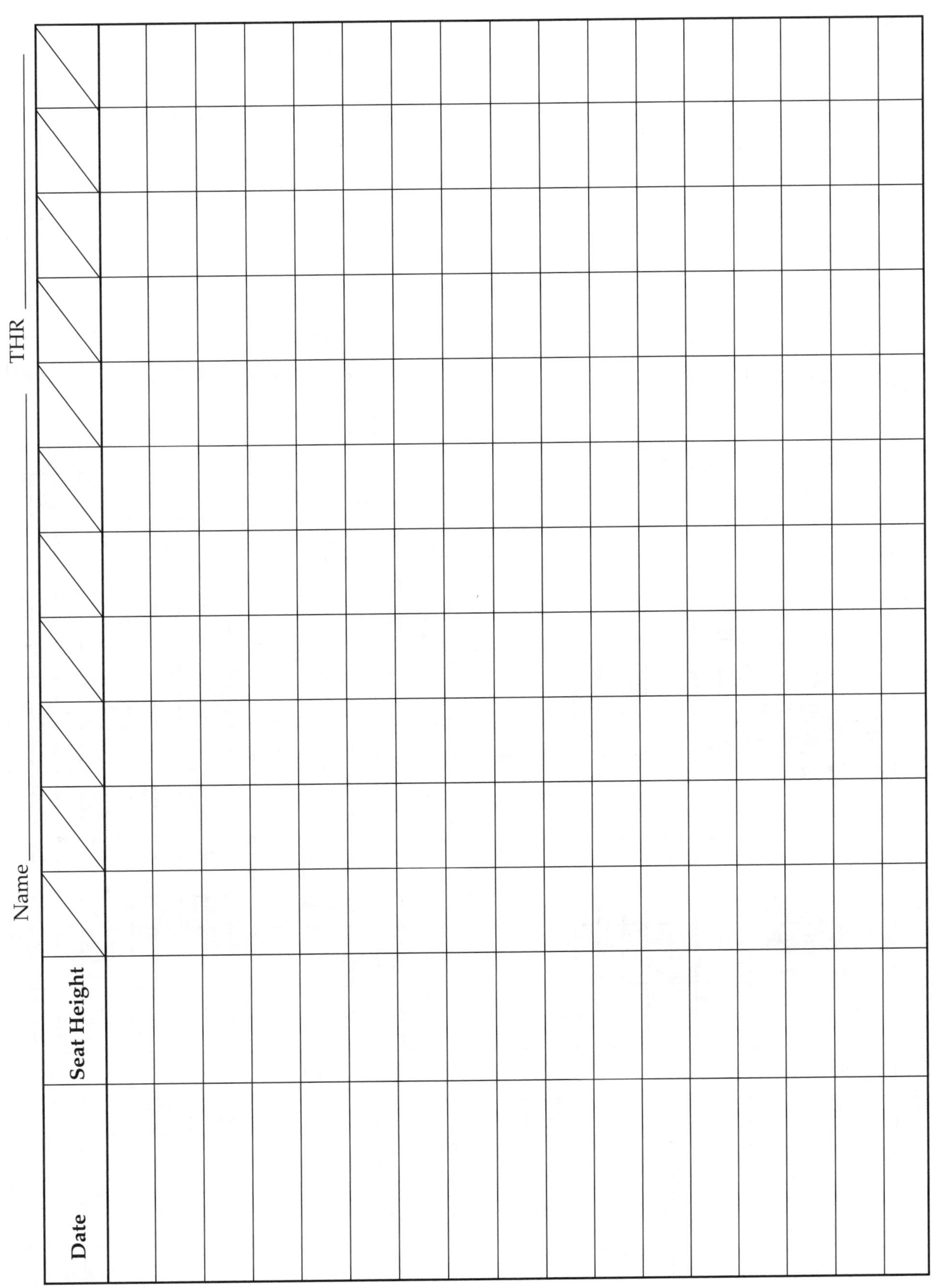

Figure 8.3 Sample workout card 2.
Reprinted, by permission, from the *YMCA Exercise Instructor Manual*, © YMCA of the USA, 1995, Human Kinetics.

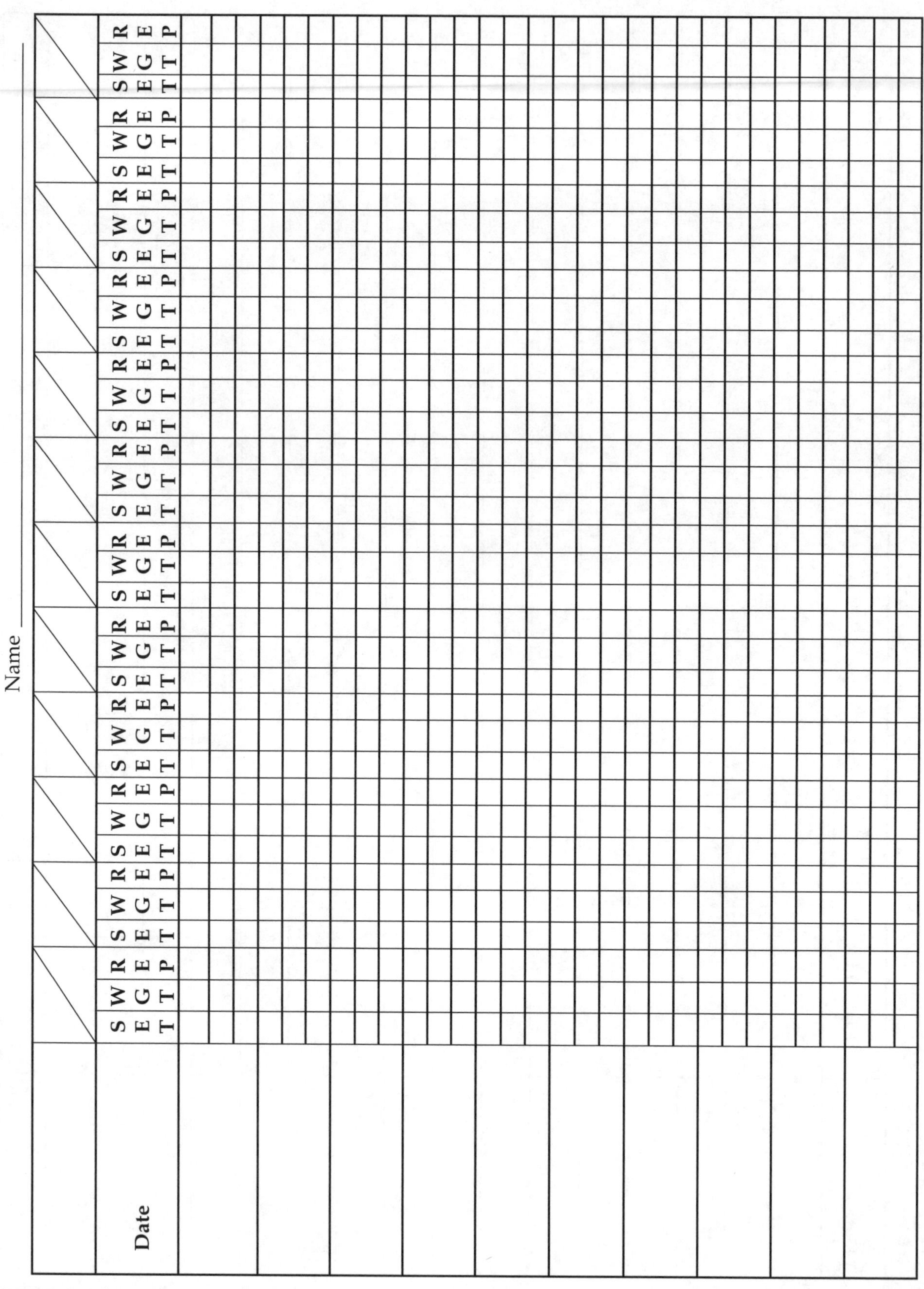

Figure 8.4 Sample workout card 3.

Reprinted, by permission, from the *YMCA Exercise Instructor Manual*, © YMCA of the USA, 1995, Human Kinetics.

9

Nutrition

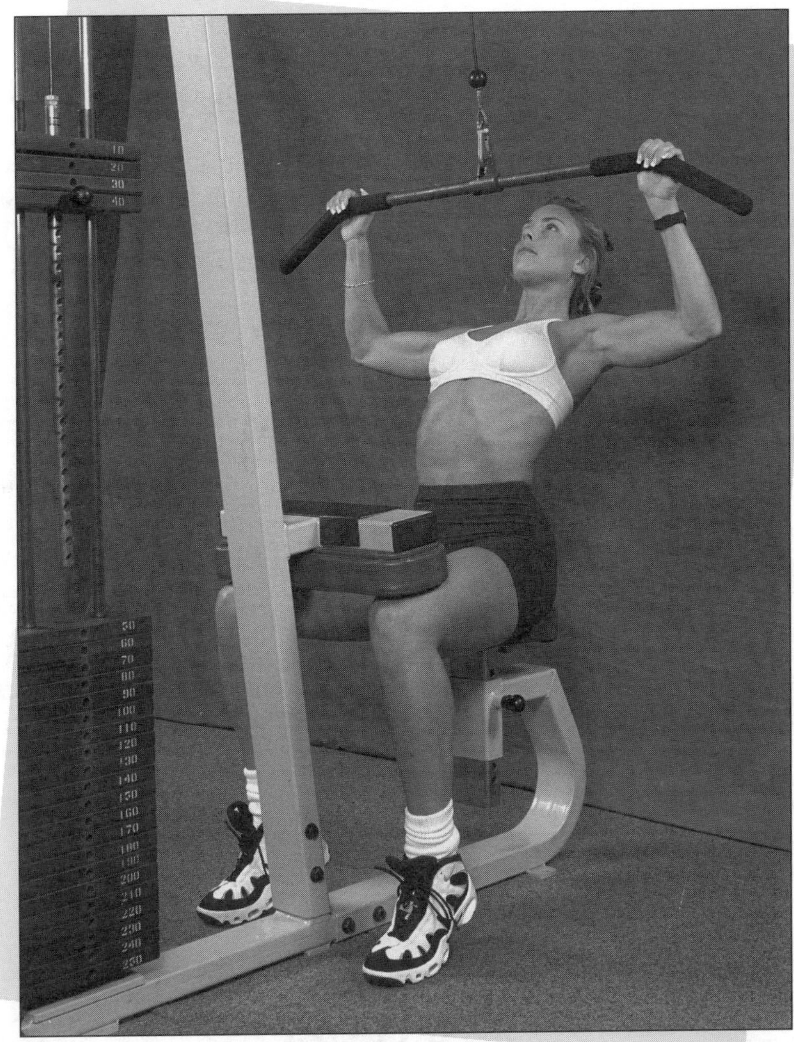

The study of nutrition involves complex theories and diverse issues. It is vital that fitness professionals understand basic nutrition principles. What people eat today affects their performance now and in later years. According to a 1991 American Dietetic Association survey of American eating habits, only 28 percent of participants rated themselves knowledgeable of basic food guidelines.

In recent years, the science of sports nutrition has dramatically altered what and how athletes eat. The emphasis is no longer on calorie counting or high protein diets, but rather on consuming ample carbohydrates for fuel, sufficient protein for building

---

From Chapter 1 of *Aerobic and Fitness Instructor's Manual*, National Dance-Exercise Instructor's Training Association (NDEITA), 1998.

muscle, and plenty of water. Caloric restriction is no longer popular. Wholesome, low fat foods are recommended. Eating regular, well-balanced meals, obtaining adequate exercise, and maintaining a reasonable body weight can substantially influence how people feel.

Dietary Guidelines

The Dietary Guidelines were developed by the Department of Health and Human Services and the U.S. Department of Agriculture to encourage healthful eating practices. They apply to healthy Americans aged two years and up.

- Eat a variety of vegetables, fruits, and grain products that are generally low in fat.
- Maintain a healthy body weight to reduce the risk of high blood pressure, heart disease, stroke, certain cancers, and Type II diabetes.
- Choose a diet low in fat and cholesterol to reduce the risk of heart attack and certain cancers.
- Use sugar only in moderation to avoid empty calories.
- Use salt in moderation to reduce the risk of high blood pressure.
- Use alcohol in moderation to avoid calories containing little nutrients.

In August 1992 the USDA and the Department of Health and Human Services introduced the Food Guide Pyramid. The Pyramid encourages Americans to eat a variety of foods to get the required nutrients, and the right amount of calories to maintain a healthy weight. The Food Guide Pyramid should be used as a general guide in choosing a healthful diet (see figure 9.1).

Essential Nutrients

Essential nutrients are those necessary for body functions that are not synthesized in the body. They include carbohydrates, protein, fat, vitamins, minerals, and water.

Carbohydrates

Carbohydrates are generally considered the most important nutrient for exercisers. Carbohydrates are the most readily available source of energy from food. Before carbohydrates can be used by the body, they must be converted into glucose, or blood sugar. Any glucose not used immediately as energy is converted into glycogen and body fat. Glycogen is stored in the liver and muscles. When more energy is needed, glycogen is converted back to glucose. Fat cannot be converted back to glucose, but is instead burned as fuel.

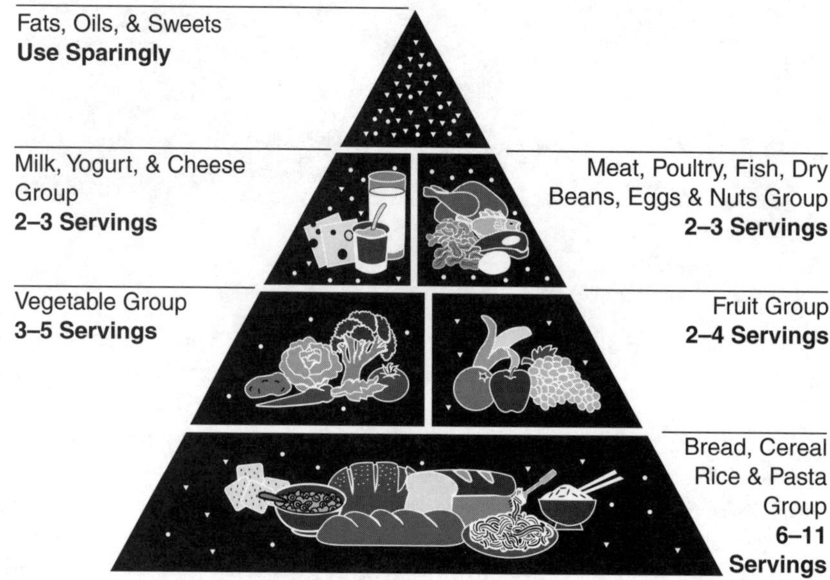

Figure 9.1 The food guide pyramid. For more information contact: U.S. Department of Agriculture, Human Nutritional Information Service, 6505 Belcrest Road, Hyattsville, MD 20782.

Substantially reducing dietary carbohydrates will result in weight loss, but primarily from loss of muscle mass and fluid. When carbohydrates are unavailable, protein will be used for energy and, as a by-product, the body eliminates fluid. This loss of fluid can result in a dramatic loss of body weight; however, this type of weight loss is temporary. Once "normal" eating is resumed, much of the apparent weight loss vanishes as the fluid is replenished.

There are three main types of carbohydrates differentiated by their chemical structure. *Monosaccharides* (glucose, galactose, and fructose) are the simplest, consisting of a single saccharide molecule. *Disaccharides* (sucrose, lactose, and maltose) consist of two saccharide molecules linked together. *Polysaccharides* (starch and cellulose) consist of a long chain of many saccharide molecules. Polysaccharides are also known as *complex carbohydrates,* and are found in cereals, potatoes, rice, pasta, and bread.

Protein

Protein is needed primarily to supply the body with amino acids. Amino acids are absorbed and used to rebuild new body proteins such as hair, skin, muscles, cartilage, hemoglobin, enzymes, hormones, and various proteins in the blood. Unused amino acids are stored as body fat. The waste products from fat conversion must be excreted in the urine, requiring additional work for the kidneys. While protein provides the basic building blocks for body tissues, research has not shown that megadoses of protein (amino acids) will increase muscle tissue growth during training or contribute significantly to energy needs.

Protein quality counts. Of the 22 amino acids, eight are considered indispensable. High-quality proteins contain all eight amino acids. These include meat, fish, poultry, eggs, and dairy products. Vegetables, fruit, legumes, and grains are lower in quality because they are missing some amino acids. Combining high and low protein foods can work well to formulate a complete protein. For example, dry beans, peas, lentils, and peanuts eaten with corn provide a quality protein. A general guide is to team grains and seeds with legumes, and any plant protein with an animal protein (see table 9.1 for examples). Tofu is made from coagulated soy milk, and it is a high-quality alternative to animal protein. It is low in saturated fats and calories, and it is cholesterol free.

Research has yet to define a specific amount of protein needed by sports-active people. Individuals who may require more protein than the current RDA include athletes, intense exercisers, and dieters who consume insufficient calories.

Fat

Fat provides more than twice as much energy as protein or carbohydrates. It carries vitamins A, D, E, and K, and it helps the body use protein and carbohydrates more efficiently. The most common form of consumable fat is in saturated fatty acids. During digestion, dietary fats are broken down into fatty acids and glycerol which are triglycerides. Triglycerides are the three molecules of fatty acids plus one molecule of glycerol. Any fatty acids not used as energy are stored as triglycerides in the adipose tissue. Stored adipose tissue, or fat, can be used to provide energy.

Saturated Fatty Acids

The major dietary source of saturated fat comes from animal products that are solid at room temperature. The vegetable oil from palm kernel, coconut, palm, and cocoa oils also contain large proportions of saturated fat. Consuming

Table 9.1 Protein Teams

Animal and grain proteins	Animal and legume proteins	Legume and grain proteins
Milk and cereal	Cheese and bean stew	Baked beans and brown bread
Cheese sandwich	Milk and rice pudding	Blackeyed peas and rice
Tuna and rice casserole	Ham and split pea soup	Beans and cornbread
Macaroni and cheese		Peanut butter sandwich
Cheese pizza		Beans and pasta

saturated fat stimulates the liver to produce excess cholesterol.

Unsaturated Fatty Acids

Mono- and polyunsaturated fats are usually liquid at room temperature. Good sources are canola, olive, and fish oils. It is heart-wise to cook with mono- or polyunsaturated fats versus saturated fats.

Vitamins

Mainstream medical researchers are paying more attention to how vitamins affect the body. Scientists are investigating possible fundamental and long-term roles that vitamins may play in forestalling and reversing certain diseases.

Vitamins help control the growth of body tissues and help the body release energy; however, very small amounts are required to accomplish this. Vitamin deficiencies can impair physical performance, but there is no evidence that vitamins taken in excess will enhance performance. Fat-soluble (A and D) vitamins are stored in the body. Excess vitamin A and D can retard growth and permanently damage organs. Water-soluble vitamins such as C are excreted in the urine. Taking vitamins will not alleviate stress, supply energy, or make up for lost sleep and missed meals.

Minerals

Minerals can be defined as chemical elements that must be present for the maintenance of health. They are important for body structures and for controlling body processes, but do not supply calories. Except for iron, minerals are not used up in the body, but are excreted after carrying out their functions. This is why mineral losses should be replaced regularly. Four significant minerals are calcium, iron, magnesium, and potassium.

Calcium

Calcium is the most abundant mineral in the body, and it is critical for strengthening teeth and bones. About 99 percent of the body's calcium is found in the skeleton. Calcium is essential for cell function, muscle contraction, blood clotting, and the transmission of nerve impulses from nerve ending to muscle fiber. A lifelong calcium-rich diet combined with weight-bearing exercise can help reduce the risk of osteoporosis. Osteoporosis affects primarily older, postmenopausal women; however, it can also affect young female athletes who have irregular menstrual periods.

Iron

Iron is essential for certain enzymes and for the formulation of hemoglobin and myoglobin. Myoglobin aids in the storage and transport of oxygen within the cells. People with diets low in iron may develop anemia, a condition that reduces the blood's hemoglobin concentration. Anemia can be categorized by general sluggishness, fatigue, and loss of appetite.

Magnesium

Magnesium is required for teeth and bone formation, muscle contraction, transmission of nerve impulses, and activation of many enzymes.

Potassium

Potassium is a mineral that, in combination with sodium and calcium, maintains normal heart rhythm, regulates the body's water balance, aids in muscle contraction, and conducts nerve impulses.

Water

Water is essential to life because it is the medium in which all metabolic reactions take place. It accounts for one-half to three-fourths of the body's weight. It regulates body temperature and carries nutrients to cells, aids in digestion, and is necessary for all chemical reactions within the body.

For exercisers, one of the most important functions of water is its cooling capacity. During exercise, heat is generated within the body as a by-product of the working muscle. Heat must be removed to maintain normal body temperature. If heat builds up, body temperature rises and performance suffers. The body loses water in the form of sweat, urine, feces, and exhaled water vapors. The amount lost as sweat depends on physical activity and the external temperature. The amount lost as urine depends on fluid intake. Sweating is a mechanism for eliminating excess heat. Sweat evaporates from the skin and the body cools down. Heavy sweating significantly reduces the body's water content. Exercisers who sweat heavily should drink at least two cups of water for each pound lost during exercise to rehydrate the body. Dark gold urine may indicate a water deficiency, assuming no influence from medications.

Fiber

Dietary fiber aids in proper digestion. It consists of the indigestible components of plants and includes certain types of polysaccharides, cellulose, hemicelluloses, gums, and pectins. Humans do not possess the necessary enzymes to digest these substances. Instead, they pass through the digestive system in the same form, unable to be used as energy.

The easiest way to increase fiber content in the diet is to increase consumption of unrefined carbohydrates such as whole-grain breads, cereals, root vegetables, potatoes, yams, and fruits.

Cholesterol

Cholesterol is a major constituent of body cells. It is involved in the formation of hormones and bile salts, and it transports fats from the bloodstream to tissues throughout the body.

Cholesterol and fat are not the same thing. Cholesterol is a fat-like substance found in all animal foods, milk products, and egg yolks. It is also found in the blood, brain, and nervous system, and it is essential to all cell structures in the body. Sex hormones and cortisone are made from cholesterol. About 1,000 mg of cholesterol are normally synthesized by the body each day.

The lean and fat parts of meat and the skin of poultry contain cholesterol. In dairy products, cholesterol is found mainly in the fat; therefore, lower fat products contain less cholesterol. Egg yolks, liver, and other organ meats are loaded with vitamins and minerals but are high in cholesterol.

The body produces low-density lipoproteins (LDLs) and high-density lipoproteins (HDLs). They comprise the majority of what is called "total cholesterol." Researchers believe the desirable cholesterol level for American adults is below 200 milligrams per deciliter (mg/dl) of blood. Epidemiological surveys indicate that the risk for heart attack at cholesterol levels of 250 mg/dl is twice that of 200 mg/dl, and at least four times as high with a level of 300 mg/dl. Genetics or a diet high in saturated fat also contribute to high cholesterol levels. High cholesterol levels indicate a higher chance of developing heart disease. The National Cholesterol Education Program recently classified total blood cholesterol levels for American adults as follows:

- **Desirable:** Less than 200 mg/dl
- **Borderline high:** 200-239 mg/dl
- **High:** 240 mg/dl and above

Alcohol

Technically, alcohol is a drug, but it is classified as a nutrient because it provides energy. Alcohol acts as a depressant to the central nervous system. Even at low levels, alcohol can slow reaction times and impair balance and coordination. Alcohol decreases the liver's output of glucose and dehydrates the body. About 20 percent of the alcohol ingested is absorbed by the stomach; the remainder is absorbed in the intestines. Alcohol is water soluble, and it is diluted by the body's water content. Organs that have a higher water content and rich blood supply, like the brain, receive the highest initial alcohol concentration. Alcohol affects all the body's cells, but the extent depends on the blood-alcohol concentration.

Food Labeling

Nutrition Panels

The new nutrition labeling requirements issued by the FDA and the USDA's Food Safety and Inspection Service were effective May 8, 1994. A revised list of nutrients should appear on the nutrition panel of all processed and packaged foods. The revisions include percentages of calories from fat, saturated fat, cholesterol, sodium, carbohydrates, protein, sodium, vitamin A, vitamin C, calcium, and iron. Listing levels of thiamin, riboflavin, and niacin is no longer required because deficiencies in these vitamins are not considered a significant public health problem.

Serving sizes will be more uniform across all product lines, and the nutritional qualities of similar products more easily comparable. They must be expressed in both metric and household measurements.

COMMON SERVING SIZES

Breads, Cereals, Rice, and Pasta

- 1 slice of bread
- 1/2 cup cooked rice or pasta
- 1/2 cup cooked cereal
- 1 ounce ready-to-eat cereal

Fruits

- 1 medium-sized piece of fruit
- 1 melon wedge
- 3/4 cup juice
- 1/2 cup canned fruit
- 1/4 cup dried fruit

Vegetables

- 1/2 cup chopped raw or cooked vegetables
- 1 cup leafy raw vegetables

Dairy Products

- 1 cup milk or yogurt
- 1-1/2 to 2 ounces of cheese

Meat, Poultry, Fish, Legumes, and Nuts

- 1-1/2 to 3 ounces cooked lean meat, poultry, or fish
- 1-1/2 cups cooked beans
- 3 eggs = 2 to 3 ounces of cooked lean meat, poultry, or fish
- 6 tablespoons peanut butter = 2 to 3 ounces of cooked lean meat, poultry, or fish

Other categories include fats, oils, and sweets that should be limited, especially when trying to lose weight.

Daily Value

Nutrients are expressed in amount per serving and also in percentages called the Daily Value. The percent Daily Value is based on a 2,000 calorie per day diet. This percentage is intended to help consumers understand the role of individual foods in the total daily diet. However, not all people require 2,000 calories per day; some require more, others less. The factors that predict calorie requirements are body size, age, height, weight, activity level, and metabolism.

Nutritional Claims

Many nutritional claims are false. For example, "light" vegetable oil is merely light in color, and "light" cheesecake is light in texture. With new labeling, any term used to describe a particular food's nutrient content will have a universal meaning. The list of acceptable claims includes such descriptions as "free," "low,""light or lite," "less," and "high." There are regulations prescribing which nutrient content claims are allowed and in what circumstances they can be used.

Only under certain circumstances can claims link a nutrient or a food to the risks of disease. The January 6, 1993, issue of the *Federal Register* permits the following nutrient-health relationships:

- Calcium and reduced risk of osteoporosis
- Dietary fiber and reduced risk of certain cancers
- Sodium and increased risk of hypertension
- Dietary saturated fat and cholesterol, and increased risk of coronary heart disease
- Dietary fat and increased risk of certain cancers

These regulations allow information on food labels that can help educate the public about recognized diet-disease relationships. Authorized claims must meet requirements to prevent label information that would be false or misleading. The FDA and USDA have begun a multiyear labeling education campaign designed to increase consumer knowledge and to help consumers make accurate and sound dietary choices.

Serving Percentages

The new labeling system does not require listing percentage of nutrients *per serving,* but lists percentages of daily values based on a 2,000 calorie diet. To calculate the percentage of nutrients per serving, the grams per serving are converted to calories. Proteins and carbohydrates have four calories per gram, and fat has nine calories per gram. The following formula calculates the total percentage of protein, carbohydrates, or fat per serving.

(Total grams of specific nutrient) multiplied by (Number of calories per gram for that nutrient) = **Calories of nutrient**

Divide (Calories of nutrient) by (Total calories per serving) = **Percent of nutrient/serving**

Example:

1 serving of Wheat n' Cheddar Snack Crackers

Total calories = 200

Fat grams = 10

Formula:

(10 grams of fat) × (9 calories/gram) = 90 calories of fat

90 calories ÷ 200 total calories = 45%

Fat = 45% of serving

Weight Control

Dieting

The media continue to inundate the public with confusing and contradicting information about diets and dieting. For years a high-protein, low-carbohydrate diet was considered the best way to lose weight. Recent evidence suggests the opposite. Consuming a diet high in complex carbohydrates and moderate in protein may be an effective way to lose weight. Evidence also suggests that it is healthier to maintain a small weight loss rather than repeatedly take off and put on weight (yo-yo dieting). The speculation is that every time a person loses and regains weight more body fat remains and more lean muscle mass is lost.

A decrease in calories and increase in physical activity will usually result in weight loss. One pound of weight is about 3,500 calories. Reducing daily intake by 250 calories would result in a loss of approximately one-half pound per week. Severe caloric restriction and overtraining can reduce metabolism, making weight loss more difficult. Although caloric restriction is often chosen above exercise as a means of weight loss, exercise is more effective for decreasing body fat. There are many benefits from regular exercise, but it is weight control that finally pushes a large percentage of people into physical activity. The American College of Sports Medicine approves a weight loss of one-half to two pounds per week.

Anorexia Nervosa

Anorexia nervosa is characterized by extreme preoccupation with weight loss, distorted body image, and an intense fear of gaining weight. Anorexics feel in control of their bodies when they are losing weight. They are obsessively challenged by seeing the scale progress downward. If not treated in its early stages, this preoccupation with weight loss seriously endangers their health, and potentially their lives.

Typically, anorexics are female, in the midteens, and from an educated, middle-class family. Anorexics are highly competitive and strive for perfection. The "perfect body" is the ultimate goal, and in their minds, they can never become too thin. Weight loss becomes an obsession, losing control becomes a great fear, and self-imposed starvation takes over. Exercise is often used in conjunction with caloric restriction to enhance weight loss. Many anorexics also abuse laxatives. Physiological characteristics of anorexics include the following:

- Dramatic weight loss, including muscle tissue
- Dry skin, which is sometimes tinged yellow from an accumulation of stored vitamin A
- Growth of fine body hair
- Intolerance to cold
- Lowered blood pressure and basal metabolism
- Anemia
- Various hormonal changes
- Retarded bone growth
- Amenorrhea (temporary cessation of the menstrual cycle)

Those with an increased risk for developing anorexia nervosa include the following:

- Females
- Those with a preoccupation for thinness
- Those constantly discussing food and body image
- Those seriously involved in activities requiring a low body weight (i.e., gymnastics, ballet, diving, modeling)
- Those from a middle to upper socioeconomic background
- Caucasians and Asians

Anorexia is very difficult to treat and should be dealt with by qualified professionals. A study from the Renfrew Center in Philadelphia, a treatment center for anorexics and bulimics, reported that females with eating disorders often begin dieting much earlier than their peers (average age 15). The prognosis for treatment is fairly good with early intervention; however, if left untreated, it is associated with early death.

Bulimia Nervosa

Bulimia is an eating disorder characterized by recurrent episodes of binge eating and purging. Eating episodes usually include at least three of the following:

- Binge consumption of high-calorie, easily ingested foods such as cookies, ice cream, etc.
- Termination of the binge by abdominal pain, sleep, or purging
- Carefully planned bingeing episodes
- Repeated attempts to lose weight, sometimes through excessive exercise
- Frequent weight fluctuations

Bulimics are also characterized by a morbid fear of fatness. Many fear they won't be able to stop bingeing voluntarily. Most bulimics report feeling depressed after a binge episode, even though the binge eating may have resulted from depression. Ninety percent of bulimics are white females, ranging from 15 to 30 years of age. They may be of normal weight or slightly underweight; however, many remain extremely thin. There are very few reports of male bulimia. Bulimics may eat as much as 6,000 calories in one sitting, and spend as much as $50 per day on food. During binges, the bulimic may have low self-esteem or feel out of control, guilty, and shameful. To control fluctuations in body weight, binge eating may be followed by vomiting. This cycle may produce a variety of health complications with potentially life-threatening consequences.

Over 40 percent of bulimics report menstrual irregularities, especially those with low body weight (less than 92 percent of ideal body weight). The effect of amenorrhea on the bone density of young female athletes is a great concern. It is estimated that 60 percent of competitive female runners are amenorrheic. Bone density of the lumbar spine is lower among amenorrheic athletes, and tibial and metatarsal stress fractures are also more common.

Binge eating can cause dilation and possible rupture of the gastrointestinal tract due to excessive food intake within a short period of time. Vomiting after bingeing may damage tooth enamel and upset the body's electrolyte balance. Repeated use of ipecac to induce vomiting can cause myocardial abnormalities. Use of laxatives by bulimics may promote a sense of purging, but seldom prevents the absorption of calories.

Exercise leaders should be alert to chronic and obsessive exercisers, especially when continued weight loss is evident. The exercise leader may choose to discuss the individual's behavior with a supervisor or trained personnel in hopes that intervention will occur. Peer support and encouragement are very important when guiding those with eating disorders to seek treatment. The following signs that may indicate a person has an eating disorder are from an article written by Dr. Peter D. Vask titled *Spotting the Problem Exerciser:*

- A need to exercise excessively
- Wide fluctuations in weight, from 5 to 10 pounds or more, that can indicate bingeing
- Fatigue, muscle cramping, lack of stamina
- Irritability or significant mood shifts, especially depression and frustration with performance
- Frequent complaints about weight that appear groundless
- Edema or fluid retention (unrelated to menstrual periods) of face, hands, or ankles
- Complaints of abdominal bloating or stomach pain that resembles heartburn
- Questions about laxatives, diuretics, or thyroid medication and their relationship to weight loss
- Reports of needing extensive dental work, having more cavities

Doctors and psychologists in the field can be contacted through the following:

The American Society of Bariatric Physicians
5200 S. Quebec Street
Englewood, CO 80111
(303) 779-4833

The American Anorexia & Bulimia Association
Regent Hospital
425 East 61st Street, Sixth Floor
New York, NY 10021
(212) 849-8686

10

Motivating Your Participants

Every personal training instructor is confronted with the challenge of motivating participants to stick with the program. Just as the individuals with whom you work have a wide range of fitness levels and abilities, so also they have a wide range of psychological outlooks on exercise. The more sensitive you are to factors that motivate exercisers to stay committed to a program, the easier it will be for you to identify participants who are more likely to drop out.

Motivation is a broad term used to describe a variety of behaviors. In general it refers to the direction or intensity of a person's behavior. Direction of behavior means whether a person approaches or avoids a particular situation. Intensity relates to the degree of effort put forth to accomplish a certain behavior.

Exercise scientists who study people's attitudes, beliefs, and personality traits are called exercise or sport psychologists. They examine factors that influence decisions to participate in exercise. Most exercise scientists would agree that a psychological prescription for exercise is not quite as easy to write as a physiological one. This chapter presents the basic elements of psychological exercise prescriptions geared toward motivating your participants to stick with their program. Some elements to take into account include participants' needs and various factors that influence participants' decisions to exercise. You can assist participants by guiding them in setting goals, providing a supportive training environment, and keeping the atmosphere positive. It will help both you and your participants if you are aware of why you chose to be a personal trainer and how you are a role model for participants.

Identifying Participants' Needs

People are motivated to fulfill their needs. If you understand what your participants' needs are and you are able to help them fulfill these needs, you possess the key to their motivation. (Martens et al., 1981, p. 49)

How can you help fulfill participants' needs if you don't know what they are? Take the time to get to know your participants. Talk with them about their fitness goals, jobs, interests, and so on. These conversations give you opportunities to learn what they like and dislike about their exercise routines. Always ask for comments in a manner that makes it easy for the participant to answer. For example, say, "Tell me your favorite thing about your workout and one thing that you would like to see changed." You can also use this time to encourage participants individually. Many sport psychologists believe that one-on-one encouragement to keep exercising is much more effective than encouragement directed at an entire group.

You can even approach this job a little more formally. After a period of time, you can conduct a short, written survey asking for participants' suggestions. Read the comments carefully and amend your program to address the responses that aren't as positive as you'd like.

Factors Influencing Decisions to Exercise

Listed in table 10.1 are some variables that have been found to influence people's decisions to exercise. Note that the main categories of exercise determinants are biological, psychological, and situational.

These factors do not operate in isolation within a person. A continual, complex interaction between these and other variables is always at work influencing decisions. Let's discuss each factor briefly and examine how you can influence it in leading your participants.

Biological

It's been shown that a participant who has more biological advantages initially (for example, is close to ideal body weight, has a greater genetic capacity to become physically fit and hence sees training benefits occurring faster, or is less predisposed to coronary heart disease) is much more motivated to begin and continue an exercise program. Unfortunately, the undermotivated, overweight, less fit individual is less likely to begin

Table 10.1 Factors Influencing Decisions to Exercise

Biological trait of the exerciser	Psychological traits of the exerciser	Situational factors
Body weight	Self-motivation	Support from family and friends
Fitness level	Attitudes and beliefs	Job status
Health status	Personality traits	Recreational habits
		Location of exercise facility
		Facility atmosphere

training and more likely to quit once he or she gets started. You need to be aware, then, that those participants who might benefit most from a personal training program are also the very people most likely to drop out.

Psychological

An exercise psychologist looks at three areas when studying the psychological traits of an exerciser: attitudes, beliefs, and personality traits.

Attitudes

A person's attitude is how he or she feels or thinks about something. Participants will begin a training with a variety of attitudes about exercise formed from past experiences as well as expectations for the new program. Although attitudes can predict the likelihood of initial involvement in exercise and the type of program selected, the fact that a person thinks of exercise as a positive experience is no guarantee that he or she will stay with the program (Dishman, 1984).

Beliefs

What a person believes about the health benefits of exercising affects his or her participation in and commitment to a program. Some people believe strongly that exercise will produce many health-related benefits, whereas others believe just as strongly that exercise will do very little for them. Participants who enter your program with a particular health problem or a belief that exercise is an ounce of prevention against future health problems will probably be more motivated to stay.

Personality Traits

Personality traits are those complex characteristics that distinguish one individual from another. One of the most studied personality traits in terms of exercise adherence is self-motivation. A self-motivated person is one who is reinforced more by his or her own ideas and goals than by those of others. Self-motivated people have much higher success rates in staying with exercise programs. These individuals seem to be better suited to overlook factors (e.g., their physical appearance, the exercise room, the convenience of the location) that may be used by other participants as excuses not to exercise.

Situational

Because biological and psychological traits are very personal factors, as an instructor you are limited in altering these influences on motivation. Situational factors, however, being more environmental in nature, are more easily altered in hopes of increasing your participants' motivation to exercise regularly. The training setting, its location and accessibility, and the atmosphere in which you conduct it are a few of the situational factors over which you have some degree of control.

Helping Participants Set Goals

Helping individuals establish realistic exercise goals is important to motivation. Many participants drop out because they expect to become immediately fit, and they are disappointed when this does not happen. You need to warn participants, in a positive manner, of the various pressures that may tempt them to drop out (hard work, discomfort, time commitment, etc.). Keep encouraging participants to make each appointment and exercise a habit. Having participants set some realistic goals to accomplish is one way to reinforce the exercise habit.

Short-term and long-term goals provide participants with objectives to work toward, and the goal-setting process is an effective means of eliciting commitment to the program. Discussing goals with each participant gives you insight to modify any unrealistic goals a person may have set. For example, a participant has set a goal of losing 20 pounds after 8 weeks of training. However, you know that exercising alone will not accomplish this goal and that 2 pounds per week ($2 \times 8 = 16$) is a recommended, safe rate of weight loss. Hence you need to explain what the participant can expect from her or his program in terms of weight loss. He or she needs to understand that diet and exercise together is the best approach to attaining and maintaining weight loss. A more appropriate short-term goal would be to lose 1 to 2 pounds a week by exercising regularly and reducing caloric intake. At this rate a safer, more desirable long-term goal of losing 10 to 15 pounds in 2 months could be accomplished. When planning goals with individual participants, take into account their physical ability, their expressed commitment, and their previous ability to accomplish goals.

Providing a Supportive Training Environment

A supportive training environment may be one of the most powerful positive reinforcers. People generally like to exercise where they are known by name, treated with respect, and instructed in a professional manner. A user-friendly facility is clean, spacious, and well lit. It has plenty of professional staff and educational materials. Specific member services may include quality equipment, easy-to-read instructional charts, spray bottles and towels at exercise stations, a convenient workout card system, easy room access, smooth traffic flow, cold water dispensers, and a systematic participant orientation program.

Physical features of the exercise facility, such as its size, furnishings, lighting and ventilation, and temperature, contribute to participants' perceptions of how enjoyable the workout environment is. Although budgetary constraints or the facility design may mean you can't have everything you want, do try to provide your participants with the best that is available.

Size of the Facility

The amount of space participants have to move around in will certainly affect their perception of the experience. Participants need to feel that there is enough room to freely perform movements and exercises without interfering with other exercisers.

Mirrors add to the attractiveness of an exercise facility and make it appear larger. Many participants also enjoy the visual feedback as they work out. Mirrors should be high quality so they maintain an accurate reflection over time.

Furnishings

The decor of the workout facility should be both professional and attractive. You can hang posters, fill bulletin boards with exercise tips, post educational materials on training-related topics, and display information participants might bring to share. Always keep the area clean and free of safety hazards such as dirt, clothing on the floor, or water tracked in on participants' shoes.

Lighting and Ventilation

Exercise facilities need to be well lit and well ventilated. Bright lighting will help participants feel good and ready to work out. Windows are a welcome addition to any exercise facility. Ceiling fans or large floor fans, if you have space for them, aid in circulating the air.

Facility Temperature

Facilities within a building or complex are typically controlled by a central thermostat. Pay attention to the temperature of the workout facility. The YMCA recommends a temperature of 68-72 degrees Fahrenheit in exercise facilities.

Creating a Positive Exercise Atmosphere

The atmosphere in which personal training sessions are conducted will affect participants' motivation. Try to create a comfortable, *noncompetitive* atmosphere in which participants will enjoy working out. Encourage participants to work out at their own pace and to have fun. As a leader you can facilitate this type of environment by always being positive and giving participants encouragement, feedback, and positive reinforcement. Try to have an uplifting mood and express confidence. If you establish a positive and helpful rapport with your participants, they will be understanding and positive toward you in return.

Being a Positive Communicator

An effective motivator is first an effective communicator. When talking with participants, keep these few points in mind:

- Don't treat participants as inferior or naive. Speak to them in the same way you want to be spoken to.
- If you ask participants for suggestions, do not ignore what they say; use their suggestions, when appropriate, to show you are listening.
- Always be positive or provide constructive feedback. No one should be embarrassed by trying to do a movement, only to be told point-blank that it is being done poorly.

- Don't become defensive when participants criticize you. Listen and try to turn the conversation into a positive situation for everyone involved.

In addition to communicating with participants, work toward being an effective communicator with your colleagues.

Providing Encouragement

Encouragement is essential not only for new personal training participants, but also for regular exercisers. For those just starting out, their feelings of insecurity and inadequacy can be offset by encouragement from you, which helps them develop confidence and competence. For regular exercisers, your encouragement may be their main source of motivation to continue training, particularly when they experience progress plateaus or lose interest in the activity. Encouragement may come in many forms, including greeting participants by name, inviting them to try new exercises, and showing enthusiasm for their training program and progress.

Giving Feedback

Your feedback should provide specific information regarding the exerciser's performance and progress. Feedback should always be honest and be given constructively. While participants need to know precisely what they are doing properly and improperly in order to improve their performance, the way in which you address participants' mistakes can affect their attitude toward training. For example, if you say, "Don't you remember you're not supposed to let your elbows come out on triceps pressdowns?" it may be taken as personal criticism. Saying "You will get better results if you keep your elbows against your sides during triceps pressdowns" instead is both more precise and more positive. The same logic applies when you comment on participants' progress. Saying "You haven't increased your workout weight at all in three weeks" is probably less effective than saying "Your training over the past three weeks indicates that you should increase your weightloads by 2.5 pounds next workout."

It is essential that you give participants feedback about their performance and progress clearly, concisely, and objectively. Remember that you can provide relevant feedback through periodic fitness evaluations as well as observation. Evaluations could include assessments of body measurements, body composition, muscle strength, joint flexibility, resting heart rate, and resting blood pressure.

Another important source of feedback for participants is their workout charts or exercise logbooks that contain written records of each training session. Self-recording has been shown to be a very effective means of motivation, particularly when reviewed regularly by concerned personal trainers.

Using Positive Reinforcement

Positive reinforcement refers to anything that maintains or increases a particular behavior. In terms of exercise adherence, positive reinforcement may include compliments on appearance, praise for performance, and rewards and incentives. While compliments are almost always welcomed, they are not always meaningful. For example, simply saying "Good job" or "You're looking good" may become so routine that it has little impact. Praise is more effective when it provides specific information. That way the exerciser knows you actually observed the behavior that prompted your comment. Here are some examples of specific positive reinforcement: "Good job. You're performing every repetition in a slow and controlled manner." "You're looking good. The back and shoulder exercises you added have improved your posture."

Rewards and incentives are most meaningful when they are based upon personal goals and abilities. The performance criteria should be challenging, yet attainable with appropriate effort. For example, an under-muscled participant may be motivated to train regularly by making the award of a t-shirt contingent upon the participant's adding three pounds of lean (muscle) weight.

Check Your Mood

It's common sense that the mood you bring into the session will affect participants. An effective instructor will leave his or her troubles outside of the exercise facility and enter with a very uplifting spirit. This is the mark of a professional.

Encourage your participants to do the same to help them get the most out of the session. Remind them that this is one hour of the day in which they can relax and do something beneficial for their minds and bodies.

Displaying Confidence

The level of self-confidence an instructor displays may influence some participants' motivation to stick with the program. Your self-confidence comes across through both your words and your actions. Verbal confidence usually takes the form of clear instructions, positive comments from systematic observations, and an assured tone of voice as you ask and answer questions. Nonverbal confidence is usually displayed by body language, appropriate and effective use of the hands to assist and direct, and pleasant facial expressions. Being well prepared to teach can only boost your level of self-confidence.

Examining Your Own Motivation

Besides considering what you can do as an instructor to motivate your participants, you should think occasionally about what motivates you to be a personal training instructor. The factors might include prestige, teaching experience, personal enjoyment, or salary. Pinpointing your reasons for being an instructor may not be easy, however, as suggested by Friedenberg (1967):

Self-appraisal is not a simple task. . . . What we must decide is perhaps how we are valuable rather than how valuable we are; the question is more qualitative than quantitative. We learn fairly accurately how we look through (other's) eyes but if we are at all wise we learn not to see ourselves through their eyes, but rather to accept their image of us as our guide to be considered in establishing our conception of ourselves. . . . Self-esteem is therefore closely related to clarification of experience; if we do not understand clearly what we have done and what has happened to us, we have no true basis for self-esteem. (pp. 106-107)

Take the time to identify your reasons for wanting to be a personal trainer. As you identify key factors that motivate you to be an instructor, ask yourself how they affect, positively or negatively, your leadership.

The Instructor as Role Model

Whether you like it or not, being a personal training instructor makes you a role model in the eyes of many participants. The stereotypical instructor is physically fit, at proper body weight, and skilled at performing movements and exercises. The stereotype may also extend to a picture of one who doesn't smoke, drink alcoholic beverages in excess, eat junk food, or indulge in any other "unhealthy" behaviors.

How you perceive yourself as a role model depends upon your own philosophy. There are many professional variations of a good role model. You should take the time to identify your beliefs and attitudes so you are ready to articulate them if the subject comes up with participants or with other instructors. Your participants' perceptions of you as a role model can be motivating or not-so-motivating factors for them. For example, participants who expect you to be in top shape and at your ideal body weight may question the benefit of your program if you are neither.

Personal training instructors who display positive attitudes and demonstrate that they value exercise typically influence their participants to do the same. A friendly, courteous, and respectful staff is the key to a friendly, courteous, and respectful membership who enjoy their exercise experiences. The three most desired instructor qualities are (1) knowledge of exercise science, (2) good teaching skills, and (3) enthusiasm. As knowledgeable instructors who communicate effectively and enthusiastically play a major role in motivating members, it is in everyone's best interest for you as an instructor to demonstrate these important characteristics.

11

Communication and Teaching Techniques

Amy Jones, M.Ed.

* Amy Jones, M.Ed., is a licensed psychotherapist and works with Fortune 500 companies undergoing change or a transition. Much of her time is spent coaching and training executives in communication and organizational effectiveness. She was formerly the director of programs for the Cooper Fitness Center in Dallas for 12 years, and she served as a technical advisor to the National Aerobic Championship. She is currently a member of the American Council on Exercise Board of Directors.

A personal trainer's relationship to a participant is clearly the helping relationship of educator to student. You are the helper or teacher; the one being helped is referred to as the student or participant. Helping relationships differ from most other kinds of relationships encountered in daily routines. Most ordinary experiences are dialogues in which both people seek personal enhancement or the mutual exchange of ideas or information. In the helping relationship, one person temporarily sets aside personal needs to help another person. The focus of the relationship is on the participant's needs and on goals that will lead to new behavior. Simply put, helping is enabling another person to change. Instead of encouraging dependence, the purpose of helping is to facilitate the participant's taking more control and becoming self-sufficient. Helping is an active process of advising, informing, correcting, and directing.

There are many kinds of helping relationships. Because there is usually a fee for service in personal training, you can be classified as a structured, professional helper, like social workers, teachers, school counselors, and legal advisors. In contrast to this professional level are unstructured levels of helping such as friendships and family relationships.

Your role is complex, as you will function as a teacher, coach, advisor, supervisor, supporter, counselor, and negotiator.

Teacher: Explaining to participants what they need to know and must do (e.g., outlining and explaining an aerobic exercise program).

Coach: Training participants in desired skills (e.g., coaching during a free-weight workout).

Advisor: Telling participants the wisest course of action (e.g., warning about dangers of an unsupervised liquid fasting program).

Supporter: Encouraging participants as they work on specific lifestyle changes (e.g., providing emotional support for a participant who has stopped smoking).

Counselor: Helping participants sort through personal problems (e.g., listening to a participant's frustrations regarding problems at work).

Negotiator: Bargaining with participants to reach an acceptable agreement (e.g., negotiating an exercise contract with a participant for a period of travel).

These roles are described only in a general sense. You should be acutely aware of your limitations and must not exceed the professional parameters of offering advice or counseling about personal problems. You can obviously listen and offer support, but you should know when to refer participants to other qualified professionals.

Stages of the Personal Trainer/ Participant Relationship

There will be distinct stages in your relationships with participants (figure 11.1), and they form a general model or framework for the divisions and related skills of the helping relationship. They may not always occur in this exact sequence, nor are all stages always present. Their length also may vary from participant to participant. Generally, the initial contact between the personal trainer and participant is made in the rapport stage. The process of gathering information after the relationship has begun forms the investigation stage. This gives way to the planning stage in which the participant's goals and steps toward them are mapped out. Finally, the action stage begins when the actual training process starts.

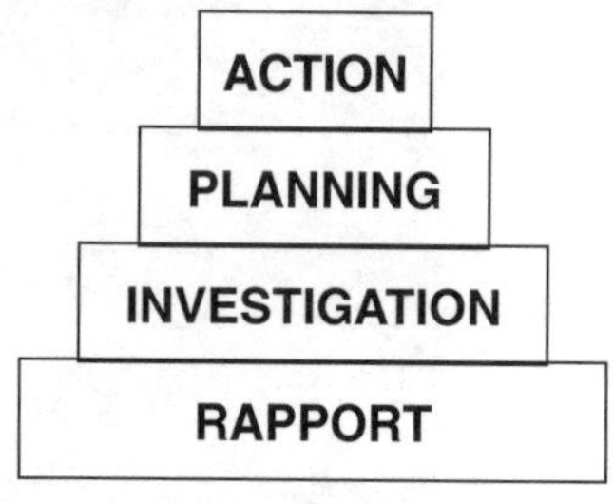

Figure 11.1 Stages of the personal trainer/participant relationship.

Each stage requires specific skills and techniques. In the beginning, for example, attentive listening skills can build the working relationship; the following stages require more decision-making and behavioral-change skills. Developing these skills can increase your effectiveness as a personal trainer. Because the personal trainer/participant relationship is dynamic and ever changing, these stages and skills overlap and may not occur in the exact order given. The specific stages and required skills are outlined as follows:

Stage 1: Rapport—interpersonal communication skills.

Stage 2: Investigation—information gathering skills.

Stage 3: Planning—problem-solving or decision-making skills.

Stage 4: Action—behavioral change skills (feedback, contracting, modeling, etc.).

Rapport Stage

The rapport stage is the foundation for the entire relationship between you and the participant. Rapport means a relationship of mutual trust, harmony, or emotional affinity. Establishing it entails building a certain level of comfort or shared understanding into a relationship. The rapport stage begins at first contact. Whether in person or on the telephone, the participant is "checking out" the personal trainer and answering the question, "Can this person help me?" Confidence or trust in your skills must be established early, because only then will the participant be willing to receive guidance.

According to Rogers et al. (1967), people in the helping profession need to communicate three basic attributes or qualities in order for the helping relationship to be successful. These three primary qualities are 1) empathy, 2) warmth, and 3) genuineness. The importance of these qualities has been demonstrated repeatedly in research by Truax and Carkuff (1967) and others. They are the foundation for a successful helping relationship and are key factors during the rapport stage.

Empathy is the ability to experience another person's world as if it were one's own. It is understanding the participant's point of view or where the participant is "coming from." The empathetic personal trainer will be able to respond appropriately to the participant's covert feelings and verbal messages by communicating perceptions to the participant. The absence of empathy may lead the participant to think the trainer does not understand what he or she is experiencing and, therefore, will block the entire helping process.

Warmth is an unconditional positive regard or a respect for another person regardless of his or her individuality and uniqueness. It bridges professional distance through friendliness and consideration regardless of a "liking" for another person. Warmth is about caring and understanding rather than judging and impersonalizing. This quality will convey a climate that communicates safety and acceptance to a participant, even when the participant is making mistakes.

Genuineness can be defined as authenticity or being honest and open without putting up a front. It is a state in which the helper's words and actions are congruent. For example, when you greet a participant with "I'm glad to see you're here today," your body language must be consistent with the words of welcome. Genuineness is the ability to relate to people without hiding behind a clipboard or white coat. It is not necessarily being fully self-revealing, but rather being committed to a responsible honesty with others.

Empathy, warmth, and genuineness are paramount in establishing trust in a working relationship. At first glance, they may seem simplistic because they are the outgrowth of ordinary effective human qualities. However, relevant research and cumulative experience point out the necessity for continuous monitoring of the timing and amount of conditions that facilitate the development of these qualities.

Interpersonal communication skills are the primary skills needed to establish rapport and thereby build a relationship. They are not only important during the rapport stage, but are necessary throughout the relationship. Interpersonal communication skills can be broadly categorized as nonverbal and verbal. The nonverbal category includes such behaviors as attending, and perceiving nonverbal and verbal messages. The verbal category includes paraphrasing, reflecting, and clarifying. Many of these skills are natural for anyone genuinely involved in helping another person, but specific communication skills can be learned, practiced, and continuously mastered.

Nonverbal Behaviors

Listening is the primary nonverbal communication skill. It is a complex concept and is not the same as hearing, which is the perception of sound through the ear. Listening obviously involves the physiology of hearing, but also is a more complex psychological procedure of involvement with the other person. In and of itself it involves skills in attending, perceiving verbal and nonverbal messages, and even verbal responding. All of these skills overlap and are difficult to treat separately.

Attending

Attending behaviors are exhibited by the listener to put the speaker at ease and entail being attentive or giving physical attention to the speaker. Instead of interrupting, the listener gives nonverbal acknowledgements during the conversation through posture, eye contact, and gestures. Verbal responses also are a form of attending. The listener may say, "Yes, I see" to encourage the speaker to continue.

Effective attending can build trust and can work wonders in human relationships. Conversely, nonattentive behavior can be devastating. For example, when you are speaking to someone who appears bored and whose eyes are continually distracted to other things, you may feel ignored and not encouraged to continue the conversation. The trainer interested in developing good attending behaviors or skills needs to be aware of the following:

1. **Posture:** When you and a participant are seated, specific postures can communicate your interest. To show involvement, face the person squarely at eye level and lean toward the person in a relaxed manner. Avoid expressing defensiveness by maintaining an open position with arms and legs uncrossed. This posture says, "I am interested in you and am ready to listen." Research has shown that these postural behaviors demonstrate to the participant the traits of empathy, warmth, and genuineness.

2. **Positioning:** Position yourself at an appropriate distance from the participant to demonstrate a respect for the participant's personal space. Hall (1966) describes an 18-inch or less distance between two people as "intimate space," an 18-inch to 4-foot distance as "personal space," a 4-foot to 12-foot distance as "social distance," and beyond 12 feet as "public distance." Most normal conversation will occur in the personal space (figure 11.2). However, the very nature of your working relationship demands at times that you enter the participant's intimate space. Because of this intimate positioning, be sensitive to the participant, particularly when hands-on work is being done. Early in the relationship you may want to ask permission to touch the participant and should take care that the participant does not misconstrue your touching or presence in her or his personal space.

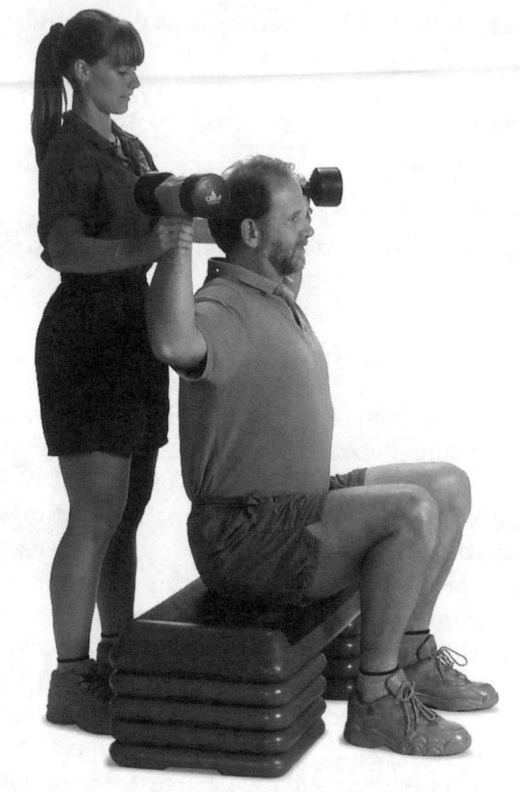

Figure 11.2 Trainer working in a client's personal space.

3. **Mirroring:** Another technique you can use to establish rapport is mimicking or mirroring. Mirroring may be either conscious or unconscious, but its purpose is to establish rapport with another person when it previously has not been. The technique of mirroring involves sensitively matching the posture and gestures of the other person, and it may include matching voice tone and tempo, and breathing patterns. These techniques often occur naturally as people interact.

4. **Eye Contact:** Eye contact is a key vehicle for indicating interest in a person. Good eye contact is not a fixed stare but rather a relaxed focus on the participant's eyes, face, and body gestures. It enables the participant to feel safe and comfortable, and it conveys your interest at the same time.

5. **Gestures:** Appropriate body movement is essential in attending. Try to use relaxed motions instead of appearing rigid and unmoving. Nervous mannerisms such as playing with objects, jingling pocket change, waving to others, and drumming fingers should be avoided.

6. **Environment:** Since much of the personal training process takes place in a gym that is usually full of talking people, blaring music, and clanging weights, a quiet place is preferable for effective communication. Pleasant surroundings facilitate conversation, so initial sessions should be conducted in a nondistracting environment. To give someone your undivided attention when distractions are present is difficult. Distractions may consist of a blaring TV or radio, a ringing telephone, people stopping by to talk, uncomfortable room temperature, and inappropriate lighting. Another type of distraction is seating arrangement. Sitting behind a desk not only puts up a physical barrier, but can be an interpersonal barrier as well. Attempts should be made to limit environmental distractions so that the participant's thoughts are not interrupted and effective communication can take place.

Perceiving Nonverbal Messages

The saying "actions speak louder than words" is especially true in communications. Mehrabian (1972) determined that 93 percent of communication is nonverbal, leaving only 7 percent for actual content of spoken words. A person's expressions, gestures, posture, and other actions provide a constant source of information. Therefore, improving your interpretation of body language is a valuable communication skill. Nonverbal messages are usually a means of expressing emotions. We search someone's face to determine feelings of anger, sadness, or disgust. Nonverbal messages tend to be more reliable than verbal messages and are essential to understanding many of the most important things others are trying to communicate to us.

The following list of nonverbal cues is not by any means exhaustive.

Feature	Nonverbal cues
Head	Nodding, cocked to side, thrown back, motioning a direction
Facial	Frowning, grimacing, animated, distracted expression
Eyes	Squinting, wide open, closed, winking, blinking, rolling, teary
Mouth	Smiling, pursed lips, lip licking, lip biting, open, closed
Skin	Blushing, paleness, perspiration, rashes
Body	Relaxed, rigid, stooped shoulders, leaning forward, leaning backward, posture chest extended out
Hands/ arms	Fidgeting, tapping, laced fingers, fisted, pointing, touching, crossed arms
Feet/legs	Foot tapping, legs crossed, legs open, knees knocking

Although voice intonation is verbal and explained in more detail later, it is appropriate to mention it as a nonverbal behavior. The sound of the voice communicates beyond the specific words. The words spoken may be fast, slow, high-pitched, loud, or whispered. The voice tells much about the mood of the speaker. For example, some people may speak very rapidly or at a high pitch when they are nervous or fearful.

General appearance also is a nonverbal cue. The way in which a person grooms and dresses is a statement to others.

One aspect of interpreting body language is noting discrepancies between verbal and nonverbal messages. It is easy to note incongruence in a person who says he is not angry while slamming his fist on the table. When you note a difference between words and nonverbal behavior, it may be helpful to search for the meaning of both. Body language can have multitudes of meanings and should be interpreted in context. A single gesture does not stand alone, but should be seen in relationship to other body movements and related to a person's words.

Misunderstandings often occur when listening only to words or observing only body language. Clarify the accuracy of your interpretation with the participant.

Perceiving Verbal Messages

To understand verbal messages, you must be able to recognize both the apparent and the underlying content. The apparent or cognitive content is comprised of the actual words and facts of the message. Cognitive messages are more easily recognized because they are stated and usually involve talking about things, people, or events and may include one or more themes or topics. The underlying or affective content is comprised of emotions, attitudes, and behaviors. Affective messages are communicated both verbally and nonverbally and are more difficult to perceive and interpret. The participant may not even be aware of his or her own feelings and might be surprised when you reveal your perceptions of what he or she is saying. Generally, emotions can be grouped into four major categories—sadness, anger, fear, and happiness—and a feeling from one category may often cover up a feeling from another.

Discriminating between cognitive and affective messages will allow you to respond appropriately to the participant. Many cognitive themes may be communicated at once, but hearing the emotional message will help you to establish priorities for cognitive topics. It seems listeners will often respond to the most recent verbal theme instead of the most important one. To illustrate, a participant says to a personal trainer in their first meeting, "There is so much going on right now. I have gained 25 pounds since starting school. I'm about to flunk chemistry and if I do, my dad said he would take me out of school. I can't concentrate and I'm not sleeping at night. It seems I just keep gaining weight." In this situation, it is necessary for the personal trainer to listen to the whole message and prioritize the cognitive themes. It may be helpful for this participant to learn some stress-reduction techniques from a qualified professional even before being put on a weight control and exercise program.

Verbal Behaviors

Verbal responses are a form of listening, and they demonstrate to the participant an understanding of what he or she is saying and feeling. Appropriate responses will encourage the participant to continue talking and will allow for more exploration. The following are commonly used verbal responses:

- **Minimal encouragers**—brief words or phrases that allow the participant to continue speaking. These verbal prods let the participant know that you are following what is being said. Example of minimal encouragers are "Mmm-hmmm," "I see," "Yes," and "Go on."
- **Paraphrasing**—a response that concisely restates the essence of the speaker's content. For example:

  –*Participant:* I didn't sleep well and don't feel like working out.

  –*Personal Trainer:* You're tired today.
- **Probing**—an attempt to gain more information. Statements such as "I'm wondering about . . . " and "Let's talk about that" will help reveal more information.
- **Reflecting**—restating feelings and/or content in a way that demonstrates understanding. You can reflect stated or implied feelings, nonverbal observation, specific content, and even what has been omitted. Examples of reflecting are "You're feeling uncomfortable about starting an exercise program," and "Sounds like you are angry at your husband for insisting that you come today."
- **Clarifying**—an attempt to understand what the participant is saying. "I'm confused about ..." and "Could you please explain that again?" are examples of clarifying statements.
- **Informing**—sharing factual information, as when you explain the pros and cons of a liquid diet.
- **Confronting**—providing the participant with mild or strong feedback about what is really going on. Confrontations are more easily heard when communicated with "I" messages such as "I feel you really don't want to be here today." Another example of confronting is "It seems to me you say . . . and yet you do . . . "
- **Questioning**—asking for a response. Questions may be closed or open. Closed questions direct participants to give a short response such as "yes"or "no." Open questions provide space for them to explore their own thoughts without being hemmed in. "What's on your mind today?" is an example of an open question.
- **Summarizing**—recapping what has been communicated and highlighting major themes. Effective summarizing can tie loose strands of a conversation together at its conclusion. A summary might begin with "Let's recap what we've discussed so far."

As mentioned earlier, the way in which we speak is often more important than what we actually say. An effective communicator is aware of the quality of delivery of the message. The elements of voice in delivery are intensity, pitch, and pace. The intensity, or force, is an important factor in delivery. Some trainers speak so softly that they cannot be heard, while others speak with such volume that they are annoying. Delivery should be loud enough to be heard, while reserving a range to emphasize important points. Working in the weight room, you may find an unusual amount of interference from others talking, background music, and weights clanging. This situation provides you with a challenge to determine an effective intensity for your voice. Decreasing voice volume in a noisy situation can actually increase the attentiveness of the other person. For example, instead of shouting to a participant in a noisy gym, you can experiment with lowering your voice volume to encourage the participant to listen more intently. This technique also will reduce vocal stress.

Pitch is the general level of the voice on the musical scale. Everyone has a characteristic pitch. Some speak in a singsong fashion while others speak in a monotone. Some people may end their sentences with an upward inflection while others end with a downward inflection. A noticeable rise in pitch level may decrease effective delivery because it usually denotes incompleteness of thought or indecisiveness. Experienced trainers cultivate a wide range of pitch, which they use effectively during delivery.

Rate means the speed of the utterance, or the number of words spoken per minute. Most people speak at the rate of 115 to 150 words per minute. Variations in rate depend upon such factors as the importance of the material, the desire for emphasis, and the mood of the content. Speaking too quickly reduces clarity and can be confusing for those listening. Even though speaking at a slower rate allows others time to absorb what is being said, speaking too slowly may bore the listener. Pausing gives people time to think about what is being said and can accentuate important information.

The rapport stage, which begins at first contact, is critical to establishing a good working relationship between the trainer and participant. Sometimes a level of comfort may be quickly established, while at other times more time and energy may have to be expended to win a participant's trust. Interpersonal communication skills can be learned and mastered. Merely reading about these skills does not necessarily improve application to everyday situations; they must be continuously practiced. Even though the rapport stage is presented as the first stage, there is really no end to it. The primary qualities (empathy, warmth, and genuineness) and the interpersonal communication skills are important and valuable throughout the entire trainer/participant relationship.

Investigation Stage

The goal of the investigation stage is to gather information about the participant's present fitness level, personal goals, and physical and psychological limitations. This may begin in the initial interview, when the participant is encouraged to talk about desires and expectations for training. Historically, health history and lifestyle questionnaire forms are filled out by the individual participant. However, you are encouraged to ask these questions orally. This method requires more time, but it can be valuable in establishing rapport. In addition, participants will probably reveal more about themselves when they observe your interest. The least interaction that should occur is that you and the participant discuss her or his written responses to the questionnaire. During the discussion you can probe, question, and clarify in order to gain more information. After all the information is gathered, you and the participant can begin planning by setting goals and making decisions about how to achieve them.

Planning Stage

Up to this point, most of your time with the participant has been spent building rapport and gathering appropriate information regarding his or her lifestyle behaviors and current fitness levels. In the planning stage, the trainer and participant begin setting goals according to the participant's needs and desires. Because there are usually several ways to reach any goal, you must make use of decision-making skills to determine the best course of action. The outcome will be more effective if the process is done together than if you dictate to the participant what to do each step of the way.

Decision making occurs frequently as we go about our daily activities; we must constantly decide how we'll spend our time, money, and energy during any given day. Many of these decisions are second nature for us, so we do not consider the process we go through in determining what is best in a particular situation. Even though there are many decision-making models, the basic process for the personal trainer/participant relationship consists of the following steps:

1. Setting goals
2. Generating alternatives

3. Exploring the alternatives
4. Making the decision
5. Formulating a plan
6. Evaluating the implementation

Setting Goals

Participants will seldom approach you with neatly stated goals. They are usually expressed in vague statements, such as "I want to be in better shape" or "I want to lose some weight." It is your responsibility to translate these general aims into precise goals.

Effective goals must be SMART, which means they are:

Specific—The goals must specifically tell what is to be accomplished. They must be easily understood and unambiguous.

Measurable—The goals must be measurable so there is no question of attainment. Examples of measurement would be percent body fat, number of pounds, or a specific fun run.

Attainable—The goals must be attainable, not too difficult or too easy. Easy goals don't motivate and overly difficult ones may frustrate.

Relevant—The goals must be relevant or pertinent to the particular interest, needs, and abilities of the participant.

Time-bound—The goals must be time-bound with specific deadlines for completion.

It is difficult to know when a participant has obtained a goal that is expressed in terms such as "I want to get in better shape." However, both parties would know when the goal is attained if it is stated as "I want to be able to walk three miles in 45 minutes by March 31st" or "I'd like to drop 20 pounds by the end of the year." According to Dick and Carey (1990), one method of clarifying a broad goal is to follow these steps:

1. Write the goal down.
2. Write down things the participant can do to demonstrate he or she has achieved the goal (e.g., lose 20 pounds, drop to 12 percent body fat, fit into a size 10 dress she hasn't worn in three years).
3. Sort through the statements and pick out the ones that best represent the original goal.
4. Rewrite the original goal to include your new statements or make smaller goals.

Express the goals in terms of participant actions rather than trainer actions. A goal stated as "The trainer will get me in shape" does not give the participant ownership of or responsibility for the goal. The goals must also be realistic. It would not be realistic for a non-runner participant to say, "I want to run a 10K next week." Realistic goals will help ensure the participant's success. Finally, setting both short- and long-range goals will be helpful. For example, a female participant who has 30 percent body fat may have a long-range goal of obtaining 20 percent body fat in six months. The short-range goal might be to reach 27 percent in the next four weeks. Setting a time line, or date of completion, often creates a sense of urgency for both the participant and the trainer and can be effective in overcoming the participant's procrastination. You also can help the beginner create behavioral goals that will remove intimidating evaluation procedures like body-fat tests, tape measures, and weight scales. An example behavioral goal can be stated as "I want to exercise three times per week, for 30 minutes of aerobic training, 20 minutes of strength training, and 10 minutes of stretching, for 12 consecutive weeks starting January 1st." In this example, the trainer and participant are establishing positive lifestyle changes rather than strictly emphasizing physiological changes.

Generating Alternatives

This step in the decision-making process involves proposing all possible alternatives for reaching the goal. This brainstorming process gives the participant more choices. For example, a participant might define a goal as "I want to get my thighs stronger for the upcoming ski season." In exploring alternatives to reach this goal, you and the participant might generate the following:

a. I could increase my thigh strength by riding the stationary cycle.
b. I could increase my thigh strength by performing squats with free-weights.
c. I could increase my thigh strength by climbing stairs.
d. I could increase my thigh strength by stepping up and down on a bench.

The participant now has several viable options for obtaining the goal.

Exploring the Alternatives

After brainstorming the list of options, the next step is to weigh or rank them. Evaluate the alternatives for implementation realities and hypothesized consequences. Some options may immediately be thrown out because they are impractical, making it easier for the participant to prioritize the remaining alternatives. From the previous example, a participant may discard option b because of its impracticality. With your help, the participant may then rank the rest of the alternatives according to interest, availability, and time.

Making the Decision

You and the participant now decide on one or more of the alternatives. Choose the most effective strategy or a combination of the options for this person at this time. For example, our skier may choose to train for skiing by doing squats with free-weights at the gym at least two days a week, and may climb stairs at home when there's not time to get to the gym.

Formulating a Plan

At this point you and the participant determine a specific sequence of action that likely will result in the accomplishment of the goals. Formulating an action plan includes who needs to do what, when, where, what materials are required, and so forth. This step is further developed as exercise programming.

Evaluating the Implementation

This step measures accomplishment in relation to the predetermined goals and may occur in a formal setting where the participant's fitness level is reassessed. The evaluation process may also occur informally during the training sessions as both participant and trainer report progress. Either way, together you determine the accomplishment and, if necessary, a new set of action steps.

Action Stage

Once rapport has been established, information has been gathered, and goals have been set, the action stage, or actual training, begins. You coach the participant toward her or his goals. As a teacher or tutor, you may use many methods of education. In a broad sense, personal training is similar to an individual approach to direct instruction, which is essentially active learning. It consists of the trainer's explaining a new concept or skill to the participant. Afterwards, the participant demonstrates understanding by practicing under the trainer's direction, while the trainer encourages the participant to continue to practice until the skills become natural. The climate of direct instruction is task-oriented and is high in expectations. The participant will be more motivated to learn in areas that he or she finds interesting and may actively resist learning in areas that he or she doesn't find interesting. You can increase motivation by teaching information that meets the needs and desires of the participant. Once an area of interest is discovered, you can use a variety of teaching techniques to help the participant feel successful with learning. According to Wlodkowski (1984), an initial small success can lead to greater confidence in the learning process, improved self-esteem, and increased motivation to learn new things. Your selection of techniques will depend upon your style and that of the participant. What works well for one person may not work for another. Having a variety of teaching techniques is essential to the success of the trainer/participant relationship.

Multisensory Input

Participants gather information through their senses (visual, auditory, kinesthetic, smell, taste), and this creates a pathway for information to be received and processed by them. Pathways often overlap, with participants showing a "preference" for gathering information in one pathway over others. Approximately 60 percent of the population prefer a primary visual pathway, while 20 percent access information auditorily and another 20 percent prefer to receive data kinesthetically. Even though a participant may enjoy charts and pictures because she or he prefers to gather information visually, that person is still able to gather information verbally, although it is not her or his dominant pathway.

You can identify which pathway the participant prefers to gather information through by observing the person's actions during learning situations and by listening for clues in the person's language (table 11.1). For example, a trainer is discussing basic anatomy with a participant using an anatomy chart on the wall. The visual learner may focus directly on the chart and may walk right up to it while the trainer is talking. The auditory learner may ignore the chart and focus directly on the trainer's words. The kinesthetic learner may touch the chart, or touch and move his or her corresponding muscles as the trainer describes them.

If you can identify the learning pathway that the participant prefers, you can match your words and behaviors to the person's preference (table 11.1). This not only enhances learning, but it also allows you to maintain rapport with the participant.

"Tell, Show, Do"
I hear and I forget.
I see and I remember.
I do and I understand.
—*Anonymous*

This proverb is at the heart of day-to-day personal training. As early as the 1930s, John Dewey advocated "learning by doing." Probably the most effective systematic method of teaching a skill is by explanation, demonstration, and execution, also known as "tell, show, do." It involves observing how something is done correctly and then performing it under the supervision of an instructor (figure 11.3). The instructor provides the student with an auditory, visual, and kinesthetic learning experience, thus stimulating all learning pathways.

Explanation

The explanation should be a concise verbal description of the skill that gives a clear understanding of what is to be accomplished. A simple skill may only require one sentence, while a more complex skill may require more detail. During

Table 11.1 Learning Pathways

	Visual	Auditory	Kinesthetic
Participant actions	Watches intently Prefers reading	Listens carefully Prefers hearing	Touches or holds Prefers to be spotted
Participant statement	"Oh, I see" "Let me see that again"	"Yeah, I hear you" "Say that one more time"	"I feel that" "This does not feel right"
Strategy	Demonstrations	Question and answer	Hands on supervision

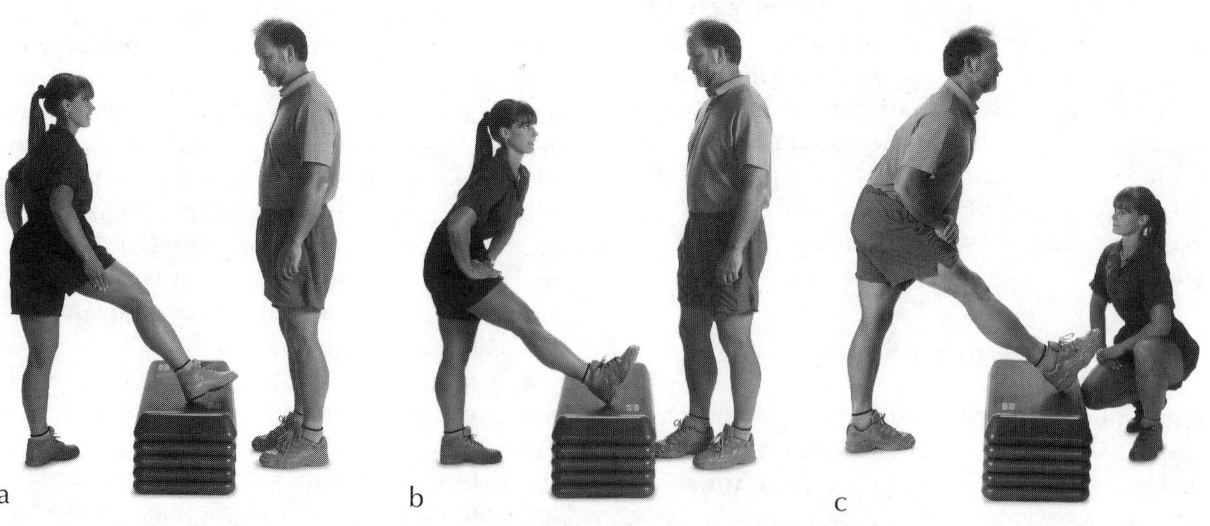

Figure 11.3 Tell, Show, Do. *(a)* Trainer explaining hamstring stretch. *(b)* Trainer demonstrating hamstring stretch. *(c)* Trainer watching client perform hamstring stretch.

this time, the participant should be told what to watch for during the demonstration. For example, the trainer might say, "I'm now going to show you how to perform a biceps curl. Watch how I control the movement and do not use momentum to help lift the weight."

Demonstration

The demonstration is the visual presentation of the skill. It is critical that it be an accurate representation of the desired action. Therefore, you must be keenly aware kinesthetically so that proper form is communicated to the participant. If you have just explained that there should be no use of momentum or swinging during the biceps curl, then you must perform the curl with complete control without using momentum for the lift.

Demonstrating the movement slowly will help the participant see what is happening. Repeating the demonstration at normal speed while reiterating the main points also will aid learning. The explanation and demonstration steps can be effectively combined in order to save time.

Performance

The performance is the participant's opportunity to practice the skill. You should carefully monitor and supervise the participant's performance to correct errors and encourage proper form. Constructive feedback and more practice time complete the learning loop. The problem in many teaching programs is that all the above steps are not followed. Often the explanation or "tell" step is not followed by the "show" and "do" steps. Telling people exactly how to perform a skill does not ensure that they will be able to do it correctly. Simply telling a participant to "stretch the hamstrings after you jog" does not ensure that the person will perform the stretch effectively. To complete the process, the participant should be shown how to perform a hamstring stretch properly and then given an opportunity to practice it while you coach proper form and execution.

You must decide if a skill should be taught as a whole or if it should be broken into parts. These methods of teaching are often referred to as the whole approach and the parts approach, respectively. Less complex skills are usually taught as a whole to establish a general idea and feel for the movement. Practicing the biceps curl from start to finish is an appropriate application of the whole approach. More complex exercises that require much attention may be demonstrated by you as a whole movement, and then broken down into lower-torso and upper-torso movements so that the student may master each part of the skill. Breaking down race walking into individual parts makes it easier to perform the activity in its entirety.

Association

You can also help the participant learn by creating links or bridges between old and new information. By discovering what the participant already knows, beginning in the rapport stage, you can build on the person's preexisting knowledge. Each participant will have her or his own unique experiences to draw from. For example, when working with a participant who skis, you can redirect the person's feet during a standing calf stretch by telling the person to "point both skis downhill." By using an association, you allow the participant to place meaning to the instruction, and, ultimately, the person learns more deeply. The association is more likely to make a lasting improvement on performance.

Modeling

Humans want to identify with other humans. We look at others and imitate traits we would like to have. The concept of emulating another's behavior or attitudes is called modeling, and the individual demonstrating the behavior is known as the model. We see many examples of modeling in our daily lives. Children adopt parent's language patterns and nonverbal cues, and they can learn aggressive behavior from watching television. Prestigious models have a profound impact on clothing and dress, hair styles, music, and food. Consider the widespread use of leg warmers in exercise classes after Jane Fonda's "Workout" videotape came on the market. According to Bandura (1977), modeling is probably the most efficient and effective form of learning a new behavior. This gives the teacher both enormous opportunity and responsibility.

Two forms of modeling are identified by Good and Brophy (1987). The first is simply imitation or "monkey see, monkey do." The observer adopts the behavior of the model, as in the leg warmer example. The second is more complex because the observer must infer attitudes, values, beliefs, or personality characteristics as a result of watching the model. The observer draws his or her own conclusions and, over time, may change his or her behavior. This is a common occurrence in the trainer/participant relationship. As a result of observing your dedication to a healthy and fit lifestyle, the participant may choose a healthier alternative to a regular Friday afternoon happy hour. In this form of modeling, people often communicate attitudes unconsciously and are unaware of the effects. Students constantly observe a teacher's approach to a subject, studying the teacher's attitudes and beliefs. They watch the way the teacher interacts with students and other colleagues, and the student may then make inferences regarding the learning process. The way in which a teacher responds to a student's question can affect the learning climate. The response, "I don't know ... let's find out," models enthusiasm for learning and makes not knowing the answer acceptable. This form of modeling is both subtle and powerful.

There are several factors that influence modeling. The first is the state of the learner. The more uncertain a learner is, the more significant the effects of the model will be. Therefore, a participant is more susceptible to the effects of your modeling at the beginning of the relationship. A second factor that influences modeling is the status of the model in the eyes of the learner. Students are more likely to adopt the behaviors of a teacher they like and respect than of one they do not.

You cannot escape being a model. However, you can decide what kind of model you will be. Who a personal trainer is and what she or he does sends loud and clear messages to the participant about what is important and how the program is really supposed to work. In other words, the way you behave is just as important as what you say. The trainer who advocates doing what he or she is unwilling to do will more than likely be unconvincing. For example, it is fruitless for a trainer to tell participants that steroids are bad for their health when it is known that the trainer uses steroids. "Do as I say, not as I do" has no place in the trainer/participant relationship. The participant views you as an expert and will generally believe everything that you say and do with regard to fitness. Therefore, it is critical that you be aware of your influence. Be competent and wise in fitness matters and obtain at least a level of fitness that corresponds to the level of teaching. Going beyond mere competence is even more desirable.

Contracting

Contracting finds its roots in the behavioral theory of reinforcement that says rewarded behavior tends to be repeated. Contracting systematically arranges the rewards so that the probability of the desired response is increased. Most behavioral contracts are verbal or written agreements between two or more people and consist of two primary parts (figure 11.4). The first part is specifying the behavior to be achieved. The second part is stating specific reinforcements that will reward the desired behavior. It may take the form of, "If you will do ________, I will do ________." A contract does not necessarily require involving other people. It is possible for a person to make an agreement with himself or herself by preparing a self-contract (figure 11.5).

All helping relationships have implied contracts or understandings that both people will have responsibilities to carry out. Verbal or informal contracts are used when there is little chance of a misunderstanding of the conditions. The written contract is used to prevent those misunderstandings and to add impact by having the participant sign his or her name to indicate a commitment.

Several features are necessary for an effective contract. The terms should be explicitly stated so that the expectations are clearly understood by all parties. An example of an unclear contract statement is "I agree to lose some weight so I may do something I enjoy." A more clearly stated contract term might be "I will lose 5 pounds and then I'll be permitted to buy that new dress." Many contracts fail because of impossible terms, so they should be feasible and reasonable. "I will lose 50 pounds this month so I can buy that new dress" is an unreasonable goal. "I will lose 1 to 2 pounds a week for the next two months" is a more reasonable goal. Composing the contract in positive rather than negative terms will encourage a more favorable attitude toward the contract. "If you do not quit smoking, I will not work with you" is a negative approach. A more positive approach would be to determine a reward given upon smoking cessation.

To ensure satisfactory results, contracts need to be evaluated frequently and perhaps renegotiated. This renegotiation can occur any time or during the formal evaluation process. What appeared to be fair and reasonable initially may not

I, the undersigned, agree to the following conditions, which I will follow to the best of my ability.

From __________ to __________, for a period of one week, I will choose to eat at meal time only.

From __________ to __________, for a period of one week, I will eat foods recommended by the American Heart Association and the American Dietetic Association.

At the end of the week, as a reward for fulfilling the above conditions, I will attend a movie or other social function with my husband.

Date ______________________________

Signature of wife ____

I, the undersigned, agree to take my wife to a movie when the above conditions are met.

Date ______________________________

Signature of husband ____

Figure 11.4 Example of an exercise contract between two people.

I will walk in my target zone a minimum of _____ minutes _____ times per week.

I will record my progress in my personal log.

The following people will help me reach my goal:

____

Person	Method
1. ______________________	1. ______________________
2. ______________________	2. ______________________
3. ______________________	3. ______________________
4. ______________________	4. ______________________

I will reward myself for adhering to the above for _____ weeks with the following:

____

____

____

I will begin the program (date) and will reevaluate it on (date).

Figure 11.5 Example of a personal exercise contract.

be so later. If a participant discovers she or he cannot meet a specified commitment, you should discuss the difficulty, and a new contract can be negotiated, drafted, and signed. This evaluation process will help ensure that the contract remains effective.

The following questions will help you troubleshoot while writing contracts:

1. Are the terms of the contract clear?
2. Is the contract fair?
3. Is the contract positive?
4. Is the target behavior clearly specified?
5. Does the contract provide for immediate reinforcement?
6. Is the reinforcement frequent and in small amounts?
7. Does the participant understand the contract?
8. Is there a time specified for evaluation?

Feedback

Feedback is a powerful contributor to effective learning and participant performance. It is any information about current or past behavior that can be used to improve performance and can be given verbally or nonverbally. It usually occurs after participants have asked a question or done something related to the exercise session. Feedback informs participants of the correctness of their performance and recognizes their effort. You will naturally respond and react to participants' behavior, and they are greatly influenced by the way you behave toward them. They monitor their trainers' reactions and adjust their performance in accordance with what they interpret.

In order for feedback to be effective, a clearly defined standard of performance must be given. For example, a trainer defines the standard of performance for proper placement and movement of the arms in race walking during the explanation and demonstration of the skill. The participant's performance is then measured and corrected according to the demonstrated criteria. The performance standard may need to be set at frequent intervals during instruction by continuing to explain and demonstrate. In order for the feedback to be effective and learning to occur, there must be a practice session that gives the participant an opportunity to correct his or her performance and reach the preset standard.

Research indicates that effective feedback has three characteristics: (1) it is specific; (2) it is contingent on performance; and (3) it provides corrective information for the learner. Specific feedback is clear about what was right and/or wrong. You may watch a participant incorrectly perform a lat pulldown on the weight equipment and then exclaim, "That's not right, Susie!" Your response does not aid Susie's understanding of the performance; it only lets her know that it was wrong. By contrast, you might respond, "Not quite, Susie, let's reverse the position of your hands." Corrective feedback helps the participant know what was wrong with the performance and what to do to get back on track. The number of different cues is infinite, and striving for unique ones will require your creativity and committed practice.

Feedback should not be given for every single move because too much of a good thing can have a negative effect; people tend to disregard excessive compliments. The feedback should match the achievement and specifically relate the response to the performance. For example, a personal trainer observing a participant performing a biceps curl might respond with "That's good," which is only a statement of general praise. However, an even more effective response would be "That's it John, you're really isolating the biceps muscle now." This response gives the participant specific information as to why the performance is correct. To maximize the effect, cues can be personalized by using a participant's name, for instance, "That's the right idea, Jennie." Typical verbal cues are:

Good	Excellent
Right	Correct
All right	OK
Very good	Fine

These words are less effective because they have been overused. Examples of other, more effective cues that you might use are:

That's an effective thought.	You are really with it today.
You've got it.	I'd give that move a 10.
You're on the money.	

Nonverbal feedback is far more effective than verbal feedback. Participants tune into facial expressions and gestures. When used properly, nonverbal cues are the epitome of personalization. How else can a "thumbs up" signal and a generous smile be interpreted? Nonverbal positive feedback interactions include:

Smiling	Making an "Okay" sign
Nodding	Patting on the back
Shaking hands	Touching
Clapping	Winking
Thumbs up	Applauding

Nonverbal negative feedback interactions include:

Frowning	Thumbs down
Shaking head	Drumming fingers
Looking away	Rolling eyes
Grimacing	

A final and important point needs to be made regarding verbal and nonverbal feedback. As in all interpersonal communication, when both verbal and nonverbal cues are given, they must be congruent. For example, if you frown while telling a participant that she or he is doing a great job, the two behaviors are incongruent and the conflicting messages are confusing. The participant will receive a mixed message and will probably believe the frown rather than the words. On the other hand, when verbal and nonverbal cuing are congruently combined, you can have a powerful influence on the participant.

References

Bandura, A. (1977). *Social learning theory.* Englewood Cliffs, NJ: Prentice Hall.

Dick, W., and L. Carey (1990). *The sytematic design of instruction* (3rd ed.). Reading, MA: Addison-Wesley.

Good, F., and J. Brophy (1987). *Looking in classrooms.* New York: Harper & Row.

Hall, E.T. (1966). *The hidden dimensions.* Garden City: Doubleday.

Krumboltz, J. (1966). *Stating the goals of counseling* (Monograph No. 1). Fullerton, CA: California Personnel and Guidance Association.

Mehrabian, A. (1972). *Nonverbal communication.* Chicago: Aldine-Atherton.

Rogers, C.R., E.T. Gendlin, D.J. Keisler, and C.D. Truax. (1967). *The therapeutic relationship and its impact.* Madison, WI: University of Wisconsin Press.

Truax, C.B., and R.F. Carkuff. (1967). *Toward effective counseling and psychotherapy.* Chicago: Aldine.

Wlodkowski, R. (1984). *Enhancing adult motivation to learn.* San Francisco: Jossey-Bass.

Suggested Readings

Bolton, R. (1979). *People skills.* New York: Simon & Schuster.

Carkhuff, R.R., and W.A.Anthony. (1979). *The skills of helping.* Amherst: Human Resource Development Press.

Jacobson, D., P.D. Eggen, and D. Kauchak.(1989). *Methods for teaching: A skills approach.* Columbus, OH: Merrill.

Kauchak, D.P., and P.E. Eggen. (1989). *Learning and teaching: Research-based methods.* Needham Heights, MA: Allyn & Bacon.

Knowles, M. (1989). *The making of an adult educator.* San Francisco: Jossey-Bass.

Mitchell, G. (1987). *The trainer's handbook.* New York: AMACOM.

Mosston, M. (1966). *Teaching physical education: From command to discovery.* Columbus, OH: Merrill.

Okun, B.F. (1987). *Effective helping interviewing and counseling techniques.* Monterey, CA: Brooks/Cole.

Rogers, C. (1961). *On becoming a person.* Boston: Houghton Mifflin.

Wheels, A. (1973). *How people change.* New York: Harper & Row.

12

Musculoskeletal Injuries

Melinda Flegel

* Melinda Flegel is an athletic trainer certified by the National Athletic Trainers' Association (NATA). She has an MS in physical education from the University of Illinois and has taught group exercise in the Philadelphia area and for the University of Illinois.

Although enjoyable and physically beneficial, any exercise program can lead to injuries and health problems. Physicians, athletic trainers, and physical therapists are concerned with injuries in sport- and exercise-related activities. With backgrounds in sports, medicine, and exercise science, these specialists are well suited to give prompt diagnosis, treatment, and rehabilitation for exercise injuries. Considering the injury potential inherent in exercise, you, like the sports medicine specialists, need to know how injuries happen, how to prevent them, and how to provide first aid (depending on your YMCA's policy for handling emergencies) when they occur.

Musculoskeletal injuries are probably the most common injuries that happen to exercise participants. Unfortunately, they are also one of the leading reasons why people stop exercising. To help prevent musculoskeletal injuries, you must focus on developing appropriate programs to develop strength, endurance, and flexibility for your participants. Even when programs are properly designed, however, injuries can happen. The road to recovery from an injury is often quicker and more complete when the participant is properly conditioned, facilitating rehabilitation of the injured area.

What can you do to minimize injuries for your personal training participants? Although this chapter will not teach you to diagnose and treat injuries, it does provide you with a basic understanding of common exercise injuries and health concerns and, more importantly, how to prevent them. An understanding of injuries will help you recognize potential safety problems and injuries and react logically if you are confronted by them.

We begin this chapter by defining some key anatomical and sports medicine terms. Then we briefly describe some common musculoskeletal injuries, with a special section on muscle soreness and fatigue, and some additional health problems related to exercise. We conclude with tips on preventing injuries and some basic first aid for treating injuries.

Anatomical and Sports Medicine Terms

To fully understand the intricacies of injuries, you need to become familiar with a few anatomical and medical terms. Let's start by taking a look at the structure of a joint (figure 12.1). Knees, elbows, and other joints consist of bones, cartilage, muscles, tendons, and ligaments.

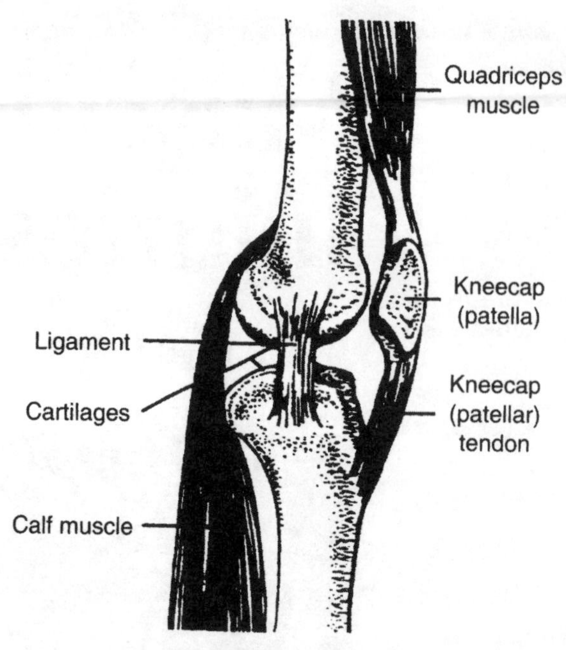

Figure 12.1 Structures of the knee joint.

Tendons and ligaments are the structures that hold joints together. Ligaments act as guide wires, connecting bone to bone. They function as the joint's primary stabilizers, and muscles serve as back-up supporters. Without ligaments and muscles, bones in a joint would easily dislocate or separate. Tendons connect muscles to bones and help make a joint move. And to protect a joint's integrity, cartilage acts as a shock absorber and prevents the bones from abrading (wearing down).

With this basic anatomy in mind, let's discuss some medical terms that you will undoubtedly come across when reading sports medicine information.

- **Strains.** Stretching and tearing injuries that affect muscles and tendons. A strain often results when a sudden or persistent stretch forces a muscle or tendon beyond its normal stretching limit. Among the structures strained most often are the calf muscles, the Achilles tendon, the quadriceps muscles, the hamstring muscles, the shoulder muscles, and the lower back.

Depending upon their severity, strains are classified in one of three categories (see figure 12.2). A Grade I strain involves stretching muscle or tendon fibers with minimal tearing. Symptoms include little or no swelling, point tenderness at the site of the injury, and mild pain when the muscle or tendon is stretched or contracted. In a Grade II strain, there is a stretching of muscle or tendon fibers accompanied by partial tearing. Grade II symptoms include pain, swelling, and possibly a slight indentation at the site of the strain. Grade III strains involve extensive tearing of muscle or tendon fibers and cause pain, swelling, and an obvious indentation at the injury site.

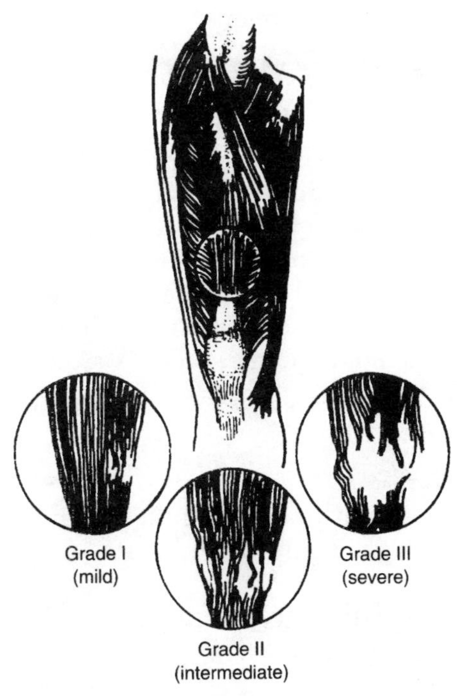

Figure 12.2 Three types of muscle strains.

- **Sprains.** Stretching and tearing injuries of the ligaments. A common cause of sprains is a sudden twisting movement that stretches or tears the ligament fibers. Sprains, like strains, can be classified according to severity, with varying levels of pain, swelling, and disability (see figure 12.3).
- **Tendinitis.** An inflammation or irritation of a tendon resulting from overuse or a forceful stretch. Those tendons most affected by tendinitis are the Achilles tendon and the elbow and shoulder tendons.
- **Chondromalacia.** A softening or abrading of joint cartilage as a natural part of aging (wear and tear) or as a result of direct injury.

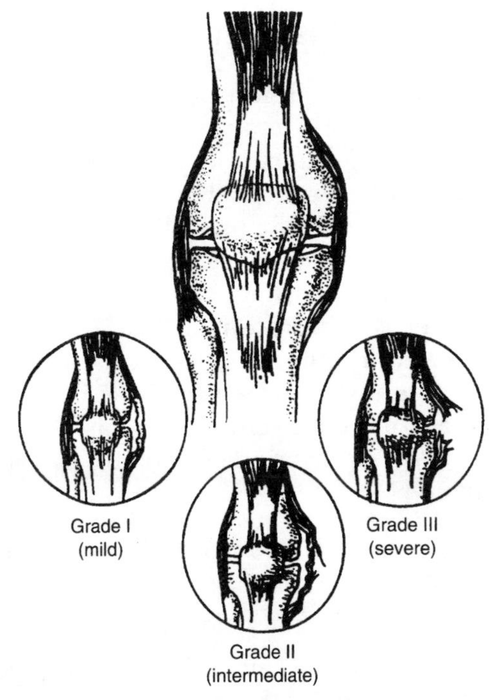

Figure 12.3 Three types of ligament sprains.

- **Periositis.** An inflammation or irritation of the membrane that covers the bones.
- **Foot pronation.** A structural condition in which the foot rolls inward, under the ankle (see figure 12.4).

With an understanding of these general terms, we can now move on to discuss some of the specific injuries suffered by exercise participants.

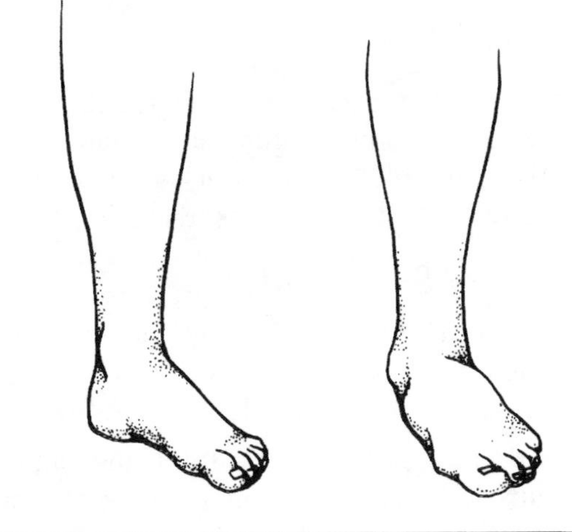

Figure 12.4 Comparison of a normal and a pronated foot.

Musculoskeletal Injuries

Most exercise-related musculoskeletal injuries fall into the category of *overuse syndrome*. Overuse injuries occur when the body is subjected to abnormal, constant, or repetitive stress or is inadequately prepared for a particular activity. With repetitive activities (jumping, running) and stressful movements (twisting, lunging), it's easy to understand why overuse injuries can occur. Individuals who are out of shape or are participating at a level too advanced for their physical capabilities are also prone to overuse syndrome. Be aware of the following signs and symptoms that indicate injury:

- Persistent pain, even when the body part is resting
- Swelling and/or discoloration
- Increased pain when body weight is placed on the injury
- Pain in a joint
- Pain/tenderness when the injured area is touched lightly
- Deviations in normal movement patterns

Common exercise-related overuse injuries are shin splints, calf muscle strain, Achilles tendinitis, bone bruises, stress fractures, arch strain, patellar (kneecap) chondromalacia, impingement syndrome, and carpal tunnel syndrome. Let's take a look at each to find out why and how it happens.

Shin Splints

A catch-all phrase used to describe aching pain in the lower leg, shin splints can be caused by a strain to lower leg muscles or tendons, by shin bone periositis, or by a stress fracture.

Causes of Shin Splints

- Abnormal foot positioning: The foot may be tilted in (pronated) unconsciously, which puts stress on the calf muscles and tendons.
- Muscle imbalance: The front and back leg muscles may not be equal in strength, causing the weaker of the two to suffer from strain.
- Excessive shock transmitted through the lower leg: Unyielding floor surfaces or poorly padded shoes force the leg to bear the brunt of the impact shock.

Calf Muscle Strain and Achilles Tendinitis

In the back of the lower leg, potential problem areas include the calf muscle and the Achilles tendon at its base. Both injuries are felt as aching or sharp pain, with calf strains being felt in the muscle belly and Achilles tendinitis in the upper-heel area. Standing or jumping on the toes or rocking back or walking on the heels can be painful in both conditions.

Causes of Calf Muscle Strain and Achilles Tendinitis

- Shortened calf muscles or Achilles tendon: Some individuals naturally have shortened calf muscles or tendons. Others have worn high-heeled shoes that let the calf muscles and tendons shorten. In either case, stretching the muscle or tendon beyond its normal limits can result in a strain.
- Inadequate stretching in warm-up or cool-down.
- Repeated stress.
- Landing on the balls of the feet without heels ever touching the floor.

Bone Bruises, Stress Fractures, and Arch Strain

With the pounding often associated with exercise, the foot is another site of frequent injury. As in all overuse injuries, hard surfaces and shoes that are improperly fitted or padded can take their toll on the feet. Foot stress most often appears as a bone bruise, a stress fracture, or an arch strain.

Bone bruises and stress fractures can occur at the heel or ball of the foot. Bone bruises are commonly felt on the sole of the foot, whereas stress fractures at the ball of the foot are usually felt on top. Stress fractures become more painful with exercise.

Causes of Bone Bruises and Stress Fractures

- Poorly padded shoes or nonyielding floor surfaces that force the foot to absorb excess shock.
- Deviations in proper running gait.

Arch strain is pain felt on the sole of the foot between the heel and the ball. Most often it results from a strain to the tendon that spans over the area.

Causes of Arch Strain

- Flat feet.
- Inadequate arch support.

Patellar Chondromalacia

The knee, like the foot and the ankle, is subjected to the shock of the body pounding against the floor or the repeated bending during strength training. A common knee problem in exercise programs is patellar (kneecap) chondromalacia.

In patellar chondromalacia, the cartilage surface on the back of the kneecap becomes irritated and begins to crack and flake. It is most noticeable as a pain underneath the kneecap that is felt when climbing stairs, sitting in a theatre, or squatting, kneeling, or bending at the knee.

Causes of Patellar Chondromalacia

- Kneecap doesn't ride properly in its groove on the thigh bone (especially in people with knock-knees or bowlegs).
- Natural wear and tear on the joint from aging.
- Direct blow to the top of the kneecap.
- Excessive kneeling or squatting.

Impingement Syndrome

In shoulder impingement syndrome, swollen rotator cuff muscles and the bursa are "pinched" by the scapula when the arm is abducted. This syndrome makes it difficult to perform exercises that require the arms to be above the head for extended periods of time. Exercises such as overhead presses, military presses, and lat pulldowns may aggravate this condition.

Causes of Impingement Syndrome

- Prior shoulder dislocation injury, which causes discomfort when the shoulder is placed in an abducted and externally rotated position such as the starting position of a bench press.
- Overstretched front or anterior ligaments of the shoulder.

Carpal Tunnel Syndrome

Most commonly seen as an occupational illness, carpal tunnel syndrome occurs in persons who do repetitive tasks such as working at a computer keyboard. It also can result from weight training and other athletic activities. Individuals with carpal tunnel syndrome may complain of numbness in the middle fingers of the hand, usually after repetitive work using the wrist and finger flexor muscles. Stretching to keep these muscles flexible can help prevent this type of injury.

Causes of Carpal Tunnel Syndrome

- Doing repetitive tasks such as typing or working at a cash register.
- Weight training.
- Engaging in athletic activities that involve extensive use of the wrist and finger-flexor muscles.

Injuries Summary

A summary of the overuse injuries common to exercisers together with their causes and symptoms is presented in table 12.1.

Let's move on to discuss a couple of general musculoskeletal problems that are also common to exercise: muscle soreness and muscle cramps.

Muscle Soreness and Fatigue

Muscle soreness and fatigue is inevitable for anyone who exercises, particularly newcomers. Most often it occurs in individuals who begin to participate either after a period of inactivity or at a higher level of difficulty. The muscles and tendons are forced to work harder than they are accustomed to, and the result is a general aching pain that can last from 1 to 3 days.

Muscle Soreness

Two general types of exercise-related muscle soreness exist. One is the immediate soreness felt during exercise or immediately thereafter. This type of soreness appears to be most directly related to the buildup in the muscle of lactic acid that has leaked out of the muscle cells. Usually this excess lactic acid is removed quite rapidly after a training session, generally within 30 to 60 minutes. Immediate soreness may also be due to

Table 12.1 Common Overuse Injuries

Injury	Common causes	Symptoms
Shin splints	Abnormal foot positioning Muscle imbalance Excessive impact shock	Dull ache in the lower leg after workout Pain on moving the foot up and down
Strains	Inadequate stretching Stretching muscles beyond their normal limits Landing on balls of feet without heels touching floor	Grade I – some tenderness, no swelling Grade II – tenderness at site, painful movement, swelling if not treated Grade III – immediate loss of function, swelling
Sprains	Sudden twisting movements	Grade I – some tenderness, no swelling Grade II – tenderness at site, painful movement, swelling if not treated Grade III – immediate loss of function, swelling
Tendinitis	Inadequate stretching Repeated stress	Tenderness
Bone bruises	Hard surfaces Poorly padded shoes	Pain at the heel or ball of the foot
Stress fractures	Hard surfaces Deviated running gait Poorly padded shoes	Pain at the fracture site Increased pain with exercise
Arch strain	Flat feet Inadequate arch support	Pain on the sole of the foot, between the heel and ball
Patellar chondromalacia	Excessive kneeling/squatting Direct blow to the kneecap Knock-knees/bowlegs Natural wear and tear	Pain underneath the kneecap
Impingement syndrome	Prior shoulder dislocation Overstretched front or anterior shoulder ligaments	
Carpal tunnel syndrome	Repetitive tasks Weight training or other athletic activities	Numbness of middle fingers
Muscle soreness—immediate	Buildup of lactic acid	Immediate discomfort
Muscle soreness—delayed	Microtrauma of muscle tissue	Discomfort 1 to 3 days after training

minor muscle or connective tissue tears, which should not be ignored.

The second type of soreness persists for one to three days following a training session. Immediately following a hard strength training session the muscles may feel tight, pumped-up, and fatigued, but not necessarily sore. However, the following day the exerciser may experience considerable muscle soreness, which may persist for another day or two. This is known as delayed onset muscle soreness (DOMS). DOMS is most likely due to microtrauma (microscopic tears) in the muscle tissue, and it usually requires a couple of days for the repair and building processes to be completed. Research indicates that eccentric muscle contractions produce more muscle microtrauma than concentric or isometric muscle contractions, and they may be the principal cause of DOMS.

Muscle Fatigue

The reasons for fatigue are varied, but they relate primarily to the intensity and duration of exercise. Skeletal muscle eventually fatigues after a period of work or exercise. During heavy strength training the primary causes of muscle fatigue are the depletion of anaerobic energy supplies and the accumulation of anaerobic byproducts such as lactic acid. However, even when a muscle is fatigued to the point that it can no longer contract concentrically, a two-minute recovery period is usually sufficient to replace the anaerobic energy stores and remove the anaerobic byproducts.

Causes of Muscle Soreness and Fatigue

- Injury or strain to the muscle or tendon.
- Insufficient supply of oxygen to working muscles.
- Insufficient levels of potassium, sodium, or other minerals in the body. These minerals are utilized in muscle contraction, so insufficient supplies disrupt normal function.

Additional Exercise-Related Health Problems

In addition to suffering musculoskeletal injuries, exercise participants can be confronted with other health problems. Participants can suffer from blisters, abrasions, fainting, and heat illnesses. Knowing the causes of these conditions can help you make preventive plans for your participants.

Blisters

Blisters are caused by friction between the skin and the shoe or sock. The friction causes the outer and middle skin layers to rub together and consequently to separate and fill with fluid.

Causes of Blisters

- Improperly fitting shoes (too tight or too loose).
- Shoes constructed of an unyielding material (especially new shoes).
- Shoes with poor ventilation.

Abrasions

Abrasions, like blisters, are often caused by friction between the skin and another surface, such as the mat, floor, or carpet.

Cause of Abrasions

- Subjecting unprotected skin to an abrasive surface, either continuously or forcefully.

Fainting

Fainting is a condition in which a person partially or totally loses consciousness for a short time. Symptoms leading to fainting may include dizziness, nausea, sweating, cold skin, or paleness.

Cause of Fainting

- Lack of blood supply to the brain, resulting from fatigue, illness, injury, or shock.

Heat Exhaustion

Heat exhaustion occurs when the body is subjected to a progressive loss of body fluid through sweating. Symptoms may include profuse sweating, pale or clammy skin, headache, dizziness, nausea, fatigue, or fainting.

Cause of Heat Exhaustion

- Failure to replace body fluids lost through sweating during vigorous activity in a hot environment. The lowered level of body fluid causes shock and circulation problems.

Heatstroke

Heatstroke is a condition in which the body's temperature suddenly rises uncontrollably. It is characterized by hot, red skin (moist or dry), extremely high body temperature, and a disruption in the sweating mechanism.

Causes of Heatstroke

- Failure to replace the body fluids lost through sweating during vigorous activity.
- Exercising in a hot, humid environment, reducing the amount of perspiration that can evaporate from the body.
- Exercising while suffering from a fever.

Now that we know the potential injuries and health problems related to exercise, let's take a look at what you can do to prevent and minimize them in your class.

Injury and Health Problem Prevention

Exercise and other physical activities can present a "catch-22" for the body. To achieve fitness benefits, the body must be stressed beyond its normal fitness level. But those same potentially beneficial stresses can harm the body if they are not properly monitored or prepared for. You can minimize injuries and health problems among participants by taking a few precautions to keep stress within healthy limits and to protect the body against specific harm.

Health Screening

Become familiar with the health screening procedures for members and program participants at your YMCA. Participants need to be aware of any conditions that may affect their participation. Reproducible screening forms can be found in appendix A. The more participants know about their health, the more likely it is that they will exercise at the proper level.

Participation

One of the most common causes of injury is overuse. To help participants avoid overuse and reduce their risk of injury, teach them the appropriate amounts of exercise to perform based on their fitness levels.

Experience

As mentioned in previous chapters, participants should be given exercise programs that are appropriate to their fitness levels. Continually urge participants to work out at their own pace and within their physical capabilities. A beginner may sustain a strain or overuse injury by trying to participate at an advanced level.

Hydration

Encourage participants to drink plenty of fluids (preferably water) at regular intervals during exercise. Water intake is necessary to replace body fluid lost in perspiration and is therefore vital to preventing heat illnesses.

Clothing

Clothing worn for exercise should be comfortable and allow adequate ventilation. Clothing that is too tight or rough can irritate the skin, causing blisters, rashes, or even abrasions. Clothing should also be of material that "breathes" to allow evaporation of sweat, which is necessary to help cool the body. Forbid participants to wear vinyl or rubber suits designed for weight reduction. Such suits prevent sweat evaporation and cause the body's internal temperature to rise. This condition can result in heat exhaustion or, worse, heatstroke.

Shoes

Good shoes can play a major role in minimizing foot and leg injuries. A properly constructed and fitted shoe will aid in shock absorption and stability, and will minimize blistering. Many participants will ask your advice for selecting good shoes. The following criteria (as illustrated in figure 12.5) are important in selecting and fitting aerobics shoes.

General Construction

- **Forefoot, rearfoot, and arch padding**—Because the arch and forefoot bear the body's weight, extra padding helps absorb shock and minimize strain to these areas. Arch support is especially needed by individuals with flat or high arches or pronated feet to maintain proper foot alignment. If the shoe is good but lacks padding, shock-absorbing inserts can be added.

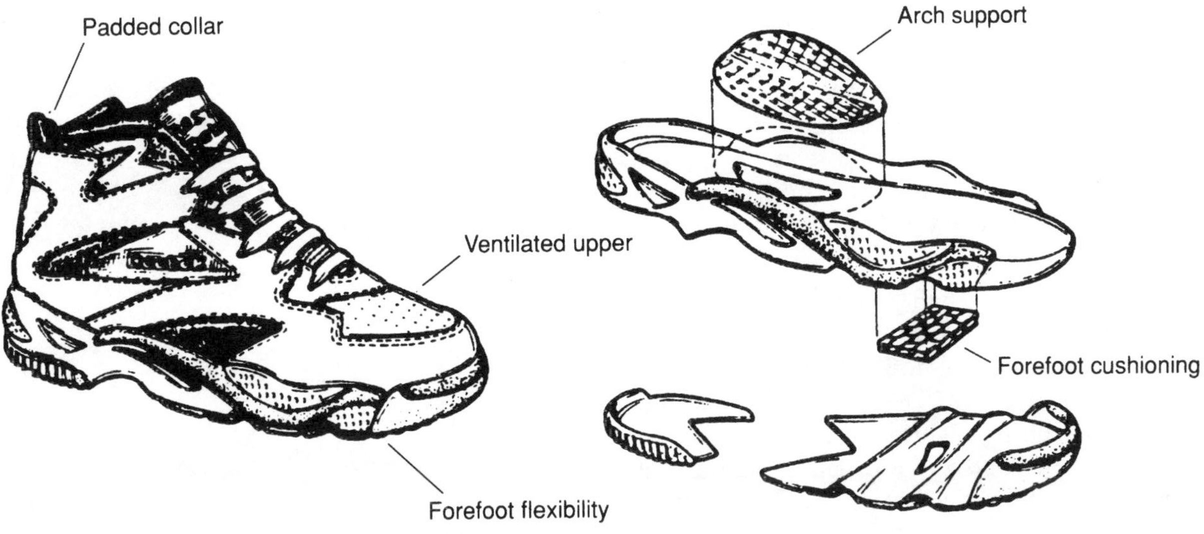

Figure 12.5 Construction of a training shoe.
Adapted, by permission, from Reebok International Ltd.

- **Heel/ankle collar**—Additional padding around the heel and ankle helps reduce stress to the Achilles tendon and improve comfort and fit.
- **Adequate ventilation**—Material that "breathes" is needed to allow sweat to evaporate. Soft leather and nylon shoes allow the best ventilation. Inadequate ventilation can lead to blisters and other skin irritations.
- **Traction**—A good exercise shoe should also provide enough traction to prevent slipping and sliding, but not so much as to let the foot grab or drag.
- **Flexibility**—The shoe must be flexible at the ball of the foot for ease of movement.
- **Lateral stability**—The sides of the shoe should be sturdy to provide stability for side-to-side motion.

Proper Fit

- Buy shoes at the end of the day to accommodate the gradual swelling that your foot experiences during the day.
- Wear athletic socks when trying on shoes.
- Make sure that there is room for toes to straighten fully. A rule of thumb is to allow a 1/2-inch space between the longest toe and the end of the shoe.
- The shoe should accommodate the widest part of the foot. Shoes that are too narrow allow the foot to hang over the sole, which can result in ankle sprains.

Using these preventive guides can help reduce the opportunities for injuries and illnesses. However all instructors will, at some time, be faced with a situation requiring first aid for participants. Some tips are in the next section.

First Aid

If an injury does occur to one of your participants, you must be prepared to handle it. Beware of treating injuries, however, as you are vulnerable to lawsuits. Improper treatment can lead to further injury or infection. Therefore, for your participants' and your own protection, limit any treatment to first aid basics.

You should obtain certification in first aid and cardiopulmonary resuscitation (CPR). Through certification you will learn how to properly care for minor injuries (scrapes, cuts, blisters), serious injuries (fractures, bleeding), and life-threatening problems (heart failure, choking). First aid classes generally require 4 to 8 hours of training, and CPR certification requires 4 to 12 hours of instruction.

Any time you suspect a serious injury or illness, follow the emergency procedures set by your YMCA and urge the affected participant to seek medical attention. If an injury or illness does occur, however, what can you do initially to help relieve pain and minimize further complications? If a musculoskeletal injury occurs, you should use R-I-C-E (rest, ice, compression, and elevation) to minimize pain and swelling.

1. **Rest**—For mild injuries, the participant should stop moving until the pain subsides. Activity usually can be resumed once the participant can move the injured area without pain or discomfort. For more severe injuries, rest should be prescribed until medical clearance for resuming participation is given by a physician.

2. **Ice**—Ice is excellent for minimizing pain and swelling. Always keep a cooler of ice and plastic bags handy. Ice should be applied directly to the injured area for 15 to 20 minutes. Crushed ice in a plastic bag works best because it can conform to the body. Avoid using commercial chemical ice. It does not cool as well, and it can cause chemical burns if its holder is accidently punctured.

3. **Compression**—Wrap an elastic bandage over the ice, starting at the farthest point away from the body and wrapping toward the body with even pressure (for example, for the ankle, start at the toes and wrap up to the lower leg). Be sure to wrap with pressure, yet not so tight as to cut off the circulation. Done properly, compression is effective in minimizing swelling.

4. **Elevation**—Raise the injured part above the level of the heart. When used in conjunction with ice and compression, elevation can help minimize swelling.

For blisters, you can apply ice to reduce heat created by the friction between the skin layers. To minimize further pressure and irritation to the area, tape a donut-shaped piece of felt or foam rubber over the blister (see figure 12.6). Do not, however, attempt to open and drain blisters. Such action may lead to infection if not performed properly.

For muscle soreness and cramps, gradual, sustained stretching can help relax the affected muscles. The muscles should be stretched for 15 to 30 seconds, just to the point where slight discomfort is felt. If performed several times, this may help relieve the pain associated with soreness or cramps.

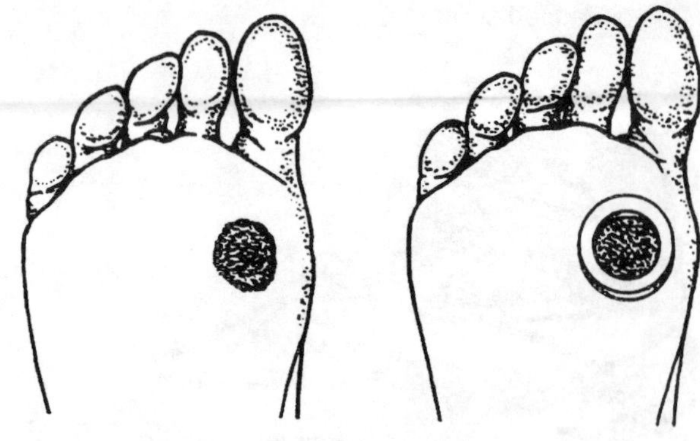

Figure 12.6 Application of a donut-shaped piece of foam rubber to a blister.

For heat illnesses, fainting, or shock, the participant should lie down. Those suffering from heat illness should be given water to drink (if conscious) and moist towels to cool the body. You should monitor breathing and heart rate as needed, and notify the appropriate YMCA staff.

Creating a Safe Environment

By applying the information and the principles in this chapter, you should be able to create a safe environment in which you and your participants can enjoy exercise. Remember, the key to preventing injuries is to exercise caution: in selecting shoes, in organizing workout sessions, in teaching proper technique, and in limiting participation. If an injury does occur, use R-I-C-E and consult a sports medicine specialist as necessary.

With proper planning you can reduce your participants' aches and pains and responsibly care for any injuries that do happen. You need to evaluate your own teaching situation and make the best possible preventive and treatment plans to serve the needs of your participants.

Preventing aches and pains and providing effective first aid can make your exercise sessions more appealing to attend. Given the typically high drop-out rate from exercise programs, the more appealing you can make your programs, the better.

13

Administrative Notes for Personal Training Instructors

The preceding chapters have presented guidelines and principles for personal training from the exercise and behavioral sciences. Applying these guidelines will make your program safer, well rounded, and more enjoyable for participants. In addition to developing knowledge of the exercise sciences, you need to consider administrative duties as you plan. Most YMCAs already have established guidelines for these administrative procedures, so in most cases your role is one of understanding what is expected, carrying out procedures in the exercise facility, and giving the YMCA administration input based on your training experience. Just as your participants benefits from the guidelines you apply from the exercise sciences, your overall program benefits from your attending to these administrative tasks. The tasks discussed here include

- legal liability,
- negligence,
- promotion,
- participant education,
- program evaluation, and
- training guidelines for members.

For those who will be supervising personal trainers at YMCAs, the final section covers the YMCA's expectations for instructors.

Legal Liability

In every exercise venture there exists the possibility that a participant may be injured, perhaps for reasons beyond your control. To avoid the risk of liability the YMCA recommends that you do the following:

- Distribute health screening (PAR-Q) forms to all participants.
- Encourage participants to undergo fitness testing and to follow an exercise program appropriate for their level of fitness.
- Teach safe exercises and proper technique.
- Maintain facilities and equipment in good working order.
- Make sure you have adequate insurance protection.

Reproducible health screening forms appear in appendix A.

By law, you are required to fulfill certain responsibilities for the welfare of your participants. You owe it to your participants to perform certain duties, and your compliance will be of utmost importance should a participant be injured in your class and file a lawsuit. The following legal duties are adapted from the American Coaching Effectiveness Program's *Coaches Guide to Sport Law* (1985) by Gary Nygaard and Thomas Boone. The duties have been modified to apply to personal training.

Proper Technique

As you know, there are proper and improper ways of structuring an exercise session, for example, in format (warming up, cardiorespiratory work, muscle conditioning, and cooling down); in proper exercise movement selection; and in appropriate frequency, intensity, and duration of exercise. Failure to teach a safe, progressive program infringes on members' right to trust you as a knowledgeable instructor.

Hand in hand with teaching proper exercise techniques should be warning participants about what could happen if they do not follow your instructions. For example, let's say that you have properly explained the physiological rationale for progressively increasing the intensity, frequency, and duration of workouts. You must also warn participants that if they exceed their predetermined intensity, symptoms of distress may stop the workout altogether. All explanations of the proper ways to exercise should be accompanied by appropriate warnings of the possible consequences if participants don't heed your instructions.

Adequate Supervision

You have learned about the importance of observation of your program participants. You owe it to your participants to be continually on the lookout for improper exercise techniques and signals of overexertion. Do not leave participants during an exercise session in which direct supervision is needed—you are in charge, and it is your responsibility to be present and prepared at all times.

Sound Planning

The primary goal of personal training is, of course, for participants to achieve training benefits. Progression toward this goal must be made slowly and in increments established to meet the fitness level of each individual. Sound planning means covering every detail in advance, from providing a safe exercise environment to teaching safe exercises to thinking through emergency procedures.

Inherent Risks

Participants need to know the risks inherent in physical activity, both those that accompany any type of exercise and those specific to their programs. For example, vigorous cardiorespiratory exercise carries the risk of muscular and cardiac problems. An inherent risk is generally defined as one incurred while working out in a safe facility with a qualified instructor. The qualified instructor is aware of and understands the inherent risks of exercise and does everything in his or her power to minimize them. Take the time to discuss inherent risks with participants at your first session, and repeat the warnings periodically.

Safe Workout Environment

The more sensitive you are to creating a safe workout environment, the more protected your participants will be. Before training begins you should check the facility for any unsafe conditions. Unsafe conditions would include water, dirt, or loose weights on the floor, uneven surfaces, poor ventilation, and so on. You need to inspect the workout environment before every session.

Additional hazards may exist such as support beams, projections hanging from the ceiling, or equipment from other programs left sitting out. Point out the potentially dangerous features of the facility. In any setting, don't forget to consider the temperature of the facility before starting the workout.

Proper Training and Certification

Lack of knowledge does not protect you from liability if you are faced with a lawsuit. The better trained you are and the more carefully you carry out proper training techniques, the better your legal protection if any injury occurs. Certification from a nationally recognized organization like the YMCA of the USA provides evidence of your competency. The YMCA of the USA recommends that all personal trainers working in YMCAs be certified as YMCA Personal Training Instructors.

First Aid and Emergency Plans

How well your first aid and emergency system works depends upon the procedures your YMCA has set up and your ability to carry them out. You should prepare in advance to effectively handle injuries or accidents. In a situation demanding first aid, remember that you will be judged negligent if you do nothing, but you will be found just as negligent if you select the correct action but perform it incorrectly.

You must be certified to administer cardiopulmonary resuscitation (CPR), and first aid training is recommended as well. Review your skills periodically and renew your certification as required. Keep a well-supplied first aid kit on hand. If possible, have access to another room where first aid can be given. Make some plan as to what will happen if a participant is injured.

Your YMCA should have a plan of action for contacting medical personnel if a person is in need of further medical treatment. This plan will depend upon available resources, such as a university health center, a private physician, an emergency squad, or an in-house physician. Have emergency telephone numbers accessible at all times, and be prepared to give a complete description of the situation over the phone. The more details you can provide, the better.

Record Keeping

Should an incident occur, you should file a written record of the cause of the injury and exactly what care you provided. If your YMCA doesn't have a standard accident report, you can obtain forms from the National Safety Council. When you fill in a report, keep your description simple, yet thorough. Record the information completely, precisely, accurately, and objectively. A written report will help you recall the details of the situation should a participant decide to press charges against you.

Evaluate the accident or injury to determine the cause or contributing factors. Once these factors are identified, do all you can to correct them or eliminate them from your program.

Negligence

If a participant sues you and the YMCA and your case is brought to trial, your behavior will be judged in light of fulfilling the duties that have been discussed. The most common lawsuit brought against fitness instructors is one of *negligence*. Negligence means that you failed to act as a reasonable and prudent instructor would have acted in a similar situation. In trying to confirm that you were negligent, the plaintiff must prove four factors:

- **Presence of the duty**—Did you owe the participant the duty in question?
- **Breach of duty**—Was that duty breached (unfulfilled)? Did you do the proper thing but do it incorrectly?
- **Cause of the injury**—Was your breach of duty the cause?
- **Extent of the injury**—What was the actual extent of the injury?

All four factors must be proven before you can be found negligent. If any one of the factors is missing, liability cannot be charged.

Check whether your YMCA provides any liability insurance. If not, it is advisable to add a clause to your personal insurance policy that will protect you if necessary.

In summary, participation in physical activity has its risks, and it is your responsibility to help protect against them. Meet the challenge of your responsibilities by thinking through your entire program, giving maximum attention to the welfare of your participants. Know your legal duties prior to leading your first training session.

Promotion of Your Program

The advertising and promotion of the personal training program are probably taken care of by others on your YMCA staff, but you should always be on the lookout for new marketing strategies. You may want to share some of the ideas here with your marketing staff.

The two main considerations in advertising are cost and time. The money and the time invested in advertising will hopefully be proportional to the number of people attracted to the program. Two methods of advertising your personal training program are printed materials and word of mouth.

Printed Materials

Printed promotion can include flyers, news releases, brochures, and so on. When writing the promotional copy include all of the pertinent information concerning the personal training program: your credentials, where and when sessions are held, and what benefits participants can expect to gain. If you create flyers, make them attractive. If possible, have them professionally printed. Post them in strategic locations for the audience you are trying to reach.

If you are trying to reach employees of a certain company, seek permission to have your notices distributed. Most businesses have a centrally located lounge or eating area with a bulletin board for notices of interest. Posting a flyer there will help reinforce your message.

News releases should be brief and descriptive. Hand-deliver them, if possible, to the local newspaper. Don't forget weekly papers, which are often looking for local news and are more likely to print public service announcements.

Word of Mouth

Perhaps the best kind of advertising is word of mouth, which also is the cheapest. Have persons in charge of groups you are interested in reaching make announcements about your program. You'll need to prepare these brief, concise announcements and see that they are delivered to the appropriate people.

Those who have worked with you before are good sources of free advertising. Personal testimonials about the fitness and fun derived from your sessions will be just as effective (if not more so) than all of the written ad copy you can generate. Consider having a participant go with you to promote your program.

Participant Education

Instructors should always be enhancing their programs with health and fitness information from reliable sources. This will add to the fitness experience for participants. Here are some practical ideas that you might find useful in your program.

Exercise Reference List

Posters, charts, and pictures help create a pleasant workout environment and serve to reinforce important ideas participants should know. They might even stimulate new questions about exercising. You need not be an expert on every topic of exercise and fitness, but you should be prepared to refer participants to reliable sources of information. These sources should be written in nontechnical, understandable language. If you are not sure you can compile such a reference list, seek out local experts in places like universities, schools, hospitals, volunteer agencies, and so on.

The following is a list of popular topics about which your participants might ask. You and your members can add other topics.

1. The body's energy systems
2. Components of physical fitness
3. Fitness appraisal
4. Heart disease and hypertension
5. Strength training
6. Smoking and exercise
7. Flexibility and stretching
8. Environmental concerns (such as altitude or weather) and exercise
9. Body composition and weight control
10. Nutrition and exercise
11. The menstrual cycle and exercise
12. Common exercise injuries
13. Stress and exercise
14. Lower back problems and exercise
15. Training programs and guidelines
16. Exercising safely
17. Diabetes and exercise
18. Pregnancy and exercise
19. Ergogenic aids (such as steroids or caffeine)

Once participants express interest in a topic, you can point them toward reliable reference books and magazine articles.

Educational Topics for Personal Training

The YMCA has developed a series of 23 fitness education topics to supplement exercise workouts. Each outline was designed as a guideline for instructors in giving minilectures as part of their training sessions. The 23 topics are as follows:

1. Orientation to exercise
2. What change you can expect and how soon you can expect it!
3. Changing exercises to fit your needs
4. Exercise exertion
5. Warm-up and cool-down
6. Objectives of YMCA programs to achieve the mission
7. What is physical fitness?
8. Exercise for older adults
9. Moving in good form
10. Walking as cardiorespiratory exercise
11. Choosing shoes for exercise
12. Choosing clothes for exercise
13. Building muscular strength for daily activities
14. Exercises to avoid and exercises to modify
15. Exercise for relaxation
16. Setting reasonable weight control goals
17. Exercise in hot weather
18. Exercise in cold weather
19. Other programs of interest at your YMCA
20. Motivating yourself to exercise
21. The basics of nutrition
22. Water
23. Self-esteem and relating to others

They appear in appendix A of this manual.

Not all instructors feel comfortable discussing all of these topics, but this does not excuse them from educating their students. There are many alternatives. Handouts can be used to present information to participants. Other YMCA staff could be scheduled to discuss fitness tips or YMCA news.

Videotapes and films are another teaching tool for you to consider. The subject matter can be used in its entirety or broken down into small segments for several sessions. You could schedule a special event every few months and show an entire film or video. A video update of fitness hints running in the YMCA lobby can pass information along as well.

Program Evaluation

To measure your program's degree of success, periodic evaluations must be conducted, both by a trained observer and your participants. Use all available data to determine how you are doing in each area of your total program. Honestly evaluate such questions as, Are participants attending regularly? Are they enjoying themselves? If the answer to these questions is no, you need to develop a plan of action for making improvements.

To have your program evaluated, develop two checklists, one for an observer, most likely your supervisor, and one for participants. Ask them to identify both strong areas and areas that need improvement. The more input you can get, the better your program can become.

Training Guidelines for Members

Quality is sometimes defined as conformance to stated objectives. If so, then the first step to a quality personal training program is to make the training objectives clear to the participants, providing specific guidelines for exercising in the fitness facility. These guidelines may be presented verbally, in a participant policy handout, and/or in a member orientation program. They also should be posted (in large print) in a prominent location.

Training guidelines may vary for cardiorespiratory equipment, weight machines, and free-weights, and they may include rules regarding appropriate exercise attire, spotters for high-risk exercises, age requirements, returning dumbbells to racks, placing barbell plates on weight trees, stripping barbells when finished, carrying gym bags, wearing music headsets, and so on. The following list shows some sample guidelines.

Training Facility Guidelines

- Wear appropriate exercise attire, including shirts and shoes, at all times.
- Put equipment back when you are finished.
- Do not bring food or beverage into the exercise facility.
- Do not bring children into the exercise facility.
- If you are under the age of 16, you can use the facility after orientation and only under direct supervision.
- Use collars on all free-weight bars.
- Do not allow socializing to interfere with others.
- Respect staff and members in the exercise facility.

Personal Behavior Guidelines

- Please train quietly.
- Please respect the exercise facility staff and other participants.
- Please use strength machines in the established order.
- Please wipe down machines after each use.
- Please complete and file your workout card each training session.

Strength Training Guidelines

- Perform each exercise in a slow and controlled manner.
- Perform each exercise through a full range of joint movement.
- Perform each exercise for one to three sets of 8 to 12 repetitions.
- When you are able to complete 12 repetitions, increase the resistance by 2.5 pounds.
- Exhale during lifting movements and inhale during lowering movements.

In addition to posting training guidelines, we recommend that you display signs that promote proper exercise technique.

Personal Training Instructor Expectations

If you supervise instructors who are conducting personal training programs, make sure that all instructors are aware of what is expected from them in their roles as personal trainers. Upon hiring personal trainers, clearly inform them of the rules and procedures to follow in carrying out their duties. The following list shows some sample guidelines for the supervision of personal training instructors.

Attire—All personal training staff are expected to wear staff shirts and identification name tags when on duty. They should complete their instructional outfits with athletic shoes and exercise shorts or sweat pants.

Absence—Any staff member who cannot report to work at the assigned time is responsible for contacting their participants, and possibly arranging a replacement from the staff list. He or she should not wait until the last minute to notify a substitute. Staff members must report all schedule changes to the Health and Fitness Director.

Attitude—The most important characteristic of a successful personal training staff member is a good attitude toward the job responsibilities and toward the participants. All staff should exhibit a positive attitude, a high level of enthusiasm, and a genuine interest in each participant's progress.

Certification—All personal training staff must have current CPR and YMCA of the USA Personal Training Instructor certification.

Cleanliness—The personal training staff is responsible for keeping the training center neat, clean, and cheerful. Whenever necessary, staff should wipe down machines (metal, plastic, and vinyl), pick up papers, reorganize the files, and keep cleanser bottles and towels at every work station.

Emergencies—All personal training staff must read, understand, and follow the YMCA emergency procedures.

First Aid—A first aid kit and ice packs are located inside the fitness center desk. The emergency telephone numbers are located above the telephone.

Hours—Part-time personal training staff usually work no more than 20 hours per week. Work schedules begin and end on the hour or the half-hour. Staff must report to work *on time* and leave work as scheduled.

Instruction—The YMCA exercise facility is an instructional facility where the goal is to teach concepts as well as skills. Staff should share the "why" as well as the "how" with participants. Staff must communicate clearly and concisely with members so members will train with good form and will understand what they are doing.

Knowledge—All personal training staff are expected to learn the basic and advanced principles and procedures for sensible fitness training. In addition to participating in required training events and certifications, staff should read and refer to the *YMCA Personal Training Instructor Manual* for information on training benefits, research, recommendations, exercise execution, program design, and related topics.

On-the-Job Behavior—Whenever staff work with members in the fitness center, it is their responsibility to be attentive and helpful. This includes teaching, modeling, providing feedback, sharing new concepts, recording, observing, and assisting members.

Personal Workouts—All personal training staff are encouraged to train regularly and correctly as good role models for members. However, staff should not workout during scheduled work hours.

Problems—Staff should not ignore or inflate problems. They should deal with problems immediately if they feel comfortable doing so. If not, they should bring the problems to the attention of the Health and Fitness Director and resolve them together. Staff should document all member problems on an Incident form.

Reference—The main reference text for staff is the *YMCA Personal Training Instructor Manual.*

Time Cards—Each staff member should complete a time card every time she or he begins and end s a work shift. The staff member should fill in the date and the hours worked.

YMCA Information—We encourage staff to become knowledgeable about general YMCA policies and procedures, as well as about other YMCA programs and activities to promote to participants.

Appendix A

Outlines for Educational Topics

This appendix contains 23 outlines for minilectures that you can use with your participants. Use these to help you organize what you say about these topics, which cover a wide range of health and fitness issues.

Minilecture 1

Orientation to Exercise

I. Why people exercise
   - A. To feel good
   - B. To meet people
   - C. To have fun
   - D. For medical reasons
   - E. To look good
   - F. To lose weight

II. Physical benefits
   - A. Improves cardiorespiratory efficiency
   - B. Improves metabolism
   - C. Improves body composition and benefits internal organs
   - D. Improves joint and muscle flexibility
   - E. Increases bone strength
   - F. Increases muscle strength
   - G. Improves balance and coordination
   - H. Promotes relaxation

III. Mental benefits
   - A. Increases knowledge of healthy habits
   - B. Increases knowledge of fitness goals
   - C. Increases knowledge of safe and efficient movement
   - D. Increases knowledge of one's own abilities

IV. Social and emotional benefits
   - A. Increases opportunities to meet people
   - B. Encourages participation in a supportive atmosphere
   - C. Increases self-esteem
   - D. Improves body image

V. Spiritual benefits
   - A. Increases respect for and appreciation of self and others
   - B. Provides opportunity to let go of daily concerns, to get in touch with yourself, and to enjoy other people
   - C. Encourages you to be uniquely YOU!

Minilecture 2

What Change You Can Expect and How Soon You Can Expect It!

I. Progress
   - A. You will progress at your own rate (influenced by your health, heredity, and motivation).
   - B. Change will occur, particularly if you
     - participate regularly,
     - work at your own pace,
     - set realistic goals, and make adjustments for day-to-day changes in your health status,
     - are free from pressure to compete, and
     - measure and celebrate your progress.

II. Regression
   - A. Beginners often overestimate the amount of change to expect.

B. However, change in the first weeks may be very noticeable.

C. A plateau period of several weeks may follow, which is normal.

D. The plateau period is followed by slow, gradual change.

III. Common changes after 4 to 6 weeks of regular participation

A. You feel better physically.

B. It is easier to reach high shelves or your feet and to fasten and unfasten seat belts.

C. House and yard work is easier and less exhausting.

D. It is easier to go up and down stairs.

E. You recover faster from colds and falls.

F. Your chronic back pain decreases.

G. Your sports performance improves.

H. You feel better about life.

Minilecture 3

Changing Exercises to Fit Your Needs

I. Taking into account differences in shape, health status, and fitness level

A. Change exercise to "fit" your individual length and circumference of limbs and trunk.

B. Follow your doctor's recommendations for exercise, based on your health status.

C. Take advantage of opportunities for fitness assessment.

II. Changing exercises for differences in shape

A. People with short arms and legs should reach "toward" instead of "to" the designated spot; static stretching may be difficult.

B. People with long arms and legs need a slower movement tempo and more space.

C. People with excess weight should exercise at a lower intensity.

III. Changing exercises for differences in fitness level

A. Exercise position and intensity should match your fitness level.

B. Exercise intensity should increase gradually as your fitness level improves.

Minilecture 4

Exercise Exertion

I. How to measure exertion

A. Target heart rate using pulse count

B. Perceived Exertion Scale

C. The talk test

II. Factors affecting exercise heart rate (HR)

A. Age

B. Weather (HR rises faster in warm weather.)

C. Health status (HR rises faster if you are sick.)

D. Medications

III. Reasonable levels of exertion

A. 55% to 70% for beginners

B. 70% to 90% for well-conditioned adults

IV. Blood pressure

A. Blood pressure increases during exercise.

B. Resting blood pressure gradually decreases with regular exercise participation.

C. Heart rate and blood pressure are *not* directly related.

Minilecture 5

Warm-Up and Cool-Down

I. Reasons for warm-up

A. Increase heart rate and muscle temperature

B. Loosen up joints

C. Prevent injury

D. Get mentally ready for activity

II. Components of warm-up

A. Part 1: active movements to get blood moving and warm muscles; 3 to 6 minutes

B. Part 2: move each joint through full range of motion; gently stretch major muscle groups; keep heart rate elevated; 5 to 10 minutes

III. Reasons for cool-down

A. Allow heart rate to gradually drop to preexercise level

B. Allow blood flow to move from large leg muscles to other organs and muscles

C. Stretch major muscle groups

D. Enjoy a period of relaxation

IV. Components of cool-down

A. Easy exercise at a moderate pace, such as walking

B. Held stretches of major muscle groups to prevent soreness or tightness

C. Relaxation period

Minilecture 6

Objectives of YMCA Programs to Achieve the Mission

I. Objectives of YMCA programs—To help people

A. Grow personally

B. Develop character

C. Improve personal and family relationships

D. Appreciate diversity

E. Become better leaders and supporters

F. Develop specific skills

G. Have fun

II. Grow personally

A. Improve physical, mental, and spiritual health

B. Set reasonable personal fitness goals and work toward them

C. Improve health knowledge

D. Improve body image and self-esteem

III. Develop character

A. Reflect on personal values

B. Reflect on the relationship between personal values and behavior

C. Reflect on the relationship between personal values and community and Christian values

IV. Improve personal and family relationships

A. Develop communication skills

B. Increase opportunities for meeting people

C. Encourage interpersonal communication

D. Encourage development of peer relationships

E. Provide intergenerational experiences

V. Appreciate diversity—This means learning about other people with a diversity of

A. Abilities and limitations

B. Philosophies

C. Ethnic and cultural traditions

D. Religious backgrounds

E. Ages

VI. Become better leaders and supporters

A. Increase opportunities to share leadership

B. Increase opportunities to provide peer support

C. Increase opportunities to provide input for programming decisions

D. Increase opportunities to become volunteer leaders

VII. Develop specific skills

A. Learn physical skills

B. Improve social skills

C. Enhance life skills

VIII. Have fun!

A. Increase opportunities to laugh and have fun

B. Increase opportunities to enjoy other people

Minilecture 7

What Is Physical Fitness?

I. Different things to different people

A. Feeling good

B. Being active without feeling fatigued

C. Coping with daily stresses and problems with a more relaxed attitude

D. Participating in daily activities with ease and enjoyment

E. Improving components of physical fitness: muscular strength and endurance, aerobic conditioning, flexibility, body composition, relaxation

II. Muscular strength and endurance

A. Definition

B. Examples

III. Cardiorespiratory fitness: Aerobic conditioning
   A. Definition
   B. Examples, including continuous and discontinuous activities
IV. Flexibility of muscles and joints
   A. Definition of joint range-of-motion exercise
   B. Definition of muscle flexibility exercise
   C. Examples of different kinds of flexibility exercises

(Relaxation is covered in Minilecture 15; body composition is covered in Minilecture 16.)

Minilecture 8

Aerobic Exercise for Older Adults

I. What is aerobic exercise?
   A. Energizing movement for all ages
   B. Large muscle activity that lasts more than 3 minutes
   C. Heart and breathing rates increased
   D. Can be done in a chair, a pool, an open indoor or outdoor space
   E. Some examples of aerobic exercise: swimming, walking, dancing, biking, running, aerobics
II. Frequency (how often)
   A. A minimum of 3 times a week
   B. A maximum of 5 times a week
III. Intensity (how hard)
   A. Harder is not better; moderate pace is fine
   B. Heart rate in target range (55% to 90% maximum HR) or perceived exertion is fairly light to very hard
   C. Able to talk comfortably
   D. Should not leave you exhausted
IV. Duration (how long)
   A. Beginners or during recovery from illness—up to 15 minutes
   B. Two options for healthy, conditioned adults
      1. 30 to 45 minutes, three times a week
      2. 15 to 30 minutes, four to five times a week

Minilecture 9

Moving in Good Form

I. Reasons for moving in good form
   A. Save energy
   B. Prevent injury
   C. Feel better and express positive self-image
II. Good body alignment
   A. Standing posture
      1. Weight carried by bones
      2. Alignment of ear, shoulder, hip joint, knee, and ankle form a straight line when body is viewed from the side
   B. Sitting posture
      1. Alignment of ear, shoulder, and hip form a straight line
      2. Knees and feet are apart, with feet flat on floor
III. Movement mechanics
   A. Walking
      1. Good alignment
      2. Smooth weight transfer
      3. Opposition arm swing
      4. Eyes focused forward instead of down
   B. Lifting
      1. Feet apart
      2. Bent knees (instead of hips)
      3. Lifted weight held close to body
   C. Carrying
      1. Weight held close to body
      2. Weight centered
   D. Pushing and pulling
      1. Feet in stride position
      2. Bent knees (instead of hips), knees in line with feet
      3. Hands and arms kept over space between feet
      4. Body weight shifted forward (push) or backward (pull)
   E. Rising from floor or chair
      1. Weight kept over feet
      2. Arms used to push on knees or against chair, if necessary

3. Weight kept over feet by bending and straightening knees and hips
4. Body lifted slowly to avoid dizziness

Minilecture 10

Walking as Cardiorespiratory Exercise

I. Variety of walking programs
  A. YMCA Walk Reebok programs
  B. YMCA self-guided walking programs
  C. YMCA walking clubs
II. Benefits of walking
  A. Familiar movement that can be done many places at a time convenient to the individual
  B. Strengthens bones
  C. Improves cardiorespiratory fitness
  D. Easy to adjust to individual fitness level
  E. Burns calories
III. Sample walk program (see *YMCA Walk Reebok Instructor Manual*)

Minilecture 11

Choosing Shoes for Exercise

I. Reasons for selecting shoes carefully
  A. Appropriate shoes that fit well prevent injury.
  B. Better fit increases foot comfort.
II. Being a wise shopper
  A. Stores that specialize in athletic shoes are more likely to have a range of sizes and salespeople who are better trained to help you.
  B. Always try both shoes on for fit and comfort; walk in them in the store before you pay for them.
III. Types of shoes
  A. Aerobic shoes are lighter in weight, have soles that accommodate side-to-side stepping, and provide additional cushioning under the ball of the foot.
  B. Walking shoes have smoother and stiffer soles, lower heels, and more solid support in the construction of shoe uppers.
  C. Running shoes have flexible soles, higher heels, and less support at the toe of the shoe.
IV. Choosing shoes
  A. Well-cushioned heel
  B. Firm heel counter
  C. Adequate internal cushioning (insole)
  D. Resilient and pliable outersole
  E. Leather or mesh upper construction
  F. Roomy toe box
  G. Adequate arch support
  H. Comfortable fit

Minilecture 12

Choosing Clothes for Exercise

I. Clothes for exercise
  A. Material should absorb perspiration.
  B. Cut should prevent chafing.
  C. Fit should allow comfortable, full range of motion.
II. Underwear
  A. An absorbent fabric like cotton is preferred.
  B. Garments should provide support without being too tight or binding.
III. Socks
  A. Look for a snug fit without rough toe seams.
  B. Cotton and wool socks absorb moisture but may cause blisters with profuse sweating.
  C. To wick moisture away from the foot, wear silk, nylon, or polypropylene next to the skin.
  D. Add extra cushioning, if needed, by wearing a second pair of socks made of wool or lightly padded terrycloth.
IV. Clothing
  A. Wear shorts, tights, or knit (or sweat) pants.
  B. Cotton T-shirts or leotards allow easy movement, keep the body warm, and absorb sweat.

Minilecture 13

Building Muscular Strength for Daily Activities

I. Daily living depends on muscular strength: Use it, don't lose it!

II. Knee extension in seated or standing position builds the quadriceps strength needed to climb stairs or get out of cars or deep chairs.

III. Biceps curls and triceps exercises build the arm strength needed for lifting and lowering, pushing, pulling, and carrying objects.

IV. Arm and leg exercise improves posture and builds the strength needed for sports and daily yard and housework.

V. Abdominal curls (plus variations) improve posture and stabilize trunk movements.

VI. Forced expiration exercises build diaphragm strength to improve depth of breathing and elimination function (bowel movement). Avoid hyperventilation.

Minilecture 14

Exercises to Avoid and Exercises to Modify

Almost any exercise can be harmful if it is improperly executed or if it is repeated too much (the repetitive motion syndrome). But there are some exercises that should be avoided. Some of these are things we all learned to do in our past exercise experiences. As our knowledge of the body and how it works advances, however, we sometimes learn that we did certain things incorrectly.

I. Exercises to avoid
   A. Standing straight-leg toe touches cause back and knee injury. Do single leg raises lying on your back instead.
   B. Deep knee bends cause knee injury. Do knee dips instead, keeping heels on the floor.
   C. Standing windmills cause back injury.
   D. Double leg lifts cause low back injury and hernias. Keep the knee of one leg bent and the foot on the floor while lifting the other leg.
   E. Straight leg sit-ups cause back injury. Do abdominal curls with knees bent.
   F. Sit-ups with feet stabilized (e.g., held down by a partner) cause back injury. Do abdominal curls lifting only the shoulders (or upper trunk) from the floor.
   G. Head or neck circles can cause damage to nerves in the neck and dizziness. Do isolated neck exercises: Turn right/left, center/down, center/diagonally down to the right or left; draw chin and head in/forward, tilt head side to side.

II. Important modifications to all exercise
   A. Protect the back by keeping it upright; bend at the knees instead.
   B. Protect the knees by keeping them lined up with the toes.
   C. Protect the arch of the foot by taking weight on the heel, then shifting weight toward the toes.
   D. Protect the back and arm joints by bending (flexing or extending) *or* turning (rotation), but not both.
   E. There are other modifications related to common performance errors.

Minilecture 15

Exercise for Relaxation

I. Importance of relaxation exercise
   A. Physiological changes
      1. Reduced blood pressure
      2. Increased release of endorphins, which act like natural sedatives
      3. Reduced muscle tension
   B. Psychological changes
      1. Release of worries and anxiety (letting go)
      2. Reduced depression
      3. Increased feelings of well-being

II. Dynamic relaxation
   A. Relaxation effect of active exercise is caused by endorphin release.
   B. Effect occurs with
      1. Noncompetitive, energetic activity
      2. Natural spontaneous laughter and enjoyment experienced with activity
      3. Balance of a challenging activity requiring coordination, such as lifting the knee and tapping it with the opposite hand, with an easy, no-fail activity like marching in place and clapping

III. Static relaxation
   A. Quiet breathing, guided muscle contraction-relaxation exercise, yoga or Tai-Chi-type exercise
   B. Guided imagery or meditation

Minilecture 16

Setting Reasonable Weight Control Goals

I. Diet
  A. "Magic Formula": Increase calorie expenditure, decrease calorie intake.
  B. Dieters should be sure to drink six to eight glasses of water a day.
  C. Safe weight loss is up to two pounds a week.
  D. Spot-reducing is a fallacy.
  E. Weight will be lost according to genetic design and order of gain.
  F. Diet change: Eat more nutritious foods, consume less, and reduce fat intake.

II. Exercise
  A. 3,500 calories equals 1 pound of fat.
  B. Fat is burned during aerobic activities.
  C. Combine exercise with diet change to maintain or build muscle mass.
  D. Real weight may not change, but body shape will change.

Minilecture 17

Exercise in Hot Weather

I. Heat stress—Heat reactions can occur at any season of the year under the right conditions. Heat stress is caused by a combination of factors:
  A. Increased humidity
  B. Increased temperature
  C. Lack of wind
  D. Solar radiation
  E. Age (Older adults are more prone to heat stress.)

II. Precautions
  A. Wear a hat with good ventilation (e.g., a hat made of loosely woven straw or natural fiber).
  B. Wear loose, absorbent (preferably cotton), light-colored clothes. Avoid wearing clothes that hold heat next to the skin, such as nylon fabric.
  C. Exercise during the cooler part of the day.
  D. Drink extra water (with no sugar or flavors added — they slow absorption).
  E. Reduce the intensity of your exercise.

III. Symptoms to watch for
  A. Dizziness
  B. Confusion or loss of consciousness
  C. Hot, dry skin
  D. Nausea
  E. Muscle cramps

IV. Remedies
  A. Get out of the sun and heat!
  B. Drink fluids.
  C. Cool the body gradually with water or a breeze (fan).
  D. Seek immediate medical aid if heat stroke symptoms occur (hot, dry skin; loss of consciousness; high body temperature).

Minilecture 18

Exercise in Cold Weather

I. Hypothermia—Hypothermia can occur at any season of the year under the right conditions. Hypothermia is caused by a combination of factors:
  A. Decreased temperature
  B. Increased humidity or moisture
  C. Increased wind
  D. Age (Older adults are more prone to hypothermia.)

II. Precautions
  A. Wear clothes that allow freedom of movement.
  B. Wear clothes in layers.
  C. Wear clothes made from materials having a high insulating value, such as wool or down.
  D. Wear ear-covering hats and warm mittens (instead of gloves).
  E. Wear a breathing mask on colder days.
  F. Keep your neck and chest covered.
  G. Exercise during the warmer parts of the day, and avoid becoming chilled.
  H. Guard against outdoor exercise on days when the windchill temperature drops below 10 degrees Fahrenheit.

III. Symptoms of hypothermia
  A. Marked shivering
  B. Numbness, loss of feeling

C. Marked muscular weakness

D. Drowsiness or loss of consciousness

E. Low body temperature

F. Personality change, impaired judgment, or mental confusion

IV. Remedies

A. Remove wet or frozen clothing.

B. Provide extra clothing, blankets, or the warmth of another body.

C. Move to a warm place indoors.

D. Provide warm, nonalcoholic drinks.

E. Warm the skin gradually in warm—not hot—water, and then dry thoroughly.

Minilecture 19

Other Programs of Interest at Your YMCA

Outline those programs currently offered at your YMCA.

Minilecture 20

Motivating Yourself to Exercise

I. Review personal goals and personal benefits of exercise based on your and participants' past experiences.

II. Give reasons people drop out of exercise programs.

A. No benefit experienced with exercise

B. Injury from muscle overuse or strains

C. Other activities in life take priority

D. Exercise program not enjoyable

E. Exercise program not challenging or interesting

F. Others

III. Identify the motivational techniques that work best for each participant.

A. Mention some of the common ways to motivate yourself to exercise:

1. Get support from family and friends.

2. Find a "buddy" to exercise with.

3. Choose a regular time to exercise that fits well in your schedule.

4. Set goals, short- and long-term.

5. Keep records on how long and often you exercise and your progress.

6. Vary the type of exercise you do and where you do it.

B. Ask each participant to identify specific techniques that may work well for him or her.

Minilecture 21

The Basics of Nutrition

I. Age and nutrition

A. Calorie needs decrease with age.

B. Rate of metabolism declines with age.

II. Roles nutrients play in physical activity

A. Carbohydrates are the primary source of energy.

B. Fat and proteins are energy producers *after* the body's glycogen stores are depleted.

C. Protein, minerals, vitamins, and water are essential to metabolic processes that produce energy.

III. Proper eating habits

A. Eat a balanced diet: grains, fruits and vegetables, dairy products, and meats.

B. Eat fewer "empty" calories, items such as candy or alcohol that have lots of calories but little nutritional value.

IV. Bad fat, good fat

A. Bad fats are cholesterol and saturated fats and are found in foods such as animal fats, organ meats, tropical oils (coconut), eggs, whole milk, butter, and cream.

B. Good fats are polyunsaturated fats and are found in foods such as safflower, olive, canola, and sunflower oils.

C. Check the labels of processed foods (including "low fat" foods) and baked goods for the types of fats used.

Minilecture 22

Water

I. The body's water needs

A. Water is used for metabolic processes—to produce energy, build muscle, repair tissue, and maintain body temperature.

B. Fluid retention is related to heart problems or inactivity, not excessive water intake.

C. Extra water is needed during warm weather, illness, and before and after vigorous exercise.

II. How much?

A. We should drink six to eight 8-ounce glasses of water a day.

B. Other fluids (juices, coffee, etc.) with added flavors and sweeteners stay in the stomach longer, and the water in them is not absorbed as well as plain water.

C. Thirst is not a good gauge of water need; though thirst may be quenched, our bodies usually need more water, especially when we are active.

III. And when?

A. Drink water throughout the day.

B. Drink water before and after exercise, in particular.

C. Even if you fear incontinence, don't stop drinking water; instead, plan ahead and locate restrooms before you need them.

D. Do Kegel exercises to help control incontinence.

Minilecture 23

Self-Esteem and Relating to Others

I. Self-concept and others

A. We all develop concepts of how well we do in many different areas in life; we are good in some, not so good in others.

B. The one area that affects our ability to succeed in all the others is our ability to relate to other people.

II. Self-esteem and helping others

A. We must first feel good about ourselves.

B. When we feel good about ourselves, we can help others.

III. How to increase self-esteem

A. We need to take steps to build our own self-esteem and avoid self-destructive messages.

B. We can choose to build on the positive aspects of those around us.

Appendix B

Health Screening, Medical Clearance, and Informed-Consent Forms

The following four forms are taken from *Principles of YMCA Health & Fitness* 3rd Edition (1999) and *YMCA Fitness Testing and Assessment Manual (2000)*. They can be reproduced and used as needed for your YMCA classes. The screening forms should be administered when participants enter a program and yearly thereafter. Copies of all completed participant forms should be retained in a records file for at least three years.

Form I—Health Screen Form (PAR-Q & YOU)

Form I is the Physical Activity Readiness Questionnaire developed by the Canadian Society for Exercise Physiology. It asks for general information about the participant's physical condition. Individuals should be instructed to follow the recommendations based on their answers prior to participating in YMCA fitness testing or exercise programs.

Forms II and IIA—Medical Clearance Form and Testing/ Program Description

The Medical Clearance Form is used by the participant's physician to report any restrictions that should be placed on the participant during fitness testing or exercise programs. The physician should see both Form II and Form IIA, which describes generally the YMCA fitness testing and exercise programs and the risks associated with each.

Form III—Informed Consent for Fitness Testing

The Informed Consent for Fitness Testing Form ensures that the participant is aware of the risks involved in the fitness testing procedures. It documents that a description of the testing procedures has been read and that all questions concerning those procedures have been answered satisfactorily.

Form IV—Informed Consent for Exercise Participation

The Informed Consent for Exercise Participation Form ensures that the participant is aware of the risks involved in exercise. It documents that the description of the exercise program has been read and all questions concerning the exercise program have been answered to the participant's satisfaction.

When and How to Use the Forms

The Health Screen Form (Form I) should be completed before a participant starts any program, even if it is just an education class. The information obtained in this form is valuable for educating participants on potential health and cardiovascular risk. Note that Form I is not intended to be a medical exam but simply a means to obtain key health information.

If a potential participant requires medical clearance, use Form II. It allows a physician to indicate that he or she thinks the individual is capable of participating in the YMCA's exercise programs. Form IIA provides a description of the YMCA exercise programs for the doctor.

The informed consent forms (Forms III and IV) are designed to notify participants of the inherent risks of fitness testing and exercise programs. Form III, Informed Consent for Fitness Testing, should be given to any person registering for a fitness test. It should be read and signed before testing starts. Form IV, Informed Consent for Exercise Participation, should be given to any participant in a supervised exercise program. It should be read and signed before exercise starts.

FORM I

Determine Your Readiness to Participate in Physical Activity

Complete the following questionnaire (reprinted from the Canadian Society for Exercise Physiology 1994) to help you determine your readiness to begin or intensify a physical activity program.

Physical Activity Readiness Questionnaire – PAR-Q (revised 1994)

PAR - Q & YOU

(A Questionnaire for People Aged 15 to 69)

Regular physical activity is fun and healthy, and increasingly more people are starting to become more active every day. Being more active is very safe for most people. However, some people should check with their doctor before they start becoming much more physically active.

If you are planning to become much more physically active than you are now, start by answering the seven questions in the box below. If you are between the ages of 15 and 69, the PAR-Q will tell you if you should check with your doctor before you start. If you are over 69 years of age, and you are not used to being very active, check with your doctor.

Common sense is your best guide when you answer these questions. Please read the questions carefully and answer each one honestly: check YES or NO.

YES	NO	
☐	☐	1. Has your doctor ever said that you have a heart condition and that you should only do physical activity recommended by a doctor?
☐	☐	2. Do you feel pain in your chest when you do physical activity?
☐	☐	3. In the past month, have you had chest pain when you were not doing physical activity?
☐	☐	4. Do you lose your balance because of dizziness or do you ever lose consciousness?
☐	☐	5. Do you have a bone or joint problem that could be made worse by a change in your physical activity?
☐	☐	6. Is your doctor currently prescribing drugs (for example, water pills) for your blood pressure or heart condition?
☐	☐	7. Do you know of any other reason why you should not do physical activity?

If you answered

YES to one or more questions

Talk with your doctor by phone or in person BEFORE you start becoming much more physically active or BEFORE you have a fitness appraisal. Tell your doctor about the PAR-Q and which questions you answered YES.

- You may be able to do any activity you want—as long as you start slowly and build up gradually. Or, you may need to restrict your activities to those which are safe for you. Talk with your doctor about the kinds of activities you wish to participate in and follow his/her advice.
- Find out which community programs are safe and helpful for you.

NO to all questions

If you answered NO honestly to all PAR-Q questions, you can be reasonably sure that you can:

- start becoming much more physically active—begin slowly and build up gradually. This is the safest and easiest way to go.
- take part in a fitness appraisal—this is an excellent way to determine your basic fitness so that you can plan the best way for you to live actively.

DELAY BECOMING MUCH MORE ACTIVE:

- if you are not feeling well because of a temporary illness such as a cold or a fever—wait until you feel better; or
- if you are or may be pregnant—talk to your doctor before you start becoming more active.

Please note: If your health changes so that you then answer YES to any of the above questions, tell your fitness or health professional. Ask whether you should change your physical activity plan.

Informed Use of the PAR-Q: The Canadian Society for Exercise Physiology, Health Canada, and their agents assume no liability for persons who undertake physical activity, and if in doubt after completing this questionnaire, consult your doctor prior to physical activity.

You are encouraged to copy the PAR-Q but only if you use the entire form

NOTE: If the PAR-Q is being given to a person before he or she participates in a physical activity program or a fitness appraisal, this section may be used for legal or administrative purposes.

I have read, understood and completed this questionnaire. Any questions I had were answered to my full satisfaction.

NAME ____________________

SIGNATURE ____________________ DATE ____________________

SIGNATURE OF PARENT ____________________ WITNESS ____________________
or GUARDIAN (for participants under the age of majority)

Supported by: CANADA Health Canada Santé Canada

FORM II

Medical Clearance Form

Dear Doctor:

____ has applied for enrollment in the
(Name of applicant)

fitness testing and/or exercise programs at the YMCA. The fitness testing program involves a submaximal test for cardiorespiratory fitness, body composition analysis, a flexibility test, and muscular strength and endurance tests. The exercise programs are designed to start easy and become progressively more difficult over a period of time. A more detailed description of the testing and exercise programs is attached in Form IIA. All fitness tests and exercise programs will be administered by qualified personnel trained in conducting exercise tests and exercise programs.

By completing the form below, however, you are not assuming any responsibility for our administration of the fitness testing and/or exercise programs. If you know of any medical or other reasons why participation in the fitness testing and/or exercise programs by the applicant would be unwise, please indicate so on this form.

If you have any questions about the YMCA fitness testing and/or exercise programs, please call.

Report of Physician

_____ I know of no reason why the applicant may not participate.

_____ I believe the applicant can participate, but I urge caution because

____

____

_____ The applicant should not engage in the follow activities:

____

____

_____ I recommend that the applicant NOT participate.

Physician signature ___________________________ Date ____________________

Address ___________________________________ Telephone _______________

City and state ______________________________ Zip _____________________

FORM IIA

Description of Fitness Testing and Exercise Programs

Dear Doctor:

The YMCA fitness testing and/or exercise programs for which the participant has applied are described as follows:

Fitness testing—The purpose of the fitness testing program is to evaluate cardiorespiratory fitness, body composition, flexibility, and muscular strength and endurance. The cardiorespiratory fitness test involves a submaximal test that may include a bench step test, a cycle ergometer test, or a 1-mile walk for best time test. Body composition is analyzed by taking several skinfold measures to calculate percentage of body fat. Flexibility is determined by the sit-and-reach test. Muscular strength and upper-body endurance may be evaluated by the 1-minute, bent-knee sit-up test or the bench press test.

Exercise programs—The purpose of the exercise programs is to develop and maintain cardiorespiratory fitness, body composition, flexibility, and muscular strength and endurance. A specific exercise plan will be given to the participant based on needs and interests and your recommendations. All exercise programs include warm-up, exercise at target heart rate, and cool-down (except for muscular strength and endurance training, in which target heart rate is not a factor). The programs may involve walking, jogging, swimming, or cycling (outdoor and stationary); participation in exercise fitness, rhythmic aerobic exercise, or choreographed fitness classes; or calisthenics or strength training. All programs are designed to place a gradually increasing workload on the body in order to improve overall fitness and muscular strength. The rate of progression is regulated by exercise target heart rate and/or perceived effort of exercise.

In both the fitness testing and exercise programs, the reaction of the cardiorespiratory system cannot be predicted with complete accuracy. There is a risk of certain changes that might occur during or following exercise. These changes might include abnormalities of blood pressure and/or heart rate. YMCA exercise instructors are certified in CPR, and emergency procedures are posted in the exercise facility.

In addition to your medical approval and recommendations, the participant will be asked to sign informed consent forms that explain the risks of fitness testing and exercise participation before the programs are initiated.

FORM III

Informed Consent for Fitness Testing

Name ____

(Please print)

The purpose of the fitness testing program is to evaluate cardiorespiratory fitness, body composition, flexibility, and muscular strength and endurance. The cardiorespiratory fitness test involves a submaximal test that may include a bench step test, a cycle ergometer test, or a 1-mile walk test. Body composition is analyzed by taking several skinfold measures to calculate percentage of body fat. Flexibility is determined by the sit-and-reach test. Muscular strength and upper-body endurance may be evaluated by the 1-minute, bent-knee sit-up test or the bench press test.

I understand that I am responsible for monitoring my own condition throughout the tests, and should any unusual symptoms occur, I will cease my participation and inform the instructor of the symptoms.

In signing this consent form, I affirm that I have read this form in its entirety and that I understand the description of the tests and their components. I also affirm that my questions regarding the fitness testing program have been answered to my satisfaction.

In the event that a medical clearance must be obtained prior to my participation in the fitness testing program, I agree to consult my physician and obtain written permission from my physician prior to the commencement of any fitness tests.

Also, in consideration for being allowed to participate in the fitness testing program, I agree to assume the risk of such testing, and further agree to hold harmless the YMCA and its staff members conducting such testing from any and all claims, suits, losses, or related causes of action for damages, including, but not limited to, such claims that may result from my injury or death, accidental or otherwise, during, or arising in any way from, the testing program.

____ Date ____________________

(Signature of participant)

____ Date ____________________

(Person administering tests)

FORM IV

Informed Consent for Exercise Participation

I desire to engage voluntarily in the YMCA exercise program in order to attempt to improve my physical fitness. I understand that the activities are designed to place a gradually increasing workload on the cardiorespiratory system and to thereby attempt to improve its function. The reaction of the cardiorespiratory system to such activities can't be predicted with complete accuracy. There is a risk of certain changes that might occur during or following the exercise. These changes might include abnormalities of blood pressure or heart rate.

I understand that the purpose of the exercise program is to develop and maintain cardiorespiratory fitness, body composition, flexibility, and muscular strength and endurance. A specific exercise plan will be given to me, based on my needs and interests and my doctor's recommendations. All exercise programs include warm-up, exercise at target heart rate, and cool-down. The programs may involve walking, jogging, swimming, or cycling (outdoor and stationary); participation in exercise fitness, rhythmic aerobic exercise, or choreographed fitness classes; or calisthenics or strength training. All programs are designed to place a gradually increasing workload on the body in order to improve overall fitness. The rate of progression is regulated by exercise target heart rate and perceived effort of exercise.

I understand that I am responsible for monitoring my own condition throughout the exercise program and should any unusual symptoms occur, I will cease my participation and inform the instructor of the symptoms.

In signing this consent form, I affirm that I have read this form in its entirety and that I understand the nature of the exercise program. I also affirm that my questions regarding the exercise program have been answered to my satisfaction.

In the event that a medical clearance must be obtained prior to my participation in the exercise program, I agree to consult my physician and obtain written permission from my physician prior to the commencement of any exercise program.

Also, in consideration for being allowed to participate in the YMCA exercise program, I agree to assume the risk of such exercise, and further agree to hold harmless the YMCA and its staff members conducting the exercise program from any and all claims, suits, losses, or related causes of action for damages, including, but not limited to, such claims that may result from my injury or death, accidental or otherwise, during, or arising in any way from, the exercise program.

______________________________________ Date ________________

(Signature of participant)

Please print:

Name ______________________________________ Date of birth __________

Address ____

Telephone ______________________

Name of personal physician ______________________________

Physician's address ______________________________________

Physician's phone ______________________

Limitations and medications ______________________________

Personal Training Terms and Definitions

The following is an alphabetical listing of common personal training terms, with a brief definition of each. It is meant to help you better understand materials from the field of health and fitness.

abduction—Sideways movement away from the body.

adduction—Sideways movement toward the body.

antagonist muscle—Muscle that lengthens as the prime mover muscle shortens. The triceps is the antagonist muscle to the biceps.

assisted training—An advanced strength training technique in which a partner helps the exerciser perform a few additional repetitions at the completion of the exercise set.

ATP (Adenosine Triphosphate)—The chemical compound that releases the energy for muscle contraction.

atrophy—Decrease in muscle cross-sectional size.

bodybuilder—Person who follows a strength training program designed to develop greater muscle size.

body composition—The ratio of lean weight (muscle, bone, etc.) to fat weight. Ideally, males should be less than 15 percent fat and females should be less than 20 percent fat.

body weight exercises—Exercises such as push-ups and chin-ups, in which one's body weight serves as the resistance.

circuit training—A system of training whereby the exerciser performs one set of exercises for each major muscle group.

concentric contraction—The muscle exerts force, shortens, and overcomes the resistance. Also known as a *positive contraction.*

concomitant—Using both arms or legs at the same time versus alternately.

controlled movement speed—Lifting and lowering the resistance in a slow and controlled manner to maintain a relatively even force output.

dynamic constant resistance exercise—Training with a resistance that does not change throughout the movement range, such as a barbell.

dynamic variable resistance exercise—Training with a resistance that changes in a predetermined manner throughout the movement range, such as a Nautilus machine.

eccentric contraction—The muscle exerts force, lengthens, and is overcome by the resistance. Also known as *negative contraction.*

extension—Movement that increases the joint angle between adjacent body parts.

fast-twitch muscle fibers—Fibers that prefer anaerobic energy sources to produce relatively high levels of force for relatively short periods of time.

first-class lever—Lever arrangement in which the axis of rotation is between the movement force and the resistance force.

flexion—Movement that decreases the joint angle between adjacent body parts.

free-weights—Handheld weights, such as barbells and dumbbells, that may be moved in virtually any direction without restriction.

full movement range—Working a muscle through a complete range of joint motion, from flexion to extension and extension to flexion.

high-endurance muscles—Muscles characterized by a large percentage of slow-twitch fibers that are more resistant to fatigue.

hypertrophy—Increase in cross-sectional muscle size.

isokinetic exercise—Training with equipment that automatically matches the resistance force to the muscle force. The amount of muscle force produced determines the amount of resistance force encountered.

isometric contraction—The muscle exerts force but does not change in length. Also known as *static contraction,* it neither overcomes nor is overcome by the resistance.

isometric exercise—Training in which the muscle force equals the resistance force in a static position. There is muscle tension but no muscle movement.

isotonic exercise—Training with equipment that provides dynamic constant resistance or dynamic variable resistance. The amount of resistance force selected determines the amount of muscle force produced.

low-endurance muscles—Muscles characterized by a high percentage of fast-twitch fibers that are less resistant to fatigue.

momentum—The quantity of motion determined by an object's mass and velocity.

motor unit—A single motor nerve and all of the individual muscle fibers that are activated by the nerve.

multi-muscle exercise—An exercise that involves two or more major muscle groups. Linear movements such as bench presses and squats are multi-muscle exercises.

muscle adaptation—The ability of a muscle to respond positively to a slightly greater training stimulus, becoming larger and stronger.

muscle balance—Training all of the major muscle groups so that a desirable strength relationship is maintained between opposing muscles.

muscle contractibility—The ability of muscle tissue to shorten when stimulated to do so.

muscle density—The ratio of muscle tissue to nonmuscle tissue within a muscle cross-section. High-density muscles are characterized by more protein filaments packed into each muscle fiber.

muscle elasticity—The ability of muscle tissue to return to its normal resting length.

muscle extensibility—The ability of muscle tissue to stretch beyond its normal resting length.

muscle fatigue—The point in an exercise set when a muscle can no longer contract concentrically and overcome the resistance.

muscle fibers—Groups of myofibrils bound together into a functional unit and innervated by a motor nerve.

muscle isolation—An attempt to exercise one muscle or muscle group at a time, by single muscle (joint) exercises.

muscle length—The actual length of a muscle between its tendon attachments. Relatively long muscles have greater size potential than relatively short muscles.

muscle pump—A temporary increase in muscle cross-sectional size due to blood/fluid congestion in the muscle tissue during high-intensity training.

myofibrils—Small cylindrical strands that run lengthwise within each muscle fiber and are composed of adjacent sarcomeres.

negative training—Advanced technique that emphasizes the negative (eccentric) phase of exercise to produce greater force output.

Olympic lifters—Athletes who strength train primarily to lift heavier weights in their competitive events—the clean and jerk and the snatch.

one repetition maximum (1 RM)—The heaviest resistance that an individual can lift one time, the 1 RM is often used as a measure of maximum strength in a given exercise.

overload—Using more resistance than the muscles are accustomed to in a gradual and progressive manner, to stimulate strength development.

overtraining—Training that does not allow the muscles to fully recover and build to slightly higher strength levels between exercise sessions. Usually rectified by reducing the training volume or taking longer recovery periods between workouts.

power—The rate of work production, power is the product of muscle force and movement speed.

powerlifters—Athletes who strength train primarily to lift heavier weights in their competitive events—the squat, bench press, and dead lift.

prepubescent—Boys and girls who have not reached sexual maturity, or puberty.

prime mover muscle—The muscle primarily responsible for performing a particular movement. The biceps are prime mover muscles for elbow flexion.

progressive resistance exercise—A training program in which the exercise resistance is gradually increased as the muscles become stronger.

reciprocal inhibition—The blocking of nerve impulses to muscles that oppose a desired movement.

recovery time—May refer to the rest period between successive exercise sets (set recovery) or the rest period between successive workouts (workout recovery).

repetitions—The number of times an exercise is performed without interruption. Lifting the barbell from the standards, performing 10 squats, then returning it to the standards constitutes one set of 10 repetitions.

sarcomere—The smallest units of contraction within a muscle, sarcomeres consist of thick myosin proteins and thin actin proteins.

second-class lever—Lever arrangement in which the resistance force is between the axis of rotation and the movement force.

set—The number of separate bouts of exercise completed. Performing 10 curls, resting 60 seconds, then performing 10 more curls constitutes 2 sets of 10 repetitions each.

slow-twitch muscle fibers—Fibers that prefer aerobic energy sources to produce relatively low levels of force for relatively long periods of time.

spotter—A training partner who provides encouragement, feedback, safety, and reinforcement during strength training sessions. The spotter should be present during high-risk exercises such as bench presses and squats, for safety purposes, and may assist with high-intensity training procedures.

stabilizer muscles—Muscles that stabilize one joint so that the desired movement can occur in another joint. The low back muscles help stabilize the torso during standing barbell curls.

strength—The ability to exert muscle force against resistance force. Strength is typically measured by the amount of resistance force that is overcome.

strength plateau—A situation in which the training program does not result in additional strength gains. Strength plateaus indicate that some aspect of the training protocol should be changed to stimulate further progress.

stress adaptation—The ability of muscle tissue to make positive strength adaptations to progressively greater training demands.

stress intensification—Gradually increasing the muscle demands by training with more resistance, more repetitions, slower movements, high-intensity techniques, or other means for making the exercise more difficult.

super-set training—A technique characterized by performing two or more sets of different exercises for a target muscle group. For example, a set of triceps pressdowns followed immediately by a set of dips for the triceps muscles.

super-slow training—A technique characterized by 10-second lifting movements to decrease momentum and increase muscle tension.

third-class lever—Lever arrangement in which the movement force is between the axis of rotation and the resistance force.

training duration—May apply to the elapsed time for a training set (set duration), or the elapsed time for a training session (workout duration).

training intensity—The degree of effort necessary to complete an exercise set or an exercise session. High-intensity training is characterized by high levels of muscle fatigue.

training principles—Research-based guidelines for developing muscle strength safely and effectively.

training specificity—Training in a particular manner to attain desired results. For example, taking short rests between sets is more effective for developing muscle hypertrophy than muscle strength.

training volume—The total amount of work accomplished (weight lifted) during a training session. One means of estimating training volume is to multiply each exercise weightload by the number of repetitions completed and summing the totals.

Valsalva response—Holding the breath while working against a resistance increases chest pressure, which may restrict blood return to the heart and greatly elevate blood pressure.

work—The product of the resistance force (weightload) times the distance it is moved. Bench pressing 200 pounds two feet produces 400 foot-pounds of force.

Bibliography

American College of Sports Medicine. 1998. The recommended quantity and quality of exercise for developing and maintaining cardiorespiratory and muscular fitness, and flexibility in healthy adults. *Medicine and Science in Sports and Exercise*, 30(6): 975-991.

American College of Sports Medicine. 1995. *ACSM's Guidelines for exercise testing and prescription* (5th ed.) Philadelphia: Lea & Febiger.

American College of Sports Medicine. 1993. *ACSM'S resource manual for guidelines for exercise testing and prescription* (2nd ed.) Philadelphia: Lea & Febiger.

American Council on Exercise. 1996. *Personal trainer manual* (2nd ed.) San Diego: American Council on Exercise.

American Council on Exercise. 1993. *Aerobics instructor manual.* San Diego: American Council on Exercise.

American Dietetic Association. 1991. Position on Nutrition for Physical Fitness and Athletic Performance for Adults.

American Heart Association. January 15, 1995. Exercise standards: A statement for healthcare professionals from the American Heart Association. *Circulation*, 91, 2.

Astrand, P.O., and K. Rodahl. 1977. *Textbook of work physiology.* New York: McGraw-Hill.

Atham, J. 1981. Strengthening muscle. *Exercise and Sport Science Reviews*, 9: 1-73.

Borg, G.B. 1982. Psychological basis of perceived exertion. *Medicine and Science in Sports and Exercise*, 14, 377-381.

Bouchard, C., R. Shepard, T. Stephens, J. Sutton, and B. McPherson. 1990. *Exercise fitness and health: A consensus of current knowledge.* Champaign, IL: Human Kinetics.

Carlton, R., and E. Rhodes. 1985. A critical review of the literature on the ratings scales of perceived exertion. *Sports Medicine*, 2, 198-222.

Charette, S.L., L. McEvoy, G. Pyka, C. Snow-Harter, D. Guido, R.A. Wiswell, and R. Marcus. 1991. *Journal of Applied Physiology*, 70(5): 1912-1916.

Decker, J.I., G. Orcutt, and P. Sammann. 1989. *Y's Way to Fitness Walking Leader's Guide.* Champaign, IL: Human Kinetics.

Dishman, R. 1984. Motivation and exercise adherence. In Silva, J. III & R. Weinberg (Eds.), *Psychological foundations of sport* (pp. 420-435). Champaign, IL: Human Kinetics.

Dishman, R., R. Farquhar, and K. Cureton. 1994. Responses to preferred intensities of exertion in men differing in activity levels. *Medicine and Science in Sports and Exercise*, 26, 783.

Durstine, L., and R. Pate. 1993. Cardiorespiratory responses to acute exercise. *ACSM's resource manual for guidelines for exercise testing and prescription* (2nd ed.) Philadelphia: Lea & Febiger.

Fleck, S.J., and W.J. Kraemer. 1997. *Designing resistance training programs* (2nd ed.) Champaign, IL: Human Kinetics.

Folinsbee, L. 1990. Exercise and the environment. Bouchard, C., R Shepard., T. Stephens, J. Sutton, & B. McPherson (Eds.) *Exercise Fitness and Health.* Champaign, IL: Human Kinetics.

Foster, C. 1975. Physiological requirements of aerobic dancing. *The Research Quarterly*, 46: 120-122.

Fox, E.L., and D.K. Matthews. 1974. *Interval training.* Philadelphia: Saunders.

Franks, D., and E. Howley. 1989. *Fitness Facts.* Champaign, IL: Human Kinetics.

Friedenberg, E. 1967. *The vanishing adolescent.* New York: Dell. [Originally published in 1959 by Beacon Press.]

Gilliam, G.M. 1981. Effects of frequency of weight training on muscle strength enhancement. *Journal of Sports Medicine*, 21: 432-436.

Graves, J.E., M.L. Pollack, A.E. Jones, A.B. Colvin, and S.H. Leggett. 1989. Specificity of limited range of motion variable resistance training. *Medicine and Science in Sports and Exercise*, 2: 84-89.

Greenberg, J., and D. Pargman. 1989. *Physical fitness: A wellness approach* (2nd ed.) Englewood Cliffs, NJ: Prentice Hall.

Guyton, A. 1974. *Function of the human body* (4th ed.) Philadelphia: W.B. Saunders.

Harre, D.(Ed.) 1982. *Principles of sports training: Introduction to the theory and methods of training.* East Berlin: Sportverlag.

Harris, K.A., and R.G. Holly. 1987. Physiological response to circuit weight training in borderline hypertensive subjects. *Medicine and Science in Sports and Exercise,* 19(3).

Haskell, W.L. 1994. Health consequences of physical activity: Understanding and challenges regarding dose-response. *Medicine and Science in Sports and Exercise,* 26, 649-660.

Herbert, W., and D. Herbert. *The Exercise Standards and Malpractice Reporter,* 1987 to present.

Heyward, V. 1998. *Advanced fitness assessment and exercise prescription* (3rd ed.) Human Kinetics.

Heyward, V.H. 1984. *Designs for fitness.* Minneapolis: Burgess Publishing.

Howley, E., and D. Franks. 1992. Health fitness instructor's handbook (2nd ed.) Champaign, IL: Human Kinetics.

Howley, E., and M. Glover. 1974. The caloric costs of running and walking 1 mile for men and women. *Medicine and Science in Sports and Exercise,* 6, 235-237.

Hunter, G.R. 1985. Changes in body composition, bodybuild, and performance associated with different weight training frequencies in males and females. *National Strength and Conditioning Association Journal,* 7: 26-28.

Hunter, G.P., J. McGuirk, N. Mitrano, P. Pearman, B. Thomas, and R. Arrington. 1989. The effects of a weight training belt on blood pressure during exercise. *Journal of Applied Sport Science Research,* 3: 13-18.

Kasch, F.W., and J.L. Boyer. 1968. *Adult fitness: Principles and practice.* Greeley, CO: All American Products and Publications.

Ketner, J.B., and M.B. Mekkion. 1995. The overtraining syndrome: A review of presentation, pathophysiology, and treatment. *Medical Exercise Nutrition Health,* 4, 136-145.

Kravitz, L., and D. Kosich. 1993. Flexibility: A comprehensive research review and program design guide. *IDEA Today,* June.

Martens, R., R. Christina, J. Harvey, and B. Sharkey. 1981. *Coaching young athletes.* Champaign, IL: Human Kinetics.

McArdle, W., F. Katch, and V. Katch. 1991. *Exercise physiology* (3rd ed.) Philadelphia: Lea & Febiger.

McDonagh, M.J.N., and C.T.M. Davies. 1984. Adaptive response of mammalian skeletal muscle to exercise with high loads. *European Journal of Applied Physiology,* 52: 139-155.

Mutoh, Y., S. Sawai, Y. Takanashi, and L. Skurko. 1988. Aerobic dance injuries among instructors and students. *The Physician and Sportsmedicine,* 16(12): 81-83, 85, 88.

National Dance Exercise Instructor Training Association. 1999. *Fitness manual.* Mineapolis: NDEITA.

National Strength and Conditioning Association. 1994. *Essentials of strength training and conditioning.* Champaign, IL: Human Kinetics.

Nieman, D. 1990. *Fitness and sports medicine: An introduction.* Palo Alto, CA: Bull Publishing.

Nygaard, G., and T. Boone. 1985. *Coaches guide to sport law.* Champaign, IL: Human Kinetics.

O'Brien, T.S. 1997. *The personal trainer's handbook.* Champaign, IL: Human Kinetics.

Ockene, I., and J. Ockene. 1992. *Prevention of coronary heart disease.* Boston: Little Brown & Company.

Painter, P., and W. Haskell. 1993. Decision making in programming exercise. In *American College of Sports Medicine's resource manual for guidelines for exercise* testing and prescription. (2nd ed.) Philadelphia: Lea & Febiger.

Parker, S., B. Hurley, D. Hanlon, and P. Vaccaro. 1989. Failure of target heart rate to accurately monitor intensity during aerobic dance. *Medicine and Science in Sports and Exercise,* 21, 230.

Pollock, M. 1973. The quantification of endurance training programs. *Exercise and Sport Science Reviews,* 1, 155-188.

Pollock, M., J. Wilmore, and S. Fox. 1984. *Exercise in health and disease.* Philadelphia: Saunders.

Raglin, J.S. 1993. Overtraining and staleness: Psychometric monitoring of endurance athletes. In *Handbook of Research on Sport Psychology.* Singer, R.B., M. Murphey, & L. Tennant (Eds.) New York: Macmillan.

Richie, D. 1989. Medical and legal implications of dance exercise leadership: The role of footwear. *Exercise Standards and Malpractice Reporter,* 3, 61.

Richie, D.H., Jr., S.F. Kelso, and P.A. Bellucci. 1985. Aerobic dance injuries: A retrospective study of instructors and participants. *The Physician and Sportsmedicine,* 13(2): 130-140.

Richie, D.H., and E.L. Washington. 1983. Musculoskeletal problems in aerobic dancers —Part I. *Dance Medicine Health Newsletter,* 2: 9-11.

Roberts, S.O. (Ed.) 1996. *The business of personal training.* Champaign, IL: Human Kinetics.

Rockefeller, K.A., and E.J. Burke. 1979. Psycho-physiological analysis of an aerobic dance programme for women. *The British Journal of Physical Education,* 13: 77-80.

Saltin, B. et al. 1977. Fiber types and metabolic potentials of skeletal muscles in sedentary men and endurance runners. *Annals of the New York Academy of Science,* 301, 3.

Shapiro, U., and D. Seidman. 1990. Field and clinical observations of exertional heat stroke patients. *Medicine and Science in Sports and Exercise,* 22, 1.

Southmayd, W., and M. Hoffman. 1981. *Sports health*. New York: Quick Fox.

Sprague, K.C. 1991. *Weight and strength training for kids and teenagers.* Los Angeles: Jeremy P. Tarcher.

Strovas, J. 1984. Aerobic dance instructors are not injury proof. *The Physician and Sportsmedicine*, 12: 24.

Thrash, K., and B. Kelly. 1987. Flexibility and strength training. *Journal of Applied Sport Science Research*, 1: 74-75.

Vaccaro, P., and M. Clinton. 1981. The effects of aerobic dance conditioning on the body composition and maximal oxygen uptake of college women. *Journal of Sports Medicine and Physical Fitness*, 21: 291-294.

Van Camp, S. 1993. Pharmacologic factors in exercise and exercise testing. In *American College of Sports Medicine's resource manual for guidelines for exercise testing and prescription.* (2nd ed.) Philadelphia: Lea & Febiger.

Vogel, J., P.B. Rock, B.H. Jones, and G. Havenith. 1993. Environmental considerations in exercise testing and training. In *American College of Sports Medicine's resource manual for guidelines for exercise testing and prescription.* (2nd ed.) Philadelphia: Lea & Febiger.

Washington, E.L., S.L. Rosenberg, B. Friedlander., and B. Carlin. 1983. Musculoskeletal problems in aerobic dancers — Part II. *Dance Medicine Health Newsletter*, 2: 11-12.

Weber, H. 1974. The energy cost of aerobic dancing. *Fitness for Living*, 8: 26-30.

Wells, C., and R. Pate. 1988. Training for performance in prolonged exercise. Lamb, D. & R. Murray (Eds.) *Prolonged Exercise* (Vol.1), 357-389. Carmel, IN: Benchmark Press.

Westcott, W.L. 1996. *Building strength and stamina.* Champaign, IL: Human Kinetics.

Westcott, W.L. 1991. *Strength fitness: Physiological principles and training techniques.* Dubuque, IA: Wm. C. Brown.

Westcott, W.L. 1989. Strength Training Resistance: Sets and Repetitions.

Westcott, W.L. 1988. Eliminating myths: Does strength training harm blood pressure. *Perspective*, 37-39 (December).

Westcott, W.L. 1987. Exercise sessions can make the difference in weight loss. *Perspective*, 13: 42-44 (February).

Westcott, W.L. 1974. Effects of varied frequencies of weight training on the development of strength. Pennsylvania State University.

Westcott, W.L., and M. Pappas. 1987. Immediate effects of circuit strength training on blood pressure. *American Fitness Quarterly*, 6: 43-44 (October).

Whaley, M., L. Kaminsky, G. Dwyer, L. Getchell, and J. Norton. 1992. Questioning the routine use of 220 - AGE heart rate formula. *Medicine and Science in Sports and Exercise*, 24, 1173.

Wilmore, J. H., and D. Costill. 1994 *Physiology of sport and exercise*. Champaign, IL: Human Kinetics.

YMCA of the USA, 2000. *YMCA Fitness Testing and Assessment Manual*, Champaign, IL: Human Kinetics.

Index

The italicized *f* and *t* following page numbers refer to figures and tables, respectively.

Additional Resources for Your Fitness Program

See the YMCA Program Store catalog for details about these additional items for your YMCA fitness program or contact the Program Store, P.O. Box 5076, Champaign, IL 61825-5076, phone 800-747-0089. To save time, order by fax, 217-351-1549. (Please call if you are interested in receiving a free catalog.)

Fitness Program Resources

0-7360-2214-7	YMCA Fitness Analyst (Comprehensive Edition)	$695.00
0-7360-2210-4	YMCA Fitness Analyst (Standard Edition)	$495.00
0-7360-3316-5	YMCA Fitness Testing and Assessment Manual	$ 32.00
0-87322-263-6	YMCA Youth Fitness Test Manual	$ 13.00
0-7360-0152-2	Promoting Physical Activity	$ 32.00
1-887781-00-5	Get Real: A Personal Guide to Real-Life Weight Management	$ 15.95
0-7360-0146-8	Get Real Instructor Manual	$ 18.00
0-88011-949-7	YMCA Personal Fitness Program Manual	$ 28.00
0-7360-0186-7	Principles of YMCA Health and Fitness (Third Edition)	$ 22.00
0-87322-884-7	YMCA Exercise Instructor Manual	$ 28.00
0-7360-1030-0	Performance Aerobics, Hi/Lo Impact 40 Audio	$ 22.95
0-88011-543-2	YMCA Walk Reebok Instructor Manual	$ 49.00
0-88011-899-7	YMCA Walk Reebok Distance/Interval Training Instructor Manual	$ 16.00
0-87322-717-4	YMCA Healthy Back Program Instructor's Guide	$ 22.00
0-87322-629-1	YMCA Healthy Back Book	$ 12.95
0-87322-692-5	YMCA Healthy Back Video	$ 19.95
0-88011-967-5	Exercises for a Healthy Back Poster	$ 15.00
0-88011-966-7	Stretching Basics Poster	$ 15.00
0-88011-823-7	Sport Stretch	$ 16.95
0-87322-770-0	Fitness Cross-Training	$ 14.95
0-88011-792-3	YMCA Fun and Fitness Activity Chart	$ 5.00
0-7360-0971-X	Y's Way to Physical Fitness Guide to Setting Workloads	$ 3.00
0-7360-1011-4	YMCA Heart Rate Check Poster	$ 15.00
0-87322-351-9	Guidelines for Employee Health Promotion Programs	$ 29.00
0-88011-942-X	Exercise for Older Adults	$ 25.00
0-87322-356-X	Active Older Adults	$ 69.00
0-88011-817-2	Guidelines for Cardiac Rehabilitation and Secondary Prevention Programs (Third Edition)	$ 35.00
0-87322-614-3	Conditioning With Physical Disabilities	$ 22.95
0-87322-392-6	Arthritis: Your Complete Exercise Guide	$ 13.95
0-87322-427-2	Diabetes: Your Complete Exercise Guide	$ 13.95

Prices shown are subject to change